HIGH POLYMERS

Vol. I: **Collected Papers of W. H. Carothers on High Polymeric Substances**
Edited by H. Mark and G. S. Whitby

Vol. II: **Physical Chemistry of High Polymeric Systems**
Second Edition. By H. Mark and A. V. Tobolsky

Vol. III: **Mechanism of Polymer Reactions**
By G. M. Burnett

Vol. V: **Cellulose and Cellulose Derivatives** (in three parts)
Second Edition. Edited by Emil Ott, H. M. Spurlin, and M. W. Grafflin

Vol. VI: **Mechanical Behavior of High Polymers**
By Turner Alfrey, Jr.

Vol. VII: **Phenoplasts: Their Structure, Properties, and Chemical Technology**
By T. S. Carswell

Vol. IX: **Emulsion Polymerization**
By F. A. Bovey, I. M. Kolthoff, A. I. Medalia, and E. J. Meehan

Vol. X: **Polymer Processes**
Edited by Calvin E. Schildknecht

Vol. XII: **Analytical Chemistry of Polymers** (in three parts)
Edited by Gordon M. Kline

Vol. XIII: **Polyethers** (in three parts)
Edited by Norman G. Gaylord

Vol. XIV: **Polyesters** (in two parts)
Edited by Norman G. Gaylord

Vol. XV: **Radiation Chemistry of Polymeric Systems**
By Adolphe Chapiro

Vol. XVI: **Polyurethanes: Chemistry and Technology** (in two parts)
By J. H. Saunders and K. C. Frisch

Vol. XVII: **Configurational Statistics of Polymeric Chains**
By M. V. Volkenstein. Translated by Serge N. Timasheff and Marina J. Timasheff

Vol. XVIII: **Copolymerization**
Edited by George E. Ham

Vol. XIX: **Chemical Reactions of Polymers**
Edited by E. M. Fettes

Vol. XX: **Crystalline Olefin Polymers** (in two parts)
Edited by R. A. V. Raff and K. W. Doak

Vol. XXI: **Macromolecules in Solution**
By Herbert Morawetz

Vol. XXII: **Conformations of Macromolecules**
By T. M. Birshtein and O. B. Ptitsyn. Translated by Serge N. Timasheff and Marina J. Timasheff

HIGH POLYMERS

A SERIES OF MONOGRAPHS ON THE CHEMISTRY, PHYSICS, AND TECHNOLOGY OF HIGH POLYMERIC SUBSTANCES

VOLUME XXII

CONFORMATIONS OF MACROMOLECULES

T. M. BIRSHTEIN and O. B. PTITSYN

Institute of High Molecular Compounds, Leningrad, USSR

Translated from the Russian Edition by

SERGE N. TIMASHEFF and MARINA J. TIMASHEFF

Scientific Editor M. V. Volkenshtein

INTERSCIENCE PUBLISHERS

a division of John Wiley & Sons

NEW YORK • LONDON • SYDNEY

Library of Congress Catalog Card Number 65-26217

PRINTED IN THE UNITED STATES OF AMERICA

INTRODUCTION TO THE ENGLISH EDITION

More than thirty years ago the first attempts were made to handle essential properties of polymeric systems with the aid of the methods of statistical mechanics. Little was known at that time on the structural details of long-chain molecules and on their natural interaction. Nonetheless, even first attempts which had to be based on many simplifying—and even oversimplifying assumptions—were obviously steps in the right direction, providing at least a preliminary understanding of such basic facts as polymerization kinetics, properties of macromolecular solutions, and rubber elasticity. As our knowledge of the exact architecture of individual macromolecules became more and more complex and the relation of the structure to solubility, crystallinity, and melting characteristics became better and better known, new material was provided for statistical treatment and an ever-increasing volume of experimental data was waiting for quantitative rationalization and coordination. The increasing number of polymer chemists and physicists who were mathematically oriented did not remain idle but attempted, almost immediately, appropriate theoretical treatment of new experimental results. For many years this went on in numerous laboratories and institutions in the form of individual efforts, each of which was characterized and limited by the special assumptions which its originator made and by the special mathematical methods which he selected for his analysis. Many of us still remember vividly the animated discussions which accompanied the developments of solution viscosity and rubber elasticity for more than ten years.

Today the time has come for a unified, overall treatment of polymer statistics based on firm and universally accepted facts and executed with the aid of rigorous and general mechanical methods. This volume represents an advanced and determined step in this direction and should be particularly welcome to the readers of our series, because it places special emphasis on the contribution of Soviet scientists whose original articles are not readily accessible for their Western colleagues. The Editors wish to express their gratitude to the authors and translators and hope that this volume will provide a substantial contribution to the progress of polymer science.

H. F. Mark
for the Editorial Board

FOREWORD

The subject of this book is the modern statistical theory of macromolecules, which is based on an examination of their conformations. This theory has uncovered the essence of several important phenomena related to macromolecules: It has given a practically complete quantitative interpretation of the behavior of macromolecules in solution, a molecular interpretation of high elasticity, and has played an important role in the development of the physics of biopolymers, i.e., of proteins and nucleic acids. In the solution of these and other problems, conformational statistics have led to essentially new results and thus made possible much greater advances than the initial model statistics of Kuhn, Guth, and Mark.

This book presents both foreign studies in the theory of macromolecular conformations and work that has been carried out over many years (1950–1963) by the theoretical group of the Institute of High Molecular Compounds of the Academy of Sciences of the U.S.S.R. in which the authors of this book have taken an active part. Considerable difficulties are encountered in the development of a theory of macromolecules which takes into account directly the concrete specifity of their chemical and stereochemical structure. It has been possible to overcome these difficulties by regarding macromolecules as rotational–isomeric cooperative systems.

It is this concept, fully confirmed by the entire development of later theoretical and experimental investigations, which forms the basis of conformational statistics. The mathematical apparatus of this theory is related to the one-dimensional model of Ising, which had been proposed for the statistical interpretation of ferromagnetism. Such an interpretation was impossible to obtain, since ferromagnetism is determined by the behavior not of a one-dimensional, but of a three-dimensional cooperative system. To the contrary, the simplest one-dimensional model of Ising is fully applicable in the present case, in view of the essentially unidimensionality of macromolecules (in the sense that the linear sequence of chemical bonds is their outstanding property). The method based on this is related to the method of chains developed by the great mathematician A. A. Markoff. The authors of this book have given an original and very elegant modification of the Ising method.

The basic physical concept of a macromolecule as a linear cooperative system, and the realization of this idea using the Ising model, were first applied to the investigation of macromolecules in solution and in the state of high elasticity. Later, American scientists started developing the conformational statistics of biopolymers; they developed, in particular, the theory of helix–coil transition, which is based on the same concept and the same method. Still later, the concept of one-dimensional cooperativity was applied by the present writer to the investigation of deoxyribonucleic acid duplication.

At the present time, it is possible to consider that a major phase in the development of the theoretical physics of polymers has been completed. It is obvious that such a development is not a goal in itself. Problems of polymer physics can be reduced to the theoretical and experimental investigation of the relation between technically important physico-mechanical properties of polymers and their chemical structure. On the other hand, macromolecular physics serves as the basis of molecular biophysics. Current problems both of the technical and biological physics of polymers consist in the investigation of the supermolecular structures which are formed by macromolecules in polymers in bulk, in concentrated solutions, and in biological systems. The statistical physics of macromolecules is the only scientific basis of these investigations, and it is already being applied. There is no doubt that in the near future the statistical theory of macromolecules will make a large contribution to technology and biology.

The book by T. M. Birshtein and O. B. Ptitsyn *Conformations of Macromolecules* is, to a certain degree, a continuation of my monograph *Configurational Statistics of Polymeric Chains*, published by the Academy of Sciences of the U.S.S.R. in 1959 and by Interscience in 1963. It has, however, a different character. It represents a compact and rigorous presentation of the main problems of the equilibrium behavior of macromolecules, which is related to their conformations, and contains a detailed analysis of the conformational transformations of biological polymers.

M. V. VOLKENSHTEIN

PREFACE

The theory of individual macromolecules represents a very interesting part of statistical physics. Every year it attracts more and more attention both as a result of the needs of the technological physics of polymers and of those of the physics of biopolymers (proteins and nucleic acids). The last decade has been marked in this field by the development of a detailed quantitative theory of the flexibility of macromolecules. The development of such a theory began with the studies of M. V. Volkenshtein who proposed the rotational–isomeric model of polymer molecules which opened the way to a quantitative approach to the problem of polymer chain flexibility. This model has been described in detail and its foundations have been presented in the monograph *Configurational Statistics of Polymeric Chains* by M. V. Volkenshtein, published in 1959. This monograph also contains a detailed presentation of the studies on the statistical theory of the flexibility of macromolecules carried out up to the year 1958–1959.

Further development of the statistical theory of polymer chain flexibility has resulted in the evolution of a more or less complete picture of the conformational structure of typical macromolecules in solution and in the state of high elasticity. As a result, it seems to us that the concept of the flexibility of a macromolecule has received for the first time a clear quantitative treatment. On the other hand, the discovery of helix–coil transitions in molecules of typical biopolymers in solution has led to the development of the theory of these phenomena. This theory proved to be quite similar to that of the flexibility of normal polymers (i.e., non-biological) both in its physical concepts and in its mathematical methods.

The present book sets as its goal a most compact presentation of the principal concepts and mathematical methods which form the basis of the modern theory of macromolecular conformations. The greatest emphasis is placed on the theory of flexibility of normal polymers, which has been developed mainly in the studies of members of the theoretical group of the laboratory of polymer structure of the Institute of High Molecular Compounds of the Academy of Sciences of the U.S.S.R. The theory of helix–coil transitions in biopolymers is also presented; this has been developed mainly by American scientists; we have tried to stress its close relation to the theory of the flexibility of molecules of normal polymers.

The term "conformations of macromolecules," as used by us, requires some explanation. In statistical physics, that part of the partition function which depends on the mutual positions of atoms that fluctuate as a result of thermal motion is called the "configurational" partition function. In stereochemistry, however, the term "configuration" refers to that structure of a molecule which is fixed at the moment of its formation and which changes only if chemical bonds are broken, while a molecular structure which fluctuates as a result of thermal motion is called "conformation." The last term was introduced for the first time by Haworth in 1928 in his book *The Constitution of Sugars* to designate different spacial distributions of atoms within a molecule which can be made to superimpose by rotation about bonds without breaking them; in this sense, this term has been widely used in the physics of macromolecules, particularly in recent years. We shall use this stereochemical term in all cases in which it is customary to talk of configurations in statistical physics.

The reading of the greater part of this book does not require any special mathematical preparation. Chapters 4 and 5 and the mathematical parts of chapters 9, 10, and 11 assume that the reader has a knowledge of the bases of matrix algebra. These sections of the book, however, can be omitted by the reader who is not interested in the mathematical side of the problem, without impeding his understanding of subsequent material.

The authors are greatly indebted to M. Z. Solomyak, who has collaborated in the preparation of the Appendix, and also to Yu. Ya. Gotlib and S. Ya. Magarik, who have read the book in manuscript form and made a number of valuable suggestions.

T. M. Birshtein
O. B. Ptitsyn

TRANSLATORS' ACKNOWLEDGMENT

Since the task of the translator of a book is the exact rendition in a second language of what has been said in the first, the primary requirement seems to be not only perfect knowledge of the two languages, but also general familiarity with the subject matter. In a book, such as the present one, even this requirement is not sufficient, and the aid of experts in the subject of the book must be invoked to make certain that all the terms used are exactly correct and that the scientific content has not been inadvertently modified even to the slightest degree. In the present case, this task was undertaken by Drs. Murray Goodman and James E. Mark, of the Polytechnic Institute of Brooklyn, who checked the entire manuscript very carefully for proper terminology and for the correctness of equations. For this, we would like to express to them our gratitude. We also wish to thank Mrs. Brita Immergut for checking the voluminous references and making all the necessary corrections.

SERGE N. TIMASHEFF
MARINA J. TIMASHEFF

CONTENTS

INTRODUCTION

The specificity peculiar to polymer physics which make it possible to regard this field as a special branch of physics are related, as is known, to the fact that polymer molecules consist of a large number of monomeric units and possess a large number of internal degrees of freedom. The flexibility of macromolecules, which accounts for the special properties of polymeric substances (especially for their high elasticity), requires, in turn, an explanation and a detailed description in terms of the chemical structure of real polymers. Therefore, the physics of individual macromolecules becomes, from a fundamental point of view, the most important part of polymer physics, since the establishment of the relation between the physical properties of macromolecules and their chemical structure must open the way to the synthesis of polymers with a prescribed set of physicomechanical properties that would satisfy practical requirements.

The first stage, which is characterized by the classical studies of Kuhn (1) and Guth and Mark (2), consisted in the development of a statistical theory of polymer chains as linear systems made up of independent elements (*statistical segments*). On the basis of this model, which takes into account the principal general property of macromolecules, namely their flexibility, Flory (3), Debye (4–6), Kuhn (32), and Kirkwood (7,8) have developed the theory of the thermodynamic, hydrodynamic and optical properties of individual molecules; in the studies of Flory (3), James and Guth (9) and other scientists, this model led to a rather complete description of the high elasticity of bulk polymers. Thus, this first stage in the development of the statistical physics of polymers has resulted in a qualitative, and to some extent semiquantitative, understanding of the principal physical properties of polymers in solution and in bulk.

Further development of the investigations set the stage for the replacement of the description in terms of models by a quantitative approach to the flexibility of polymers in terms of their chemical and stereochemical structures. At a first glance it might appear that the theory of polymer structure is much more complicated than that of simple liquids. In reality the situation is just the reverse. In simple liquids the state of each molecule depends on the states of (on the average) equivalent neighbors which surround it. A liquid forms as a whole a three-dimensional cooperative system, a rigorous statistical treatment of which meets with very serious difficulties [see for example, Hill (10)]. In polymers, those neighboring monomer units which form part of the same chain are much closer to each other and, on the average, interact with each other much more strongly than do neighboring monomer units which belong to different chains. It is sufficient to note that such characteristics of polymers in bulk as their thermodynamic properties, the photoelastic effect, the dielectric constant, and even the crystallizability are determined not so much by intermolecular interactions as by chain flexibility. Therefore, polymers can be considered, as a first approximation, as ensembles of linear sequences of monomer units which interact with each other, i.e., as *one-dimensional cooperative system;* on the other hand, intermolecular interactions, as well as interactions of remote (along the chain) monomer units, can be looked upon as correcting factors. The development of the theory of a one-dimensional cooperative system is a comparatively simple task; methods of solving this problem have been developed by Ising (11) and Kramers and Wannier (12) [see also Newell and Montroll (13)], in connection with the requirements of the theory of ferromagnetism. The first application of these methods to the theory of polymer chains is found in the study of Volkenshtein and Ptitsyn (14), published in 1953. At the present time the application of the mathematics of the Ising model to the theory of macromolecules is generally accepted; this has made possible important achievements in the development of theories of physical and electrochemical properties of macromolecules in solution, of helix–coil transitions in synthetic polypeptides and nucleic acids, of deoxyribonucleic acid duplication, etc. The bases of the matrix method for calculating the partition function and mean properties of a one-dimensional cooperative system are presented in the present book. This method has been generalized by Gotlib (15) and Birshtein and Ptitsyn (16,17) and applied by them to the calculation of the mean properties of macromolecules in solution.

The mathematics of Ising, and Kramers and Wannier relate the physical properties of a one-dimensional cooperative system to the state of its elements. Their application to macromolecules has become possible as a result of the concept, proposed by Volkenshtein (18) and repeatedly confirmed by experiments, of the rotational-isomeric structure of polymeric chains. This concept makes it possible to speak of a discrete set of states (conformations) of monomer units. Ptitsyn and Sharonov (19) have hypothesized of an analogy between the short-range one-dimensional order in an amorphous polymer chain and the long-range one-dimensional order in a crystalline chain. This hypothesis, the validity of which can be considered as proven now for a majority of polymers, has permitted the development of the quantitative rotational-isomeric theory of the physical properties of macromolecules in solution and in the high elastic bulk state. The present book is devoted principally to a presentation of this theory.

The treatment of a macromolecule as a one-dimensional cooperative system proved to be particularly fruitful in the theory of biopolymer molecules and their synthetic analogs (polypeptides and polynucleotides). It is well known that, under certain conditions, such molecules can retain an ordered conformation not only in the crystalline state but also in solution (20). This conformation is maintained by intramolecular forces (for example, hydrogen bonds), which have a strong cooperative character in the sense that the breaking of one bond is not advantageous, since this does not lead to the realization of additional degrees of freedom; only with the simultaneous breaking of a large number of adjacent hydrogen bonds can this occur. As a result, the interdependence between the states of adjacent monomer units (i.e., the degree of cooperativity of the macromolecule) is considerably greater than in molecules of nonbiological polymers; this explains the sharp change in the state of biological macromolecules with a relatively small change in external parameters. The transition of such macromolecules from an ordered (helical) to a disordered (coiled) state usually takes place in a rather narrow interval of temperature or solvent composition (20).

At the present time, *helix–coil transitions* in biological macromolecules and their synthetic analogs are the subject of very intensive studies, both experimental and theoretical. This is quite natural, since such transitions are probably quite directly related to a number of extremely important life processes. While, at the present time, the study of these phenomena outside of living organisms meets with great difficulties, investigations of helix–coil transitions can be carried out under quite varied conditions by bringing to bear the entire arsenal of modern physical methods. Treatment of the results obtained on the basis of the statistical theory, which relates the position and width of the transition region to the parameters of the macromolecules, makes it possible to obtain valuable information on intramolecular interactions in biopolymer molecules.

The theory of the helix–coil transition has been developed, starting from the year 1958, by a large number of scientists [in particular Zimm (21–24)], as a theory of cooperative conformational transformations in one-dimensional systems. In this work, it was found quite convenient and fruitful to use those statistical methods of Ising (11) and Kramers and Wannier (12) which also form the basis of the rotational-isomeric theory of the physical properties of common (i.e., nonbiological) macromolecules. The statistical theory of helix–coil transitions is presented elsewhere in this book (Chapters 9–11).

The theory of a macromolecule as a linear cooperative system does not take into account the interactions of all the atoms of a chain. Since the forces which act between atoms diminish more or less rapidly with an increase in distance, the interactions between atoms which are not bonded to each other fall into two categories. The first class consists of *short-range interactions*, i.e., of interactions operating between atoms separated on the average by small distances and depending on one or several angles of internal rotation. Quite naturally such interactions, which basically can be reduced to the repulsion of atoms with overlapping electron clouds, are characteristic not only of macromolecules but also of low molecular compounds. They result in the presence of a restricting potential of internal rotation and in the well-known phenomenon of rotational isomerism; this is quite important for an understanding of the thermodynamic and spectroscopic properties of molecules (see Chapter 2). It is evident that it is the short-range interactions which are accounted for in the treatment of macromolecules as one-dimensional cooperative systems.

The second class consists of *long-range interactions* or excluded volume effects,* i.e., of interactions between atoms which, on the average, are at a considerable distance from each other, but which randomly approach each other in the process of the fluctuating coiling of the chain. To this class belong, first of all, the repulsive forces which arise when two atoms approach each other to a distance smaller than the sum of their van der Waals radii, and also the attractive forces which are operative between atoms at greater distances, as well as forces which act between the segments of the chain and the solvent molecules.

The validity of such a classification of the intramolecular interactions in macromolecules is based on the fact that the influence of volume effects on the macromolecular properties under investigation can be excluded if the measurements are carried out at the so-called θ-point (3) or "Flory point" (analogous to the point of inversion in real gases). At this point, the effect of attractive and repulsive forces upon the macroscopic properties of the chain (for example, on its dimensions) compensate each other. Furthermore, as has been shown in specially designed experiments, certain prop-

* In this book, which is dedicated to the treatment of macromolecules as linear cooperative systems, long-range interactions are not considered; the theory of long-range interactions is presented in the well known monograph by Flory (3) and also in the review literature (25).

erties of macromolecules, for example, the mean-square dipole moment (26–28) or the mean optical anisotropy (29), are generally little affected by long-range interactions. In the case of the dipole moment, this result is confirmed also by statistical calculations (30). In concentrated polymer solutions or in polymers in bulk, long-range intramolecular interactions become indistinguishable from intermolecular ones and make a general contribution to the dependence of the energy of a sample on its volume. At constant volume the physical properties of a sample are determined primarily by short-range intramolecular interactions, i.e., by the flexibility of the chain.

The effect of long-range interactions on the properties of macromolecules of biological polymers or their synthetic analogs in an ordered (helical) state is obviously quite small, since in this state, distant atoms approach each other very rarely due to the stretched form of the chain. In the coiled state, however, long-range interactions (under conditions not approaching θ conditions) can have a considerable effect on the properties of the molecules and, thus, on the helix–coil transition (31).

References

1. Kuhn, W., *Kolloid-Z.*, **68,** 2 (1934).
2. Guth, E., and H. Mark, *Monatsh. Chem.*, **65,** 93 (1934).
3. Flory, P. J., *Principles of Polymer Chemistry*, Cornell Univ. Press, Ithaca, N. Y., 1953.
4. Debye, P. J. W., *J. Phys. Colloid Chem.*, **51,** 18 (1947).
5. Debye, P. J. W., *J. Chem. Phys.*, **14,** 636 (1946).
6. Debye, P. J. W., and A. M. Bueche, *J. Chem. Phys.*, **16,** 573 (1948).
7. Kirkwood, J. G., and J. Riseman, *J. Chem. Phys.*, **16,** 565 (1948).
8. Kirkwood, J. G., *J. Polymer Sci.*, **12,** 1 (1954).
9. James, H. M., and E. Guth, *J. Polymer Sci.*, **4,** 153 (1949).
10. Hill, T., *Statisticheskaya Mekhanika*, IL, Moscow, 1960 (originally published as *Statistical Mechanics*, McGraw-Hill, New York, 1956).
11. Ising, E., *Z. Physik*, **31,** 253 (1925).
12. Kramers, H. A., and G. H. Wannier, *Phys. Rev.*, **60,** 252 (1941).
13. Newell, G. F., and E. W. Montroll, *Rev. Mod. Phys.*, **25,** 353 (1953).
14. Volkenshtein, M. V., and O. B. Ptitsyn, *Dokl. Akad. Nauk SSSR*, **91,** 1313 (1953)
15. Gotlib, Yu. Ya., *Zh. Tekhn. Fiz.*, **29,** 523 (1959); *Soviet Phys.-Tech. Phys.*, **4,** 465. (1959).
16. Birshtein, T. M., and O. B. Ptitsyn, *Zh. Tekhn. Fiz.*, **29,** 1048 (1959); *Soviet Phys.-Tech. Phys.*, **4,** 954 (1959).
17. Birshtein, T. M., candidate dissertation, Institut Vysokomolekulyarnykh Soedinenii, Akad. Nauk SSSR, Leningrad, 1959.
18. Volkenshtein, M. V., *Konfiguratsionnaya Statistika Polimernyikh Tsepei*, Izdatel'stvo Akad. Nauk SSSR, Moscow, 1959 (published in translation as *Configurational Statistics at Polymeric Chains*, Interscience, New York, 1963).

19. Ptitsyn, O. B., and Yu. A. Sharonov, *Zh. Tekhn. Fiz.*, **27,** 2744 (1957); *Soviet Phys.-Tech. Phys.*, **2,** 2544 (1957).
20. Doty, P., in *Sovremennye Problemy Biofiziki*, IL, Moscow, 1961, Vol. I, p. 138 (originally published as *Biophysical Science: A Study Program*, J. L. Oncley, F. O. Schmitt, R. C. Williams, M. D. Rosenberg, and R. H. Bolt, Eds., Wiley, New York, 1959).
21. Zimm, B. H., and J. K. Bragg, *J. Chem. Phys.*, **28,** 1246 (1958).
22. Zimm, B. H., and J. K. Bragg, *J. Chem. Phys.*, **31,** 526 (1959).
23. Zimm, B. H., and S. A. Rice, *Mol. Phys.*, **3,** 391 (1960).
24. Zimm, B. H., *J. Chem. Phys.*, **33,** 1349 (1960).
25. Ptitsyn, O. B., *Usp. Fiz. Nauk*, **69,** 371 (1959); *Soviet Phys.-Usp.*, **2,** 797 (1959).
26. Marchal, J., C. Wippler, and H. Benoit, *Compt. Rend.*, **241,** 1266 (1955).
27. Marchal, J., and H. Benoit, *J. Polymer Sci.*, **23,** 223 (1957).
28. Marchal, J., and Ch. Lapp, *J. Polymer Sci.*, **27,** 571 (1958).
29. Tsvetkov, V. N., V. E. Bychkova, S. M. Savvon, and N. K. Nekrasov, *Vysokomol. Soedin.*, **1,** 1407 (1959); *Polymer Sci. USSR*, **1,** 584 (1960) (abstract).
30. Oky, T., *Busseiron Kenkyu*, **7,** 260 (1960).
31. Ptitsyn, O. B., *Biofizika*, **7,** 257 (1962).
32. Kuhn, W., H. Kuhn and P. Buchner, *Ergeb. Exakt. Naturw.*, **25,** 1 (1951).

Chapter 1

FLEXIBILITY OF MACROMOLECULES AND THEIR PHYSICAL PROPERTIES

1.1. Methods of Studying the Flexibility of Macromolecules

The specific physical properties of macromolecules are due to their **flexibility,** which is related to the large number of internal degrees of freedom determined by rotation about single bonds. From this point of view, a polymeric molecule can be regarded as a macroscopic system: it is possible to talk about its *macro state,* which is characterized, for example, by the end-to-end distance of the molecule and its dipole moment, and its *micro state,* characterized by the mutual positions of all the bonds within the molecule relative to each other, i.e., by its conformations (by the set of internal rotation angles).* It is evident that the number of micro states is very much larger for a coiled macro state of the molecule, in which the end-to-end distance is much less than maximal, than for the extended state. As a result, a free macromolecule in solution or in an amorphous bulk polymer has the form of a coil. When polymers are extended the coils unwind; this determines their ability to undergo large reversible deformations (high elasticity) (1,2).

Unfortunately, there are no direct methods for investigating the possible conformations of free macromolecules which characterize their flexibility in detail. The average values of various quantities which characterize macromolecules (dimensions, dipole moments, optical anisotropy, etc.), however, are determined not only by the values of the same quantities for monomeric units, but also by the average positions of the latter relative to each other; these depend on the flexibility of the macromolecules. As a result, the observed average properties of macromolecules are measures of their flexibility and, with suitable theoretical analysis, they make it possible to obtain complete information on the mechanism of polymer chain flexibility.

* The contribution to the flexibility of a macromolecule from other degrees of freedom (deformation of chemical bonds and valence angles) is usually quite small and can be neglected completely relative to the contribution due to rotation about single bonds.

At the present time, experimental data are available on the dimensions (i.e., the mean-square end-to-end distance of the molecule),* the mean-square dipole moments, and the mean optical anisotropies for a large number of different types of polymers. The most reliable method for measuring the dimensions of macromolecules is that proposed by Debye (1); it is based on the investigation of the angular dissymmetry of light scattered by a solution of a polymer whose molecules are not negligibly small with respect to the wavelength of the light. The angular distribution of the relative intensity of scattered light has the form

$$P(\vartheta) = \frac{1}{n^2} \sum_{p,\, t=1}^{n} \overline{\left(\frac{\sin \mu r_{p,\, t}}{\mu r_{p,\, t}}\right)} \tag{1.1}$$

where ϑ is the angle of scattering; n is the number of scattering centers (monomer units) in the chain, $r_{p,\, t}$ is the distance between the pth and tth scattering centers, $\mu = (4\pi/\lambda') \sin \vartheta/2$, and λ' is the wavelength of the light in the solution. The averaging is carried out over all conformations of the chain. Expanding the $P(\vartheta)$ function, eq. (1.1), in series of $\sin(\vartheta/2)$, we obtain at small ϑ, making no assumption on the structure of the chain,

$$P(\vartheta) = 1 - \frac{\mu^2}{6n^2} \sum_{p,\, t=1}^{n} \overline{r_{p,t}^{2}} + \ldots = 1 - \frac{\mu^2 \overline{R^2}}{3} + \ldots \tag{1.2}$$

Here $\overline{R^2}$ is the mean-square radius of gyration of the chain, given by

$$\overline{R^2} = \frac{1}{n} \sum_{p=1}^{n} \overline{s_p^{\,2}} \tag{1.3}$$

where s_p is the distance between the pth monomer unit of the chain and its center of gravity. The right-hand side of eq. (1.2) follows from the relation

$$\frac{1}{2n^2} \sum_{p,\, t=1}^{n} \overline{r_{p,t}^{\,2}} = \frac{1}{2n^2} \sum_{p,\, t=1}^{n} \overline{(\mathbf{s}_p - \mathbf{s}_t)^2} = \frac{1}{n} \sum_{p=1}^{n} \overline{\mathbf{s}_p^{\,2}} = \overline{R^2} \tag{1.4}$$

since

$$\sum_{p=1}^{n} \mathbf{s}_p = \sum_{t=1}^{n} \mathbf{s}_t = 0$$

* As has been pointed out already, the flexibility of macromolecules is determined from their dimensions at the Θ-point (in an ideal solvent), at which the influence of long-range interactions is absent. In order to determine these dimensions, it is necessary either to carry out the measurements directly at the Θ-point or to eliminate the effect of long-range interactions with the use of existing theories.

Thus, the method of light scattering permits one, in principle, to obtain the value of the mean-square radius of gyration of the macromolecule, independently of any assumption about its structure. In the case of sufficiently long and flexible chains in ideal solvents, the distances between the overwhelming majority of scattering centers (with the exception of the nearest ones along the chain) obey a normal (Gaussian) distribution law (see Chapter 5). For such chains,

$$\overline{R^2} = \tfrac{1}{6}\overline{h^2} \qquad (1.5)$$

where $\overline{h^2}$ is the mean-square distance between chain ends. For short or stiff chains, the relation between $\overline{R^2}$ and $\overline{h^2}$ can be more complicated [see, for example, Benoit and Doty (2)]. We shall not dwell on this point, however, since we shall be concerned primarily with the examination of the conformations of long flexible macromolecules.

Because of experimental difficulties, it is customary to measure either the values of $P(\vartheta)$ down to $\vartheta \approx 30°$, and then to extrapolate to $\vartheta = 0°$ [Zimm method (3)], or to measure the ratio $P(\vartheta = 45°)/P(\vartheta = 135°)$ [Debye method (1)]. This ratio can be used to determine $\overline{R^2}$ with the aid of a theoretical expression relating $P(\vartheta)$ with $\overline{R^2}$ at any ϑ. For linear monodisperse Gaussian chains,* Debye has obtained

$$P(\vartheta) = (2/x^2)[e^{-x} - (1 - x)] \qquad (1.6)$$

where $x = \mu^2\overline{R^2}$.

Another method of determining the dimensions of macromolecules is the study of their hydrodynamic properties under rotational motion (viscosity, flow birefringence) or translational motion (diffusion, sedimentation in an ultracentrifuge). The theory relating these properties to the dimensions of the macromolecules is based on the assumption of definite models, both of the chain geometry and of the degree of its hydrodynamic permeability to solvent. The generally accepted point of view at the present time is that of Flory (4), according to which long flexible macromolecules carry along in their motion almost all the solvent trapped in their volume, so that their hydrodynamic properties are similar to those of continuous particles. As a result, the intrinsic viscosity of macromolecules is expressed by an equation similar to the Einstein equation:

$$[\eta] = \lim_{c\to 0} [(\eta - \eta_0)/\eta_0 c] = \Phi(\overline{h^2})^{3/2}/M \qquad (1.7)$$

* For the sake of brevity, macromolecular chains in which the distance between any pair of monomer units obeys a Gaussian distribution function are called Gaussian.

TABLE 1.1. Mean-Square End-to-End Distances of Macromolecules in Solution

Polymer	Repeating unit	$(\overline{h^2}/\overline{h^2}_{\text{fr.rot.}})^{1/2}$	Method	References
Polyisobutylene	$-CH_2-C(CH_3)_2-$	2.3 1.7–1.8	LS V	17 18–20, 119
Polypropylene	$-CH_2-CH(CH_3)-$	1.8	V	21
Polybutylene	$-CH_2-CH(CH_2CH_3)-$	1.8	V	22
Poly(vinyl bromide)	$-CH_2-CH(Br)-$	1.9	LS,V	23
Polystyrene	$-CH_2-CH(C_6H_5)-$	2.2–2.4	LS,V	4,17,19,20, 24–32
Poly-2,5-dichlorostyrene	$-CH_2-CH(C_6H_3Cl_2)-$ (2,5-dichlorophenyl)	2.5	LS	33
Poly-3,4-dichlorostyrene	$-CH_2-CH(C_6H_3Cl_2)-$ (3,4-dichlorophenyl)	2.9	LS	34
Poly-4-vinylpyridine	$-CH_2-CH(C_5H_4N)-$ (4-pyridyl)	2.2	V	35
Poly-α-vinylnaphthalene	$-CH_2-CH(C_{10}H_7)-$ (α-naphthyl)	3.2	LS	36
Poly(acrylic acid) (unionized)	$-CH_2-CH(C(=O)OH)-$	1.8	V	37
Poly(vinyl acetate)	$-CH_2-CH(O-C(=O)-CH_3)-$	2.3	LS	38
Poly(vinyl benzoate)	$-CH_2-CH(O-C(=O)-C_6H_5)-$	2.4	V	39
Poly(methyl methacrylate)	$-CH_2-C(CH_3)(C(=O)-OCH_3)-$	2.0–2.2	LS,V	37,40,41, 106

(*continued*)

TABLE 1.1 (*continued*)

Polymer	Repeating unit	$(\overline{h^2}/\overline{h^2}_{fr.rot.})^{1/2}$	Method	References
Poly(ethyl methacrylate)	$-CH_2-C(CH_3)(C(=O)OCH_2CH_3)-$	1.9	LS	42
Poly(butyl methacrylate)	$-CH_2-C(CH_3)(C(=O)O(CH_2)_3CH_3)-$	2.1	LS	43
Poly(2-ethylbutyl methacrylate)	$-CH_2-C(CH_3)(C(=O)OCH_2CH(C_2H_5)C_2H_5)-$	2.3	LS	44
Poly(hexyl methacrylate)	$-CH_2-C(CH_3)(C(=O)O(CH_2)_5CH_3)-$	2.4	LS	45
Poly(octyl methacrylate)	$-CH_2-C(CH_3)(C(=O)O-(CH_2)_7-CH_3)-$	2.3	LS	46
Poly(lauryl methacrylate)	$-CH_2-C(CH_3)(C(=O)O(CH_2)_{11}CH_3)-$	2.8	LS	47
Polydimethylsiloxane	$-O-Si(CH_3)_2-$	1.4[a]	V	48,120–122
Polyhexene-1-sulfone	$-S(=O)_2-CH_2-CH((CH_2)_3CH_3)-$	2.1[b,c] 1.6[b,c]	LS, V	49,107
Natural rubber (*cis*-1,4-polyisoprene)	$-CH_2(H)C=C(CH_3)CH_2-$	1.5[c]	V	50
cis-1,4-Polybutadiene	$-CH_2(H)C=C(H)CH_2-$	1.6	V	51
Gutta-percha (*trans*-1,4-polyisoprene)	$-CH_2(H)C=C(CH_3)CH_2-$	1.3[c]	V	50

[a] In calculation of $\overline{h^2}_{fr.rot.}$, the angle at Si was taken to be tetrahedral, and that at O as 143°.

[b] The values 2.1 and 1.6 were obtained in different Θ-solvents, i.e., in hexyl chloride and methyl ethyl ketone–isopropanol mixtures, respectively.

[c] In the calculation of $\overline{h^2}_{fr.rot.}$ the angles between single bonds were taken to be tetrahedral, and those between single and double bonds as 120°.

where η is the solution viscosity, η_0 is the solvent viscosity, c is the weight concentration of the polymer, M is the molecular weight, and Φ is a coefficient which depends on chain geometry. For linear Gaussian chains, which serve as models for real linear macromolecules in Θ-solvents, $\Phi = 2.86 \times 10^{23}$ (5,6).* Furthermore, long-range interactions decrease Φ (7–12), while branching of the macromolecule increases Φ (13,14). The normally used empirical value, $\Phi = 2.1 \times 10^{23}$,* is based on measurements on linear macromolecules in good solvents, in which long-range interactions play a considerable role.

The rotational diffusion coefficient of macromolecules, which is closely related to the intrinsic viscosity (15,16), can be determined from measurements of the angle of orientation of the dynamic birefringence of polymer solutions.

Polymer chain dimensions can be determined also from the translational frictional coefficient F, which is determined from measurements of the diffusion and sedimentation coefficients of macromolecules. For hydrodynamically impermeable macromolecules

$$F = P(\overline{h^2})^{1/2}\eta_0 \tag{1.8}$$

where P is a coefficient which depends on chain geometry. For linear Gaussian chains, $P = 5.20$ (10,11), while the dependence of the coefficient P on long-range interactions and chain branching is similar to that of the coefficient Φ; this dependence, however, is weaker.

A summary of experimental results on the dimensions of macromolecules is given in Table 1.1. This table contains the ratios of the mean-square dimensions $(\overline{h^2})^{1/2}$ of macromolecules in Θ-solvents (in which long-range interactions are excluded) to the mean-square dimensions $(\overline{h^2}_{\text{fr. rot.}})^{1/2}$, calculated with eq. (1.14) for free rotation (in all cases, except in those specially indicated, the valence angles were considered to be tetrahedral). The quantity $(\overline{h^2}/\overline{h^2}_{\text{fr. rot.}})^{1/2}$ represents a measure of the restriction to free rotation in the chain. The method used to determine the dimensions, i.e., light scattering (LS) or viscometry (V), is indicated in the fourth column of the table. In order to calculate $\overline{h^2}$ by the second method, we have used the theoretical value, $\Phi = 2.86 \times 10^{23}$ for the Θ-solvents.† Only those dimensions directly measured in a Θ-solvent are given in the table; dimensions calculated from experimental data in other

* *Note:* This value corresponds to $[\eta]$ expressed in CGS units (cm. ^{3}/g.).

† Normally the empirical (averaged over all solvents) value of $\Phi = 2.1 \times 10^{23}$ is used. This results in an increase in $(\overline{h^2})^{1/2}$ of approximately 10% over the values given in Table 1.1.

solvents with the help of long-range interaction theory are not given. All data are for room temperature and atactic polymers (see Section 1.2).

The dipole moments of macromolecules are determined from measurements of the dielectric constants of dilute polymer solutions; in such measurements, the data must be analyzed on the basis of the polarization theory of the condensed phase (since even in infinitely dilute polymer solutions, each dipole is present in the field of other dipoles of the same molecule). Modern theories of the dielectric polarization of the condensed phase (52–54) lead to eq. (1.9) for the mean-square dipole moment per monomer unit in the chain.

$$\frac{\overline{\mu^2}}{n} = \frac{9kT(\epsilon - n_0^2)(2\epsilon + n_0^2)}{4\pi N_A \epsilon (n_0^2 + 2)^2} V_M \tag{1.9}$$

Here ϵ is the dielectric constant of the medium, n is the degree of polymerization (the number of monomer units in the macromolecule), n_0 is the refractive index of the medium, V_M is the molar volume of a monomer unit, μ is the dipole moment and N_A is Avogadro's number. Values of $\overline{\mu^2}/n$ have been obtained for many molecules in solution by using this equation or, more exactly, its generalization (54) for two-component systems, i.e., solutions. Values close to those have been obtained also from measurements of the dielectric properties of polymers in bulk (55–57). The difference between the $\overline{\mu^2}/n$ values and the dipole moments of monomer units m* shows the correlation of the orientations of neighboring dipoles; this is due to the presence of fixed valence angles and to the restriction of internal rotation.

The ratios of the root mean-square dipole moments of chains, $(\overline{\mu^2})^{1/2}$, to those of freely joined chains, $(\overline{\mu_0^2})^{1/2} = n^{1/2}m$ are given in Table 1.2. All data are for room temperature and atactic polymers.

The third quantity which gives information on chain flexibility is the mean optical anisotropy of the molecules; this can be determined from the dynamic birefringence of polymer solutions (16,66,67) (if the effects of macro and micro shapes are excluded from it) or (with less precision) from the photoelastic effect in highly elastic polymers.

A complete compendium of experimental data on the optical anisotropy of macromolecules is given in the review papers of Tsvetkov (16,118), while the theory of optical anisotropy of macromolecules is developed primarily in the studies of Gotlib (109–112) and presented in the monograph of Volkenstein (68) [see also (113–115)]. The optical anisotropy values of

* The dipole moment of a monomer unit is usually taken as the dipole moment of a hydrogenated monomeric molecule.

TABLE 1.2. Mean-Square Dipole Moments of Macromolecules in Solution and in the Highly Elastic State

Polymer	Repeating unit	$(\overline{\mu^2}/nm^2)^{1/2}$	References
Poly-*p*-chlorostyrene	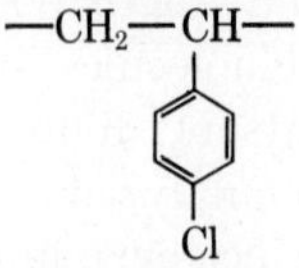 $-CH_2-CH-$ with C_6H_4-Cl (para)	0.65–0.75	55,57,58
Poly-*p*-bromostyrene	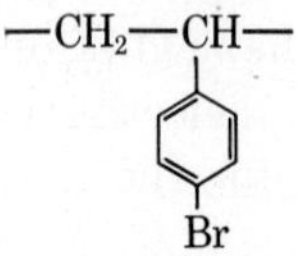 $-CH_2-CH-$ with C_6H_4-Br (para)	0.71	55
Poly-*p*-iodostyrene	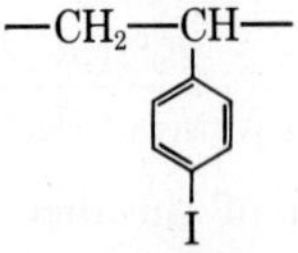 $-CH_2-CH-$ with C_6H_4-I (para)	0.71	55
Poly-*o*-chlorostyrene	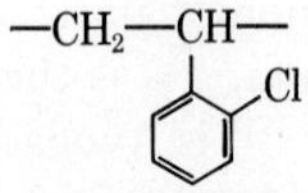 $-CH_2-CH-$ with C_6H_4-Cl (ortho)	1.3	55
Poly-*o*-bromostyrene	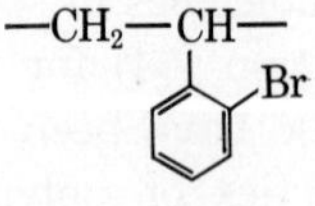 $-CH_2-CH-$ with C_6H_4-Br (ortho)	1.1	55
Poly(vinyl chloride)	$-CH_2-CH(Cl)-$	0.87	58,59
Poly(methyl methacrylate)	$-CH_2-C(CH_3)(C(=O)OCH_3)-$	0.73–0.81	56,60–63
Poly(ethyl methacrylate)	$-CH_2-C(CH_3)(C(=O)OCH_2CH_3)-$	0.77–0.79	56
Poly(*n*-propyl methacrylate)	$-CH_2-C(CH_3)(C(=O)O(CH_2)_2CH_3)-$	0.75–0.77	56
Poly(isopropyl methacrylate)	$-CH_2-C(CH_3)(C(=O)OCH(CH_3)_2)-$	0.78–0.81	56

(*continued*)

TABLE 1.2 (*continued*)

Polymer	Repeating unit	$(\overline{\mu^2}/nm^2)^{1/2}$	References
Poly(*n*-butyl methacrylate)	CH_3 $-CH_2-C-$ $O=C-O(CH_2)_3CH_3$	0.74–0.77	56
Poly(*tert*-butyl methacrylate)	CH_3 $-CH_2-C-$ $O=C-C(CH_3)_3$	0.79	116
Poly(phenyl methacrylate)	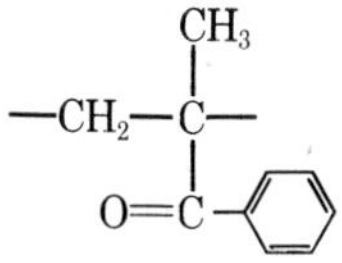 CH_3 $-CH_2-C-$ $O=C-C_6H_5$	0.74	62
Poly(*p*-chlorophenyl methacrylate)	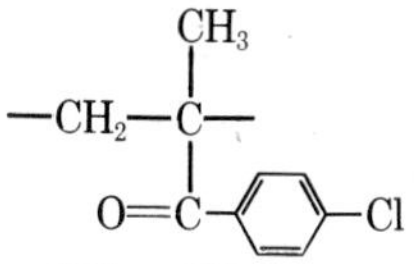 CH_3 $-CH_2-C-$ $O=C-C_6H_4-Cl$	0.59	62
Poly(methyl acrylate)	$-CH_2-CH-$ $O=C-OCH_3$	0.82	64
Poly(ethyl acrylate)	$-CH_2-CH-$ $O=C-OCH_2CH_3$	0.87	64
Poly(*n*-propyl acrylate)	$-CH_2-CH_2$ $O=C-O(CH_2)_2CH_3$	0.87	64
Poly(*n*-butyl acrylate)	$-CH_2-CH-$ $O=C-O(CH_2)_3CH_3$	0.82	64
Poly(vinyl acetate)	$-CH_2-CH-$ O $O=C-CH_3$	0.91	64
Poly(vinyl propionate)	$-CH_2-CH-$ O $O=C-CH_2CH_3$	0.93	64
Poly(vinyl butyrate)	$-CH_2-CH-$ O $O=C-(CH_2)_2CH_3$	0.90	64
Poly(vinyl isobutyl ether)	$-CH_2-CH-$ O $C(CH_3)_3$	0.87	117
Poly(ethylene oxide)	$-CH_2-CH_2-O-$	0.87	65

macromolecules are quite sensitive to the structure (valence angles, rotation of side groups, etc.) of the monomer units of a polymer chain, and, as a result, they can yield quite valuable and, in some cases, unique information. The present book, however, deals primarily with the mechanism of the flexibility of macromolecules, while the effect of the flexibility of a chain on its optical anisotropy is determined mainly by the influence of the flexibility on the mean chain dimensions (108). Therefore, we shall not dwell on the analysis of experimental data, nor on the development of the theory of polymer chain optical anisotropy.

1.2. Early Studies on the Conformational Statistics of Polymer Chains

As was already pointed out in the Introduction, a quantitative interpretation of the flexibility of polymer chains requires the development of a theory which relates the physical properties of individual macromolecules to parameters that characterize their flexibility. The basic aim of the conformational statistics of macromolecules is the development of such a theory. Starting with Chapter 2, we shall present the present-day status of this problem; at this point, however, we shall give a brief survey of early studies on the conformational statistics of polymer chains [for details, see Volkenshtein (68)].

The end-to-end distance of polymer chains consisting of N units is given by

$$\mathbf{h} = \sum_{i=1}^{N} \boldsymbol{l}_i \tag{1.10}$$

where $\boldsymbol{l}_i$ is a vector directed along the ith unit, with a length equal to that of the unit. As a result

$$\overline{h^2} = \sum_{i=1}^{N} \sum_{j=1}^{N} \overline{(\boldsymbol{l}_i, \boldsymbol{l}_j)} = \sum_{i=1}^{N} \boldsymbol{l}_i^2 + \sum_{i=1}^{N} 2 \sum_{j=1}^{i-1} \overline{(\boldsymbol{l}_i, \boldsymbol{l}_j)} \tag{1.11}$$

For a hypothetical freely jointed chain of N units with length l $\overline{(\boldsymbol{l}_i, \boldsymbol{l}_j)} = 0$ for $i \neq j$, and

$$\overline{h^2} = Nl^2 \tag{1.12}$$

For a polymer chain with units of identical length and with identical fixed valence angles and free rotation about all bonds (69,70),

$$\overline{h^2} = Nl^2 \frac{1 + \cos \alpha}{1 - \cos \alpha} - 2l^2 \cos \alpha \frac{1 - \cos^N \alpha}{(1 - \cos \alpha)^2} \tag{1.13}$$

where l is the length of a unit and $\pi - \alpha$ is the valence angle (for a hydrocarbon chain, this is close to a tetrahedral angle, i.e., to 109° 28′). With $N \gg 1$

$$\overline{h^2} = Nl^2(1 + \cos\alpha)/(1 - \cos\alpha) \tag{1.14}$$

In the same way, the dipole moment of the macromolecule is

$$\boldsymbol{\mu} = \sum_{i=1}^{N} \mathbf{m}_i \tag{1.15}$$

where $\mathbf{m}_i$ is the dipole moment of the ith monomer unit and n is the degree of polymerization. The mean-square value of the dipole moment may be calculated by using eq. (1.11), with $\mathbf{l}_i$ and $\mathbf{l}_j$ replaced by $\mathbf{m}_i$ and $\mathbf{m}_j$. For a hypothetical freely jointed chain, we obtain

$$\overline{\mu^2} = nm^2 \tag{1.16}$$

where m is the absolute value of the dipole moment of a monomer unit. For a chain with fixed valence angles and free rotation (55,69,71,72)

$$\overline{\mu^2} = nm^2\left(1 - 2\frac{\cos\alpha\cos\vartheta_1\cos\vartheta_2}{\sin^2\alpha}\right) \tag{1.17}$$

where ϑ_1 and ϑ_2 are the angles between the direction of the dipole and the two C—C bonds attached to it. For example, for chains of the type $(\text{—CH}_2\text{—CHR—})_n$ with tetrahedral valence angles, $\overline{\mu^2} = (11/12)nm^2$, while for chains of type $(\text{—CH}_2\text{—CR}_2\text{—})_n$, $\overline{\mu^2} = (3/4)nm^2$. (Here R is a polar side group). In real molecules, internal rotation is always more or less restricted, because of interactions between nonbonded atoms and atomic groups. As can be seen from Tables 1.1 and 1.2, restriction of internal rotation in macromolecules is reflected to a considerable degree in their dimensions and their dipole moments: the average dimensions of the majority of typical macromolecules of the vinyl series are 2 to 2.5 times greater, while their dipole moments are, as a rule, smaller than in macromolecules with free rotation.

The earliest studies on the conformational statistics of macromolecules which took restriction of internal rotation into account started with the assumption that the rotations about neighboring single bonds of the principal chain are independent of each other. The theoretical investigation of this question was initiated by Bresler and Frenkel (73), who examined a model having torsional oscillations and derived an equation which was valid for long chains ($N \gg 1$) with highly restricted rotation* (see Chapter 3)

$$\overline{h^2} = Nl^2\left(\frac{1 + \cos\alpha}{1 - \cos\alpha}\right)\frac{2}{1 - \eta} \tag{1.18}$$

Here $\eta = \overline{\cos\varphi}$ is the mean value of the cosine of the angle of internal rotation, φ.† Later, Debye (74), Taylor (75), and H. Kuhn (76) derived the more general expression:

$$\overline{h^2} = Nl^2\left(\frac{1 + \cos\alpha}{1 - \cos\alpha}\right)\left(\frac{1 + \eta}{1 - \eta}\right) \tag{1.19}$$

The equation of Bresler and Frenkel ($1 - \eta \ll 1$), and that also derived by Sadron (77) (with $\eta \ll 1$), follow from this equation. A still more general equation, not limited to high values of N, has been derived by Benoit (78). An examination of the regions of applicability of these equations and their detailed derivations has been reported by Volkenshtein and Ptitsyn (79,80). The calculation of the dependence of $\overline{h^2}$ on η was carried out by two methods: either by establishment of the recurring relation between the mean cosines of the angles formed by the units which are separated by the kth and $(k - 1)$th intermediate units, or by the consecutive projection of each unit on systems of coordinates related to pairs of preceding units. In later studies on the averaging of the vector characteristics of macromolecules the second method, which was first proposed by Eyring (69) was generally used [see also (79,80)]. It is presented in Chapter 5 in a generalized form. The first method was developed in the investigations of Gotlib (109–112) and Birshtein (113–115) on the averaging of the tensor characteristics of macromolecules.

Equation (1.19) is valid for polymers with symmetric side groups, of type $(\text{—CR}_2\text{—})_n$ or $(\text{—CR}_2\text{—CR}_2'\text{—})_n$ (polyethylene, polyisobutylene, etc.), in which the internal rotation potential is symmetric about the *trans*-position:

$$U(\varphi) = U(-\varphi) \tag{1.20}$$

* While the Bresler-Frenkel equation has been obtained for a model with torsional oscillations, it is actually valid for any symmetric potential under the conditions that $N \gg 1$ and $1 - \eta \ll 1$.

† The internal rotation angle φ_i defines the inclination of the plane, which passes through the ith and $(i - 1)$th units of the chain, relative to the plane which passes through the $(i - 1)$th and $(i - 2)$th units. We measure this angle from the *trans* position of the units, in which the $(i - 2)$th, $(i - 1)$th and ith units lie in a single plane and the ith unit is parallel to the $(i - 2)$th unit.

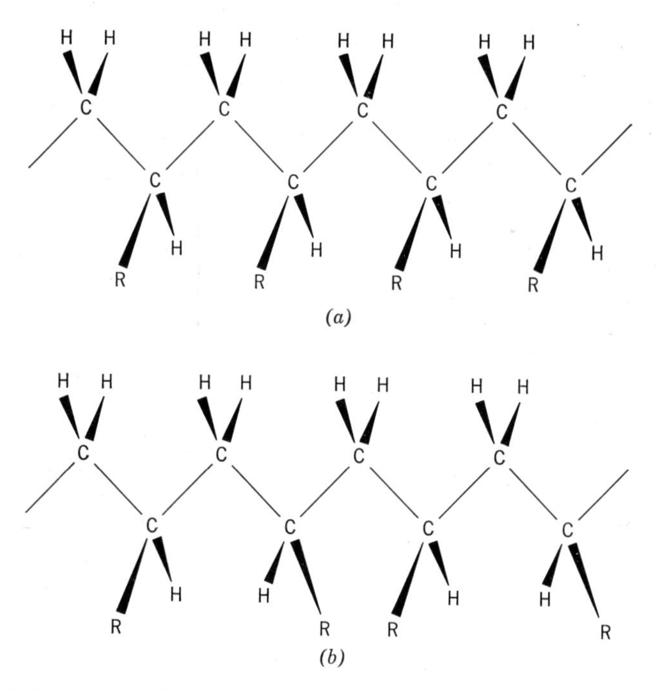

Fig. 1.1. Stereoregular macromolecules of the vinyl series: (*a*) isotactic; (*b*) syndiotactic. The thin lines lie in the plane of the drawing, the heavy lines protrude on both sides of this plane and are drawn in perspective.

Most polymers of the vinyl series, such as polystyrene, poly(methyl methacrylate), etc., have asymmetric side groups, i.e., they belong to the type $(\text{—CRR}'\text{—})_n$ or $(\text{—CH}_2\text{—CRR}'\text{—})_n$. The condition of symmetry, eq. (1.20), is not fulfilled for such polymers, and their dimensions are characterized by their values not only of $\overline{\cos \varphi}$ but also of $\overline{\sin \varphi}$. Birshtein and Ptitsyn (81,82) were the first to examine the mean dimensions of chains with asymmetric side groups, taking into account the fact that, in such cases, the conditions of internal rotation are a function of stereoisomerism, i.e., of the positions of identical side groups in the chain. As is well known, Natta and his co-workers and later many others, have synthesized sterically regular polymers (83–88): these may be *isotactic*, in which each monomer unit of a planar *trans* chain can be obtained from the previous one by parallel translation (89), or *syndiotactic*, in which transition from one monomer unit to the next requires parallel translation along with mirror image reflection (89). In the case of vinyl polymers of type $(\text{—CH}_2\text{—CHR—})_n$, this means that, in an isotactic polymer, the R groups are located on one side of the planar *trans* chain, while, in syndiotactic polymers, they alternate on the two sides (Fig. 1.1). Irregular (atactic) polymers are characterized by a definite *microtacticity*, i.e., by the probability of monomer units being attached in an isotactic or syndiotactic manner.

From the symmetry conditions of isotactic chains of the type $(\text{—CH}_2\text{—CHR—})_n$ and the assumption of the independent rotations about neighboring units, it was shown (82) that such chains must be characterized by values of $\overline{\cos\varphi}$ identical for all units and values of $\overline{\sin\varphi}$ identical in absolute value, but alternating in sign (if all the rotation angles are measured in the same direction). In similar manner it was shown that syndiotactic chains of the type $(\text{—CH}_2\text{—CHR—})_n$, with independent rotations about neighboring units, must be characterized by values of $\overline{\cos\varphi}$ identical for all units and values of $\overline{\sin\varphi}$ identical in absolute value but alternating in sign in pairs. (The sign of $\overline{\sin\varphi}$ is determined, apparently, by the direction of the predominant twist about a given unit.) These differences in the direction of the predominant twist result in different equations for the mean dimensions of isotactic and syndiotactic molecules (82):

$$\overline{h_i^2} = Nl^2\left(\frac{1+\cos\alpha}{1-\cos\alpha}\right)\frac{1-\eta^2-\epsilon^2}{(1-\eta)^2+\epsilon^2} \tag{1.21}$$

and

$$\overline{h_s^2} = Nl^2\left(\frac{1+\cos\alpha}{1-\cos\alpha}\right)\frac{1-(\eta^2+\epsilon^2)^2}{(1-\eta)^2+(\eta-\eta^2-\epsilon^2)^2} \tag{1.22}$$

where $\epsilon = \overline{\sin\varphi}$. Examination of these equations shows that, for identical values of η and ϵ, $\overline{h_i^2} < \overline{h_s^2}$, i.e., isotactic chains must be shorter than syndiotactic ones, under the assumption of independent rotation about neighboring units. As we shall see below, in actuality, rotations about neighboring units can in no way be regarded as independent; therefore, comparison of this theoretical calculation with experiment makes no sense. The dimensions of atactic chains have been examined by Birshtein and Ptitsyn (82) and recently in greater detail (but with the same approximation) by Suzuki (90).

In a number of investigations (91–94), the mean dimensions of chains of the type $(\text{—CH}_2\text{—CHR—})_n$ were calculated without taking into account the stereochemical structure of the macromolecules, with the assumption that all the units are characterized by values of $\overline{\cos\varphi}$ and $\overline{\sin\varphi}$ identical in sign and value, i.e., by an identical direction of the predominant twist. As a result, the equation obtained in these studies,

$$\overline{h^2} = Nl^2\left(\frac{1 + \cos \alpha}{1 - \cos \alpha}\right) \frac{(1 + \eta)^2 + \epsilon^2}{1 - \eta^2 - \epsilon^2} \tag{1.23}$$

is not consistent with the stereochemistry of polymer chains and, particularly, does not take into account the differences between isotactic and syndiotactic polymers.

The mean dimensions of macromolecules have been calculated also for more complicated structures within the approximation of independent rotations: for chains with alternating values of $\overline{\cos \varphi}$ and valence angles (95), for molecules of rubber and gutta-percha (71,95–97), cellulose (96), polypeptides (96), and, finally, for the general case of macromolecules with any number of segments in the repeating unit (93,94).

Debye and Bueche (58) first took into account qualitatively the restriction of internal rotation in the theory of dipole moments of macromolecules. The quantitative theory of dipole moments of macromolecules (within the approximation of independent rotations about neighboring units) was developed by Birshtein and Ptitsyn (98) in 1954. The following equations [eqs. (1.24)–(1.27)] taking restriction of internal rotation into account were derived for chains of various types.

$(\text{—}CR_2\text{—})_n$:

$$\overline{\mu^2} = 0 \tag{1.24}$$

$(\text{—}CH_2\text{—}CR_2\text{—})_n$:

$$\overline{\mu^2} = \frac{nm^2}{1 + \cos \alpha}\left(\frac{1 + \eta}{1 - \eta}\right) \tag{1.25}$$

$(\text{—}CH_2\text{—}CHR\text{—})_n$ (isotactic):

$$\overline{\mu^2}_i = \frac{nm^2}{1 - \eta^2 - \epsilon^2}\left[\frac{11}{12}(1 + \eta^2 + \epsilon^2) + \frac{\eta}{2} - \frac{4}{3}\frac{\epsilon^2}{(1 - \eta)^2 + \epsilon^2} + \frac{2\sqrt{3}}{3}\epsilon\right] \tag{1.26}$$

$(\text{—}CH_2\text{—}CHR\text{—})_n$ (syndiotactic):

$$\overline{\mu^2}_s = nm^2\frac{1 - \eta^2 - \epsilon^2}{(1 - \eta)^2 + (\eta - \eta^2 - \epsilon^2)^2} \times \left[\frac{11}{12}(1 + \eta^2 + \epsilon^2) - \frac{4}{3}\eta + \frac{2\sqrt{3}}{3}\epsilon\right] \tag{1.27}$$

Here m is, as before, the dipole moment of a monomer unit; the valence angles are considered to be tetrahedral. Equations for $\overline{\mu^2}$ of chains of type $(\text{—CHR—})_n$ were also derived.

Equations (1.26) and (1.27) contain the term $(2\sqrt{3}/3)\epsilon$ which is a function of the sign of ϵ. This sign is taken as negative if the dipolar R groups repel each other more strongly than the nondipolar ones, and as positive in the opposite case. All other conditions being equal, $\overline{\mu^2}$ will be smaller with negative than with positive ϵ; this is not surprising, since in the first case the dipoles partly compensate each other. Examination of eqs. (1.26) and (1.27) shows (98) that, for identical η and ϵ, $\overline{\mu_s^2} < \overline{\mu_i^2}$, the difference between $\overline{\mu_s^2}$ and $\overline{\mu_i^2}$ being quite large (considerably larger than that between $\overline{h_s^2}$ and $\overline{h_i^2}$). This is due to the fact that the differences between the mean-square dipole moments of isotactic and syndiotactic chains are determined not only by the differences in the directions of the predominant twists (as for $\overline{h_s^2}$ and $\overline{h_i^2}$), but also directly by the difference in the mutual orientations of the polar side groups. In this case also, however, the real conformations of the monomer units in isotactic and syndiotactic chains must be taken into account in the development of theory sufficiently quantitative to permit comparison with experiment.

Expressions for $\overline{\mu^2}$ have been derived for heterochain polymers in a number of studies: for polydimethylsiloxane $[\text{—Si(CH}_3)_2\text{—O—}]_n$ (72), poly(ethylene oxide) $(\text{—CH}_2\text{—CH}_2\text{—O—})_n$ (65), and polyoxymethylene $(\text{—CH}_2\text{—O—})_n$ (99,100).

It is evident that, with the availability of the proper theory, experimental data on the dimensions and dipole moments of macromolecules could serve as a basis for the quantitative investigation of polymer chain flexibility. Attempts at such an investigation, however, with the use of the theoretical expressions for $\overline{h^2}$ and $\overline{\mu^2}$ given in this section would obviously result in failure. In fact, these expressions have been obtained with the assumption that the rotations about neighboring chain units are independent. This means that the total potential energy of the chain, which is a function of all the angles of internal rotation, can be decomposed into a sum of terms, each of which is a function only of one angle of internal rotation:

$$U(\varphi_1, \varphi_2, \ldots, \varphi_N) = \sum_{i=1}^{N} U(\varphi_i) \tag{1.28}$$

In other words, only the interactions between atoms which are directly linked to two neighboring atoms of the main chain are taken into account, while all other interactions are neglected. Until quite recently, such an approximation was not only accepted in statistical physics of macromolecules, but also was widely used (and is still used) in studies of the thermodynamic properties of low molecular compounds [in particular, in the determination of the potential barriers which restrict internal rotation, from the temperature dependence of the heat capacity (101)]. It should be noted, however, that this assumption has never been verified by any more or less convincing reasoning and, actually, was dictated only by the requirements of convenience and ease of calculation.

At this point we shall not delve into an analysis of the nature of the potential restricting internal rotation (see Section 2.2); we shall note only that the forces of interaction must increase sharply with a decrease in distance between the atoms. At the same time, it should be pointed out that simple calculations, as well as studies of appropriate models, have demonstrated that atoms which are not bonded to two neighboring atoms of the chain can approach each other quite closely, both in low and high molecular weight compounds; therefore, under no circumstances is it possible to neglect the interactions between them. Using the empirical potential of intramolecular interactions which they had derived, Lassettre and Dean (102) showed as early as 1949 that the conformations of isobutane, $CH(CH_3)_3$, and tetramethylmethane, $C(CH_3)_4$ are determined by the interactions between the methyl end groups, which depend not on one, but on two angles of internal rotation. Later, Ptitsyn and Sharonov showed (103) that the major part of the energy difference between the rotational isomers of *n*-butane* is determined by the interactions of non-neighboring atomic groups. A detailed investigation of the restricting potential in *n*-butane carried out recently by Borisova and Volkenshtein (105) confirmed the important role played by interactions between non-neighboring groups in this compound.

Thus, correlations between neighboring rotations play an important role, even in linear low molecular weight hydrocarbons with small side groups, and the condition of eq. (1.28) is not fulfilled. This must be even more the case of polymer chains with large side groups (polyisobutylene, polystyrene, etc.) for which conformations are determined principally by interactions between their large side groups, as has been demonstrated by calculations as well as by an examination of models (see Chapter 3). This is confirmed by the sharp difference between the conformations in the crystalline state of isotactic and syndiotactic chains of the type $(—CH_2—CHR—)_n$; this difference is determined by the different mutual orientations of the large groups. Furthermore, the helical crystalline conforma-

* Volkenshtein (104) earlier pointed out the necessity of taking into account the correlations between rotations about the various single bonds of *n*-butane.

tion of isotactic chains shows that there is a considerable difference between the angles of rotation of two neighboring bonds. At the same time, the assumption that the rotations about neighboring bonds are independent of each other requires that these angles be equal in value and opposite in sign (82), as was pointed out in connection with eq. (1.21).

From what has been said above, it follows that the approximation of eq. (1.28) neglects those interactions which play a decisive role in most polymers. Thus, under no circumstances, can it serve as a basis for a quantitative theory of macromolecules. *Any quantitative theory of macromolecules absolutely must take into account the correlation between rotations about neighboring bonds, i.e., it must consider a macromolecule as a one-dimensional cooperative system.* Comparison of such a theory with experiment is obviously impossible without knowledge of the real conformations of the monomer units of the chain. Thus, if the first aim of a theory of macromolecules is the determination of the relation between the physical properties of polymer chains and the conformations of their monomer units, then its second aim is the development of methods for determining these conformations.

References

1. Debye, P. J. W., *J. Phys. Colloid Chem.*, **51,** 18 (1947).
2. Benoit, H., and P. Doty, *J. Phys. Chem.*, **57,** 958 (1953).
3. Zimm, B. H., *J. Chem. Phys.*, **16,** 1093 (1948).
4. Flory, P. J., *Principles of Polymer Chemistry*, Cornell Univ. Press, Ithaca, N. Y., 1953.
5. Auer, P. L., and C. S. Gardner, *J. Chem. Phys.*, **23,** 1546 (1955).
6. Zimm, B. H., *J. Chem. Phys.*, **24,** 269 (1956).
7. Ptitsyn, O. B., and Yu. E. Eizner, *Zh. Fiz. Khim.*, **32,** 2464 (1958).
8. Ptitsyn, O. B., and Yu. E. Eizner, *Zh. Tekhn. Fiz.*, **29,** 1117 (1959); *Soviet Phys.-Tech. Phys.*, **4,** 1020 (1959).
9. Ptitsyn, O. B., and Yu. E. Eizner, *Vysokomol. Soedin.*, **1,** 966 (1959).
10. Yamakawa, H., and M. Kurata, *J. Phys. Soc. Japan*, **13,** 94 (1958).
11. Kurata, M., and H. Yamakawa, *J. Chem. Phys.*, **29,** 311 (1958).
12. Kurata, M., H. Yamakawa, and H. Utiyama, *Makromol. Chem.*, **34.** 139 (1959).
13. Zimm, B. H., and R. W. Kilb, *J. Polymer Sci.*, **37,** 19 (1959).
14. Bueche, F., *J. Polymer Sci.*, **41,** 549 (1959).
15. Kuhn, W., H. Kuhn, and P. Buchner, *Ergeb. Exact. Naturw.*, **25,** 1 (1951).
16. Tsvetkov, V. N., *Zh. Vses. Khim. Obshchestva im. D. I. Mendeleeva* **6,** 428 (1961).
17. Kunst, E. D., *Rec. Trav. Chim.*, **69,** 125 (1950).
18. Fox, T. G, Jr., and P. J. Flory, *J. Am. Chem. Soc.*, **73,** 1909 (1951).
19. Krigbaum, W. R., and P. J. Flory, *J. Polymer Sci.*, **11,** 37 (1953).
20. Bawn, C. E. H., and R. D. Patel, *Trans. Faraday Soc.*, **52,** 1669 (1956).
21. Danusso, F., G. Moraglio, and G. Gianotti, *Rend. Ist. Lombardo Sci. Lettere*, **A93,** 666 (1959).

22. Danusso, F., G. Moraglio, and G. Gianotti, *Rend. Ist. Lombardo Sci. Lettere,* **A94,** 566 (1960).
23. Ciferri, A., and M. Lauretti, *Ann. Chim.* (*Rome*), **48,** 198 (1958).
24. Outer, P., C. I. Carr, and B. H. Zimm, *J. Chem. Phys.*, **18,** 830 (1950).
25. Fox, T. G, Jr., and P. J. Flory, *J. Am. Chem. Soc.*, **73,** 1915 (1951).
26. Krigbaum, W. R., L. Mandelkern, and P. J. Flory, *J. Polymer Sci.*, **9,** 381 (1952).
27. Oth, J., and V. Desreux, *Bull. Soc. Chim. Belges,* **63,** 285 (1954).
28. Krigbaum, W. R., and D. K. Carpenter, *J. Phys. Chem.*, **59,** 1166 (1955).
29. Notley, N. T., and P. J. W. Debye, *J. Polymer Sci.*, **17,** 99 (1955).
30. Chinai, S. N., P. C. Scherer, C. W. Bondurant, and D. W. Levi, *J. Polymer Sci.*, **22,** 527 (1956).
31. Rossi, C., U. Bianchi, and V. Magnasco, *J. Polymer Sci.*, **30,** 175 (1958).
32. Eskin, V. E., *Vysokomol. Soedin.*, **1,** 138 (1959); *Polymer Sci. USSR,* **1,** 174 (1960)
33. Eskin, V. E., and K. Z. Gumargalieva, *Vysokomol. Soedin.*, **2,** 265 (1960); *Polymer Sci. USSR,* **2,** 320 (1961) (abstract).
34. Eskin, V. E., and L. N. Andreeva, *Vysokomol. Soedin.*, **3,** 435 (1961); *Polymer Sci. USSR,* **2,** 536 (1961) (abstract).
35. Boyes, A. G., and U. P. Strauss, *J. Polymer Sci.*, **22,** 463 (1956).
36. Eskin, V. E., and O. Z. Korotkina, *Vysokomol. Soedin.*, **2,** 272 (1960); *Polymer Sci. USSR,* **2,** 247 (1961).
37. Newman, S., W. R. Krigbaum, C. Laugier, and P. J. Flory, *J. Polymer Sci.*, **14,** 451 (1954).
38. Shultz, A. R., *J. Am. Chem. Soc.*, **76,** 3422 (1954).
39. Sakurada, I., Y. Sakaguchi, and Sh. Kokuryo, *Kobunshi Kagaku,* **17,** 227 (1960).
40. Cantow, H.-J., and O. Bodmann, *Z. Physik. Chem.* (*Frankfurt*), **3,** 65 (1955).
41. Chinai, S. N., and C. W. Bondurant, Jr., *J. Polymer Sci.*, **22,** 555 (1956).
42. Chinai, S. N., and R. J. Samuels, *J. Polymer Sci.*, **19,** 463 (1956).
43. Chinai, S. N., and R. A Guzzi, *J. Polymer Sci.*, **21,** 427 (1956).
44. Didot, F. E., S. N. Chinai, and D. W. Levi, *J. Polymer Sci.*, **43,** 557 (1960).
45. Chinai, S. N., *J. Polymer Sci.*, **25,** 413 (1957).
46. Chinai, S. N., A. L. Resnik, and H. T. Lee, *J. Polymer Sci.*, **33,** 471 (1958).
47. Chinai, S. N., and R. A. Guzzi, *J. Polymer Sci.*, **41,** 475 (1959).
48. Flory, P. J., L. Mandelkern, J. B. Kinsinger, and W. B. Schultz, *J. Am. Chem. Soc.*, **74,** 3364 (1952).
49. Ivin, K. J., and H. A. Ende, *J. Polymer Sci.*, **43,** S17 (1961).
50. Wagner, H. L., and P. J. Flory, *J. Am. Chem. Soc.*, **74,** 195 (1952).
51. Danusso, F., G. Moraglio, and G. Gianotti, *J. Polymer Sci.*, **51,** 475 (1961).
52. Fröhlich, H., *Teoriya Dielektrikov* IL, Moscow, 1960 (originally published as *Theory of Dielectrics*, Oxford, Clarendon Press, 1958).
53. Buckingham, A., *Proc. Roy. Soc.* (*London*), A238, 235 (1956).
54. Mikhailov, G. P., and L. L. Burshtein, *Usp. Fiz. Nauk,* **74,** 3 (1961); *Soviet Phys.-Usp.*, **4,** 389 (1961).
55. Fattakhov, K. Z., *Zh. Tekhn. Fiz.*, **24,** 1401 (1954).
56. Mikhailov, G. P., and L. L. Burshtein, *Zh. Tekhn. Fiz.*, **29,** 192 (1959); *Soviet Phys.-Tech. Phys.*, **4,** 165 (1959).
57. Birshtein, T. M., L. L. Burshtein, and O. B. Ptitsyn, *Zh. Tekhn. Fiz.*, **29,** 896 (1959); *Soviet Phys.-Tech. Phys..*, **4,** 810 (1959).
58. Debye, P., and F. Bueche, *J. Chem. Phys.*, **19,** 589 (1951).

59. Imamura, Y., *Nippon Kagaku Zasshi*, **76**, 217 (1955).
60. Marchal, J., and H. Benoit, *J. Polymer Sci.*, **23**, 223 (1957).
61. Marchal, J., and Ch. Lapp, *J. Polymer Sci.*, **27**, 571 (1958).
62. Burshtein, L. L., and G. P. Mikhailov, *Zh. Tekhn. Fiz.*, **27**, 694 (1957); *Soviet Phys.-Tech. Phys.*, **2**, 624 (1957).
63. Mikhailov, G. P., and L. L. Burshtein, *Fiz. Tverd Telz*, **1**, 632 (1959); *Soviet Phys.-Solid State*, **1**, 574 (1959).
64. Mikhailov, G. P., and L. L. Burshtein, *Vysokomol. Soedin.*, in press.
65. Marchal, J., and H. Benoit, *J. Chim. Phys.*, **52**, 818 (1955).
66. Tsvetkov, V. N., *Usp. Khim., Tekhnol. Polimerov*, **2**, 171 (1957).
67. Tsvetkov, V. N., *Vestn. Gos. Leningr. Univ., Ser. Fiz. Khim.*, **22**, No. 4, 39 (1961).
68. Volkenshtein, M. V., *Konfiguratsionnaya Statistika Polimernykh Tsepei*, Izdatel'stvo Akad. Nauk SSSR, Moscow, 1959 (published in translation as *Configurational Statistics of Polymeric Chains*, Interscience, New York, 1963).
69. Eyring, H., *Phys. Rev.*, **39**, 746 (1932).
70. Fuoss, R. M., and J. G. Kirkwood, *J. Am. Chem. Soc.*, **63**, 385 (1941).
71. Wall, F. T., *J. Chem. Phys.*, **11**, 67 (1943).
72. Sauer, R. O., and D. J. Mead, *J. Am. Chem. Soc.*, **68**, 1794 (1946).
73. Bresler, S. E., and Ya. I. Frenkel, *Zh. Eksp. Teoret. Fiz.*, **9**, 1094 (1939); Ya. I. Frenkel, *Sobranie Trudov* (Collected Works), Vol. 2, Izdatel'stvo Akad. Nauk SSSR, Moscow, 1958.
74. Debye, P. J. W., Report No. 637 to Rubber Reserve Company, 9.04, (1945); *Collected Papers of Peter J. W. Debye*, Interscience, New York–London, 1954.
75. Taylor, W. J., *J. Chem. Phys.*, **15**, 412 (1947).
76. Kuhn, H., *J. Chem. Phys.*, **15**, 843 (1947).
77. Sadron, C., *J. Chim. Phys.*, **43**, 145 (1946).
78. Benoit, H., *J. Chim. Phys.*, **44**, 18 (1947).
79. Volkenshtein, M. V., and O. B. Ptitsyn, *Dokl. Akad. Nauk* SSSR, **78**, 657 (1951).
80. Volkenshtein, M. V., and O. B. Ptitsyn, *Zh. Fiz. Khim.*, **26**, 1061 (1952).
81. Birshtein, T. M., and O. B. Ptitsyn, *Zh. Fiz. Khim.*, **26**, 1215 (1952).
82. Birshtein, T. M., and O. B. Ptitsyn, *Zh. Fiz. Khim.*, **28**, 213 (1954).
83. Natta, G., *J. Polymer Sci.*, **16**, 143 (1955).
84. Natta, G., *Makromol. Chem.*, **16**, 213 (1955).
85. Natta, G., *Angew. Chem.*, **68**, 393 (1956).
86. Natta, G., *Chim. Ind.* (*Paris*), **77**, 1009 (1957).
87. Natta, G., *Makromol. Chem.*, **35**, 94 (1960).
88. Natta, G., *Nuovo Cimento* (*Suppl.* **1**), **15**, 3 (1960).
89. Natta, G., and F. Danusso, *J. Polymer Sci.*, **34**, 3 (1959).
90. Suzuki, Y., *J. Chem. Phys.*, **34**, 79 (1961).
91. Tang, A.-C., *J. Chim. Soc.*, **18**, 103 (1951).
92. Sack, R. A., *J. Chem. Phys.*, **25**, 1087 (1956).
93. Chung, C.-S., *Acta. Sci. Natur.*, No. 1, 139 (1956).
94. Chen, H.-F., and Ho Fu-Chen, *Acta Sci. Natur.* No. 2, 203 (1956).
95. Chistorazum, A. A., *Dokl. Akad. Nauk SSSR*, **89**, 999 (1953).
96. Benoit, H., *J. Polymer Sci.*, **3**, 376 (1948).
97. Tang, A.-C., and J.-C. Liu, *J. Chinese Chem. Soc.*, **18**, 110 (1951).
98. Birshtein, T. M., and O. B. Ptitsyn, *Zh. Tekhn. Fiz.*, **24**, 1998 (1954).
99. Uchida, T., Y. Kurita, and M. Kubo, *J. Polymer Sci.*, **19**, 365 (1956).

100. Uchida, T., Y. Kurita, N. Koizumi, and M. Kubo, *J. Polymer Sci.*, **21**, 313 (1956)
101. Godnev, I. N., *Vychislenie Termodinamicheskikh Funktsii po Molekularnym Dannym* (Calculation of Thermodynamic Functions from Molecular Data), Gostekhizdat, Moscow, 1956.
102. Lassettre, E. N., and L. B. Dean, Jr., *J. Chem. Phys.*, **17**, 317 (1949).
103. Ptitsyn, O. B., and Yu. A. Sharonov, *Zh. Tekhn. Fiz.*, **27**, 2744 (1957); *Soviet Phys.-Tech. Phys.*, **2**, 2544 (1957).
104. Volkenshtein, M. V., *Dokl. Akad. Nauk SSSR*, **49**, 111 (1945).
105. Borisova, N. P., and M. V. Volkenshtein, *Zh. Strukt. Khim.*, 2, 469 (1961).
106. Fox, T. G, *Polymer*, **3**, 111 (1962).
107. Ivin, K. J., H. A. Ende, and G. Meyerhoff, *Polymer*, **3**, 129 (1962).
108. Birshtein, T. M., M. V. Volkenshtein, Yu. Ya. Gotlib, and O. B. Ptitsyn, *Vysokomol. Soedin.*, **4**, 670 (1962); *Polymer Sci. USSR*, **3**, 973 (1962) (abstract).
109. Gotlib, Yu. Ya., M. V. Volkenshtein, and E. K. Byutner, *Dokl. Akad. Nauk SSSR*, **49**, 935 (1945).
110. Gotlib, Yu. Ya., *Zh. Tekhn. Fiz..*, **27**, 707 (1957); *Soviet Phys.-Tech. Phys.*, **2**, 637 (1957).
111. Gotlib, Yu. Ya., *Zh. Tekhn. Fiz.*, **28**, 801 (1958); *Soviet Phys.-Tech. Phys.*, **3**, 749 (1958).
112. Gotlib, Yu. Ya., *Uch. Zap. Leingr. Ped. Inst. im. A. I. Gertsena*, **141**, 121 (1958).
113. Birshtein, T. M., *Zh. Tekhn. Fiz.*, **28**, 813 (1958); *Soviet Phys.-Tech. Phys.*, **3**, 760 (1958).
114. Birshtein, T. M., *Vysokomol. Soedin.*, **1**, 798 (1959); *Polymer Sci. USSR*, **1**, 276 (1960).
115. Birshtein, T. M., and E. A. Sokolova, *Vysokomol. Soedin.*, **1**, 1026 (1959); *Polymer Sci. USSR*, **1**, 397 (1960).
116. Mikhailov, G. P. and L. L. Burshtein, *Vysokomol. Soedin.*, **6**, 1713 (1964).
117. Takeda, M., Y. Imamura, S. Okamura, and T. Higashimura, *J. Chem. Phys.*, **33**, 631 (1960).
118. Tsvetkov, V. N., *Usp. Fiz. Nauk*, **81**, 51 (1963); *Soviet Phys.-Usp.*, **6**, 639 (1963).
119. Kuwahara, N., M. Kaneko, Y. Miyake, and J. Furuichi, *J. Phys. Soc. Japan*, **17**, 568 (1962).
120. Schulz, G. V., and A. Haug, *Z. Physik. Chem. (Frankfurt)*, **34**, 328 (1962).
121. Haug, A., and G. Meyerhoff, *Makromol. Chem.*, **53**, 91 (1962).
122. Crescenzi, V., and P. J. Flory, *J. Am. Chem. Soc.*, **86**, 141 (1964).

Chapter 2

INTERNAL ROTATION AND ROTATIONAL ISOMERISM

2.1. Brief Survey of Experimental Data

First, let us examine the problem of monomer unit conformations in typical cases. This problem is, obviously, related to the general problem of the internal rotation in molecules, which is always more or less restricted. This is indicated first of all by the fact that the contributions to the heat capacities of molecules containing single C—C bonds lie between those typical for rotational and vibrational motions. The restriction of internal rotation, which results in the temperature dependence of the probability of various states of molecules, is further confirmed by the temperature dependence in such molecules of various physical properties (heat capacity, dipole moment, nuclear magnetic resonance absorption, intensities of spectral lines, etc.) which are determined by the relative positions of groups attached to the C—C bond. The pertinent experimental data have been presented in literature reviews (1–5, 74,75).

At the present time the best method for the study of molecular structure (6,7) is that of microwave spectroscopy. This method permits determination of the characteristics of the internal rotation in two ways: first, from the change with temperature of the intensity ratios of rotational transition bands which correspond to the rotation of whole molecules in the fundamental and excited states of the torsional oscillations and, second, from the splitting of rotational bands due to transition over the internal rotation barrier. Also noteworthy is the application of the method of nuclear magnetic resonance [see, for example, (8,9)] to the investigation of rotations within molecules. During the early years of the development of this technique, investigations were centered on the temperature dependence of the width or second moment of the band; this dependence is determined by internal rotation. More recently, high resolution spectra have also come into usage; these yield more detailed information on the location of atomic groups within molecules (10).

If at least one of the rotating groups has C_{3v} symmetry, characterized by the presence of a threefold axis of symmetry which coincides with the axis

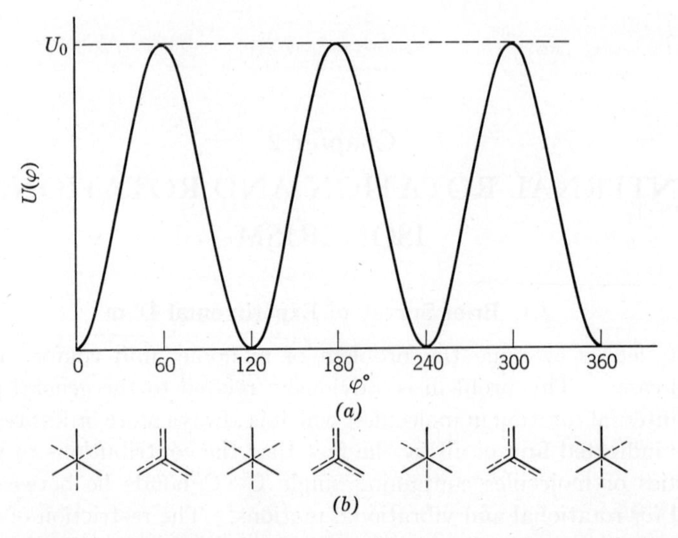

Fig. 2.1. (*a*) Plot of internal rotation potential energy as a function of the angle of rotation φ, with C_{3v} symmetry of the rotating groups, and (*b*) the corresponding conformations of the molecule. U_0 is the height of the potential barrier.

of rotation and by three planes of symmetry which pass through the axis of rotation (methyl groups, for example, have such symmetry), then the internal rotation potential energy obviously does not change if the angle of internal rotation φ is replaced by angle $\varphi \pm 2\pi/3$, as well as if angle $+\varphi$ is replaced by $-\varphi$ (angle φ is measured from the minimum of the potential curve). A particular case of such potential is shown in Figure 2.1. Expanding the potential energy $U(\varphi)$ in a Fourier series and taking the indicated symmetry conditions into account, we obtain

$$U(\varphi) = \frac{1}{2} \sum_{n=1}^{\infty} U^{(3n)} (1 - \cos 3n\varphi) \tag{2.1}$$

Experimental data show [see, for example, (3)] that, if the C—C bond is formed by tetrahedral carbon atoms (i.e., it is not adjacent to a C═C bond), the potential energy minimum corresponds to the *staggered conformation* of the molecule (see Fig. 2.1). Should a double bond be attached to one of the carbon atoms, however, it assumes an *eclipsed conformation* with respect to one of the atoms of the C_{3v} symmetry group (11).

Microwave spectroscopic investigation of the splitting of rotational bands has shown that in all cases, for example, in methylsilane, CH_3—SiH_3 (12), acetaldehyde, CH_3—CHO (13), and propylene oxide, CH_3—

CHCH$_2$O (14), the coefficient $U^{(3)}$ in series (2.1) is greater than $U^{(6)}$ by at least one order of magnitude. Even if the symmetry of the molecule results in a zero coefficient $U^{(3)}$, $U^{(6)}$ amounts to only a few calories per mole, i.e., there is practically free rotation. This is true if the second rotating group has C_{2v} symmetry, e.g., nitromethane, CH_3—NO_2 (15) and methyl difluoroborane, CH_3—BF_2 (16). As a result, it is sufficient to keep only the first term of the series in eq. (2.1) for practically all molecules with C_{3v} symmetry, i.e., the potential energy of internal rotation can be regarded as

$$U(\varphi) = (U_0/2)\,(1 - \cos 3\varphi) \tag{2.2}$$

where $U_0 \equiv U^{(3)}$ is equal to the height of the potential barrier (see Fig. 2.1).

In this case, the internal rotation appears to involve torsional oscillations inside potential wells located close to the staggered conformations, with jumps over barriers which correspond to the eclipsed conformations. The heights of the barriers, which in the past were determined mainly from heat capacity, are measured now with great accuracy by microwave spectroscopic methods (3,4,74,75). The height of the barrier U_0 is 2.7–3.0 kcal/mole in the most simple ethane molecule, CH_3—CH_3 (76). The value of U_0 increases, as a rule, by 10–30% for the replacement of each H atom by CH_3, Cl, F, or CN, reaching, for example, for hexachloroethane, CCl_3—CCl_3, values of the order of 10 kcal/mole (77). Furthermore, the height of the barrier decreases with an increase in the length d of the axis of rotation, from 3 kcal/mole for CH_3—CH_3 (d = 1.54 Å) to 1.7 kcal/mole (78) for CH_3—SiH_3 (d = 1.93 Å), ≈1 kcal/mole (77) for SiH_3—SiH_3 (d = 2.34 Å) and practically to zero (79) for H_3C—C≡C—CF_3 (d = 4.1 Å). Tables of barrier heights have been compiled for a large number of compounds; they can be found in reviews (3,4,74,75) and in Volkenshtein's recent monograph (2).

If none of the rotating groups has C_{3v} symmetry, the internal rotation potential energy curve acquires a more complicated form. The molecular conformations corresponding to the relative minima of the potential curve correspond in this case of nonbonded atoms to different mutual arrangements. Therefore, in general they have different potential energies at the minimum point and different shapes of the potential curves in the vicinity of the minimum. These stable molecular conformations, which differ from each other, can be obtained from each other by rotation about single bonds and thus, are called *rotational isomers*. For example, in 1,2-substituted ethanes (Fig. 2.2) the rotational isomers correspond approximately to the staggered positions of the bonds; moreover, the *trans* conformation (φ =

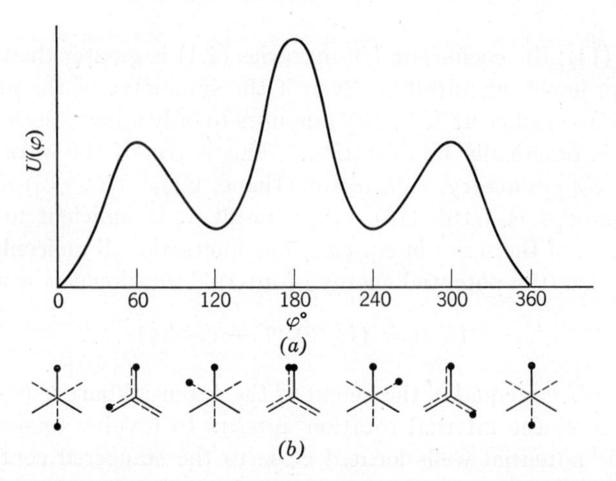

Fig. 2.2. (*a*) Plot of internal rotation potential energy as a function of the angle of rotation φ for 1,2-dichloroethane, and (*b*) the corresponding conformations of the molecule, showing position of the Cl atoms.

0°), in which the substituents are removed from each other to the maximal distance, as a rule, has an energy lower than the *gauche* conformations ($\varphi = \pm 120°$). In this case, the internal rotation involved torsional oscillations inside potential wells, with jumps between rotational isomers. For normal values of the energy barriers ($\approx$3 kcal/mole) the frequency of jumps at room temperature is of the order of 10^{10} sec.$^{-1}$; as a result, the rotational isomers cannot be resolved. Therefore, the majority of the equilibrium properties of the molecules (for example, the dipole moment, the polarizability tensor, the optical activity, etc.) are quantities averaged over the properties of the rotational isomers. However, molecular properties which manifest themselves over times shorter than the lifetime of the rotational isomers enable us to establish the separate existence of the rotational isomers. Spectral lines are such properties; their frequencies are different for different rotational isomers.

The phenomenon of rotational isomerism was discovered by Kohlrausch in 1932 (17) by means of Raman spectroscopy. It is well known now that the majority of compounds have rotational isomers. This has been established by studies of their infrared absorption spectra, Raman spectra, and lately also of high resolution nuclear magnetic resonance spectra and microwave rotation spectra. That rotational isomerism exists in the corresponding compounds is proven by the fact that the number of spectral bands is greater than that theoretically possible for a single conformation of the molecule. Thus, a detailed investigation of the vibrational spectra of various chlorine-substituted isoparaffins has made it possible to single out the characteristic frequencies of the valence vibrations of the C—Cl bond for *trans* and *gauche* isomers (18,19). On the other hand, the change of spectral band intensities with temperature, which results from a displacement of the equilibrium between rotational isomer makes it possible to determine the energy differences between the rotational isomers. When a compound is crystallized, its spectrum, as a rule, becomes simpler because of the freezing out of the less stable rotational isomers.

In a number of cases, microwave spectral data make possible the determination not only of the energy differences between the rotational isomers, but also of the corresponding angle. Thus, it was found that in 1,2-dichloroethane, the *gauche* isomers are rotated by an angle of 100–120° relative to the *trans* position, in 1,2-dibromoethane by an angle of 120–130° (1,20), and in 1-fluoro-2-chloroethane by an angle of 110° (21). Valuable information on rotational isomerism can be obtained from studies of the temperature dependence of dipole moments, Kerr constants, optical activities, and other properties of the molecules, as well as by the methods of electron diffraction, x-ray diffraction, and ultrasound absorption.

In most investigations, the energy differences ΔU between rotational isomers are found to lie in the range of 0.5–1.5 kcal/mole (for example, for butane, $CH_3CH_2—CH_2CH_3$, $\Delta U = 0.8$ kcal/mole; for dichloroethane, $\Delta U = 1.2$ kcal/mole). For polar molecules, ΔU is usually a function of the surrounding medium, because of stabilization of the more polar rotational isomers by intermolecular interactions (22–24). Nevertheless, in the vast majority of cases, the molecules crystallize in the state which corresponds to the most stable rotational isomer in the gas phase (1), i.e., intramolecular interactions play the decisive role. Detailed surveys of experimental data on rotational isomers and tables of the energy differences for various molecules can be found in the literature (1,2,5).

2.2. Theory of the Restricting Potential

The theory of the restricting potential is still practically undeveloped, despite the fact that the problem of the internal rotation of molecules has been subjected to extensive experimental investigations. A rigorous quantum mechanical calculation based on the consideration of the electrostatic interactions between all the electrons and nuclei of a molecule must, in principle, give the energy values of all the conformations of a molecule and, consequently, of all the heights of the barriers and energy differences be-

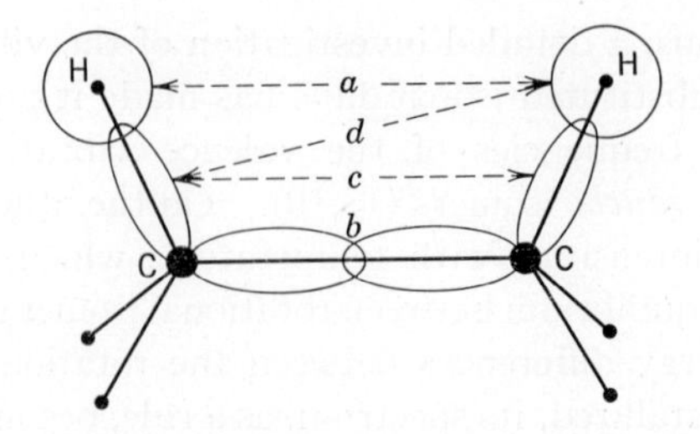

Fig. 2.3. Schematic representation of interactions in the ethane molecule: (*a*) interaction between H atoms; (*b*) interaction between the electrons which form the C—C bond; (*c*) interaction between the carbon atom electrons which form the C—H bonds; (*d*) interaction with H atoms of carbon atom electrons which form the C—H bonds.

tween the rotational isomers. The calculation of the restricting potential, however, demands particularly high precision of results obtained by approximate quantum mechanical methods. The restricting energy is considerably smaller than the total energy of the molecule; therefore, in such calculations, the heights of the barriers and the energy differences between rotational isomers turn out to be small differences between large numbers. As a result, up to the present, there is no sufficiently rigorous quantum mechanical calculation of the potential curve even for the simplest case, namely the ethane molecule.

In calculating the restricting potential in ethane, it is sufficient to take into account only those interactions, shown schematically in Figure 2.3, which are a function of the internal rotation angle φ. As has been shown by Eyring (25), the interaction between the hydrogen atoms even in the eclipsed conformation is quite small and results in a value of the potential barrier one order of magnitude smaller than experimental. The interactions between the electrons which form the C—C bond are a function of angle φ only if this bond does not possess cylindrical symmetry, this can be the result of, for example, a contribution of the 4*f*-state; however, the evaluation carried out by Eyring and co-workers has shown that such a contribution to the barrier of the ethane molecule is small (26). The hypothesis that the cause of the restricting potential is the absence of cylindrical symmetry of the C—C bond has been discussed by other authors as well (27). This idea seems to have been abandoned at the present time, since the exchange interactions between the electrons of carbon atoms of the C—C bond must lead to an increase in the stability of the eclipsed rather than the staggered conformation (the first has the greater overlap of electron clouds) (4,28). Let us examine now the mutual interactions of the electrons of carbon atoms which form the C—H bonds, as well as their interactions with the hydrogen atoms. If the electrons of the hydrogen atoms are in the 1*s* state, while the valence electrons of the carbon atoms are in the hydridized sp^3 state, it can be shown (4) that within the two-center approximation normally used in quantum mechanical calculations, which neglects interactions between three or more electrons, these interactions are independent of the internal rotation angle and, therefore, make no contribution to the potential barrier. Pauling has shown, however (29), that the interaction between the carbon atom electrons which form the C—H bonds results in the formation of a potential barrier if hybridization with the *d*- and *f*-states is taken into account. Pauling made a rough estimate of the contributions of these states to the wave function of the carbon atom electrons which form the C—H bond and has obtained a value of the order of 2%. The value of the potential barrier obtained in this way is close to experimental, the lowest energy being for the staggered conformation.

Harris and Harris (30) have made an attempt at the quantum mechanical calculation of the energy of an ethane molecule as a function of the angle of internal rotation. In this calculation the molecule was divided into fragments which contained one C—C bond (axis of rotation) and two C—H bonds C—H attached to the axis. The fact that addition of such fragments results in three C—C bonds is not important, since the excess energy is not dependent on the angle of internal rotation and has no effect on the potential barrier. On solution of the six-electron problem for the HC—CH system, taking into account only sp^3 hybridization of the valence electrons of the carbon atom, and summation over the three fragments, the internal rotation barrier in ethane was found to be 7.5 kcal/mole. This value was obtained as the difference between the energy values (736.9–729.4 kcal/mole) of the eclipsed and staggered conformations, with the staggered conformation energetically more favorable. Because of the roughness of the model and of the approximations used, there is no need to discuss this value of the height of the barrier. There is, however, one basic difference between the results of Harris and Harris (30) and those of Pauling (29), and it lies in the interpretation of the barrier in ethane. According to Harris and Harris the barrier is formed only with sp^3 hybridization of the valence electrons of the carbon atom, while according to Pauling (29), who started from the two-center approximation, it is necessary to take *d*- and *f*-states into account.

Most of the theories of the restricting potential are semiempirical in character because of the above-mentioned difficulties which arise when an attempt is made at a rigorous quantum mechanical approach to the problem of internal rotation. These theories can be classified into two groups, depending on what is regarded in them as the principal cause of the restriction. The first group of theories starts with the assumption that the cause of the restriction of rotation is the interaction between nonbonded atoms (type *a* of Fig. 2.3), which can be examined by analogy with intermolecular interactions. At short distances, such as are found in neighboring atoms of a single molecule, such an interaction is repulsive and, therefore, must lead to enhanced stability of the staggered conformations of ethane and its derivatives, as was first noted in 1891 (31).

The first semiempirical calculation of the steric repulsion of nonbonded atoms (32) [see also (33)] was based on a potential energy equation of the type

$$U = \sum_{i,j} \frac{K_{R^{(i)}R^{(j)}}}{r_{ij}^{s}} \tag{2.3}$$

where r_{ij} is the distance between the ith and jth atoms of the molecule, and $K_{R^{(i)}R^{(j)}}$ and s are empirical constants which describe the interaction between atoms $R^{(i)}$ and $R^{(j)}$. Values of $s = 5$ and $K_{HH} = 4.99 \times 10^5$ cal-Å^5/mole (32) were found from the heights of the barriers in ethane and tetramethylmethane, in which all the $R^{(i)}$ and $R^{(j)}$ are hydrogen atoms. This made it possible to describe the barriers in a number of hydrocarbon molecules containing methyl groups. Later, similar calculations were carried out with a somewhat different dependence of the energy on interatomic distances, for example, with the aid of the Lennard-Jones potential (34,35). With this method, it is usually possible to calculate the potential barriers in some molecules from the barriers in other molecules of similar structure. However, the values of the potential barriers and the energy differences between the rotational isomers of the simplest hydrocarbons could not be accounted for simultaneously in terms of a single dependence of energy on distance. The cause of this difficulty becomes evident in the light of the work of Mason and Kreevoy (36). These authors did not select values of the potential specifically to describe the intramolecular interactions, but they took values directly from experimental data on intermolecular interactions of atoms with electron clouds of similar structure (for example, instead of the halogens they used the inert gases, which are next to them in the periodic table). Pair-interaction potentials, determined for short distances from experiments on the scattering of atomic beams and for large distances from an analysis of second virial coefficients and transport phenomena in gases, have the form

$$U(r) = \begin{cases} Ke^{-ar} - (K'/r^6) & r \geq r_1 \\ K''/r^s & r_2 \leq r \leq r_1 \end{cases} \quad (2.4)$$

where $a = 3.0$–4.6 Å^{-1}, $s = 7$–10. The internal rotation energy curves calculated on the basis of these potentials have a shape close to cosinusoidal in the region of the minimum. The values of the potential barriers obtained were found usually to be half of the experimental ones; thus, a study (36) which proved directly the important role of steric interactions in the restriction of internal rotation also indicated clearly that this interaction is not the sole cause of the restriction.

A second large group of theories has been devoted to the analysis of other causes of the restriction. These involve an examination of the interaction between the charge clouds of the bonds linked to the axis of rotation (type *c*, Fig. 2.3). In a number of studies (37–40) this was taken into account as an electrostatic multipole i.e., dipole and quadrupole (37–39) or octapole (40) interaction between the charges of the bonds. This is equivalent to expansion in series in multipoles of the coulombic integral in the expression for an interaction of type *c*. Such an expansion permits the electrostatic interaction to be expressed in terms of a given number of parameters which, in principle, can be determined in an independent manner (dipole and quadrupole moments of the bonds). It is preferable, however, to consider these parameters as empirical, especially since there is doubt about the convergence of the series at such short distances between the charge clouds of the bonds.

Thus, in the theory of Lassettre and Dean (37,38), who limited themselves to the dipole and quadrupole moments of the bonds, the determining role was played by quadrupole–quadrupole interactions. Here, the values of the bond quadrupole moments, which are necessary for the interpretation of the observed values of the potential barriers, were found to be considerably larger than the experimental ones (41). In the similar calculations of Oosterhoff (39), who started from a somewhat different distribution of charges in a bond, it was necessary to postulate an anomalously large dipole moment for a C—H bond in order to explain the potential barrier of ethane. Finally, Au Chin-Tang (40) examined the multipole interaction taking into account all terms up to octapole and found that the internal rotation potential is given by eq. (2.2) for molecules with C_{3v} symmetry; furthermore, the height of the potential barrier is directly proportional to the product of the octapole moment of the interacting rotating bonds and inversely proportional to the seventh power of the length of the axis of rotation. The results of this study indicate that the electrostatic interaction of the bonds always leads to staggered conformations. Since the octapole moments of the bonds are not known, the theory of Au Chin-Tang is a semiempirical one; it permits the calculation of potential barrier values in some molecules from the values in others. These calculations give good results; furthermore, the values of the octapole moments turn out to be of a reasonable order of magnitude.

The study of Pauling (29), which has been mentioned above, also belongs to this group. It is devoted to the theoretical examination of interactions of type *c* (see Fig. 2.3); however, the exchange interaction and not the coulombic interaction was considered, in contrast with other studies (37–40). An attempt was made recently to evaluate the exchange intergrals of the interactions of a number of bonds by semiempirical means, starting from the ultrafine splitting of nuclear magnetic resonance spectra, which is determined by these integrals (42). The value of the potential barrier of ethane, calculated on the basis of semiempirical values of the interaction integrals, was found to be 2.3 kcal/mole; this is in good agreement with experiment.

2.3. Calculation of the Restricting Potential in the Simplest Molecules

On summing up, it can be noted that two effects play an important role in the restriction of internal rotation; these are the steric interaction of nonbonded atoms and the interaction of bonds adjacent to the axis of rotation (the so-called bond orientation effect), which results always in the stability of staggered conformations (29,40) ["*the principle of staggered bonds*" (43,44)]. The steric interaction, which at short distances can be reduced mainly to steric repulsion, stabilizes those conformations which correspond to the maximal separation of nonbonded atoms; in small molecules, these conformations are staggered as a rule; in macromolecules which have bulky side groups, however, the case might turn out to be different (see below).

The effect of bond orientation must be approximately identical in various staggered conformations. Therefore, if all the rotational isomers have staggered conformations, the energy difference between rotational isomers must be determined mainly by the steric interaction between nonbonded atoms; this has been confirmed in the calculations of Mason and Kreevoy (45) for ethane derivatives. The determining role of steric interactions in the conformations of molecules has been pointed out repeatedly by Mizushima (1,35), Bunn (43,44), Kitaigorodskii (46), and others. It is understood that in those cases in which the rotational isomers do not correspond to staggered conformations, the energy difference can depend also on the effect of bond orientation. Even in these cases, however, steric interaction plays a determining role, since it is impossible to have molecular conformations in which the distance between any pair of atoms is considerably shorter than the sum of their van der Waals radii.

This justifies the assumption that the most stable conformations (rotational isomers) of molecules can be determined, without detailed knowledge of the internal rotation potential, by direct comparison of the interatomic distances in the various conformations with the sum of the van der Waals radii of these atoms or groups. It is possible to speak of the "principle of the best intramolecular packing" of atoms. This requires maximal interatomic distances of a given molecule consistent with the fixed bond distances; in this, the valence angles, which can be deformed much more easily than the valence bonds, can be opened in order to decrease overlap of the van der Waals atomic radii (47). By applying this principle, it seems possible to predict the most probable conformations of most molecules with internal degrees of freedom, including macromolecules.

A more quantitative approach to this problem consists in describing the steric interaction of nonbonded atoms not by means of the van der Waals radii, but in greater detail by means of semiempirical interaction potentials of the type used in the study of Mason and Kreevoy (36). In this approach it is necessary to take into account also the interaction of bonds linked to the axis of rotation.

There is no theoretical method of calculating the effect of bond orientation, which would be at all reliable nor any semiempirical one; however, if the potential curve of the internal rotation of ethane is considered to be wholly determined by this effect because of the small van der Waals radius of the hydrogen atom, it becomes possible to determine its value by an empirical method. It may be assumed, as a first approximation, that the contribution of bond interactions to the internal rotation potential energy of other hydrocarbon molecules is the same as in ethane. This really means that of the interactions which involve the participation of bonds linked to the axis of rotation, the main role is played by interactions of type *c* and not *d* (see Fig. 2.3). In such a case the potential energy of internal rotation in hydrocarbon molecules can be expressed approximately in the form

$$U(\varphi) = (U_{or}/2)\,(1 - \cos 3\varphi) + \sum_{i,k} U(r_{ik}) \tag{2.5}$$

where U_{or} is the contribution to the potential barrier of the effect of bond orientation (it is more or less similar to the potential barrier of ethane), and $U(r_{ik})$ is the potential energy of the interaction between the nonbonded ith and kth atoms of the chain; this is a function of the distance r_{ik} between them and, thus, of the internal rotation angle φ.

The decomposition of the intramolecular interaction energy into the ethane potential $(U_{or}/2)$ $(1 - \cos 3\varphi)$, and the steric terms, $U(r_{ik})$, which are functions only of the distances between the interacting atoms, is based on the fact pointed out above that the steric potential, $\Sigma_{ik} U(r_{ik})$, makes no significant contribution to the potential barrier of ethane because of the small van der Waals radius of the hydrogen atom. It is, of course, possible that this barrier is determined not only by the effect of bond orientation, but by other factors (for example, by the dependence of the potential of H···H interaction on the angle between the C—H bonds as well as on the distance between the H atoms). Equation (2.5), however, is not based on any particular assumptions about the causes of the potential barrier of ethane and, therefore, is quite justified in a strictly empirical manner.

In the case of molecules which contain bonds with sizable dipole moments, eq. (2.5) must be supplemented by additional terms which take into account the electrostatic interaction of the electron clouds of the bonds linked to the axis of rotation. In a number of investigations [see, for example, Fordham (48)], this effect is described as the interaction of "physical dipoles," i.e., of partial charges located at the ends of bonds and equal to the ratio of the dipole moment of the bond to its length. Naturally, the validity of this description requires justification; we shall not dwell on these questions in detail, however, since in what follows we shall be concerned principally with the conformations of nonpolar macromolecules.

Calculation of the internal rotation potential energy with eq. (2.5) requires knowledge of the interaction potentials between nonbonded H···H, C···C, and C···H atoms. Two groups of potentials have been proposed for interactions between nonbonded H atoms. The first group contains the interaction potential of the H atoms of H—H bonds, obtained by Lennard-Jones (49) from the second virial coefficient of gaseous H_2, and calculated theoretically by Eyring (25), and the potential of the interaction of free H atoms, calculated by Hirschfelder and Linnet (50) and applied particularly by Mason and Kreevoy (36,45). According to the potential curves (25,49,50), which are similar to each other, the repulsion of free H atoms or of the H atoms in H_2 molecules becomes significant when they approach each other to a distance of

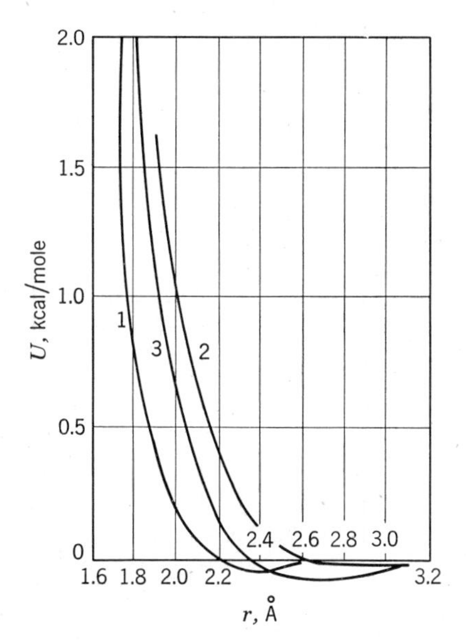

Fig. 2.4. Potentials of interaction between the nonbonded H atoms of C—H bonds (H···H), atoms as proposed by (*1*) Hill (52), (*2*) Bartell (53), and (*3*) Kitaigorodskii (54, 55).

≈ 2.4–2.5 Å, while the minimum in the potential energy is at a distance of >3 Å.

On the other hand, the interaction between the H atoms of C—H bonds is quite different: significant repulsion sets in only when they approach each other to a distance of ≈ 1.9 Å, while the potential curve has a minimum at a distance of 2.4 Å. [The crystallographic van der Waals radius of an H atom in a C—H bond is 1.2 Å (51).] The interaction between nonbonded H atoms in C—H bonds is described by another group of potentials, proposed by Hill (52), Bartell (53), and Kitaigorodskii (54,55) from crystallochemical and thermodynamic data on the intermolecular interactions of the simplest hydrocarbons (Fig. 2.4). The potentials have the form

$$U(r) = Ke^{-ar} - (K'/r^6) \tag{2.6}$$

where the values of the constants K, K', and a are given in Table 2.1. Examination of Figure 2.4 shows that the potential of Bartell results in a much stronger repulsion between the H atoms at short distances than the potential of Hill, while the potential of Kitaigorodskii lies between those of

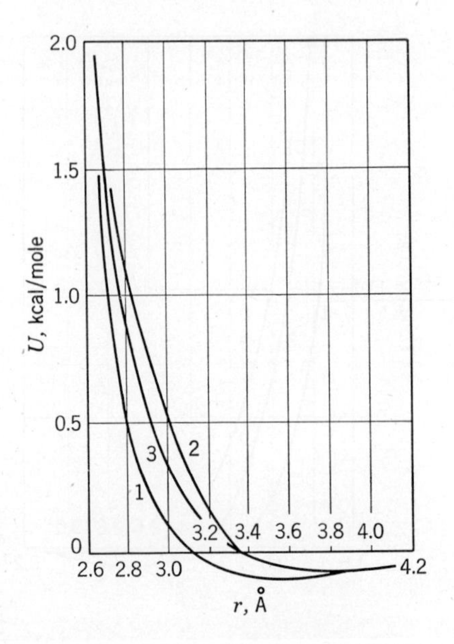

Fig. 2.5. Potentials of interaction between nonbonded C atoms (C···C), as proposed by (*1*) Bartell (53), (*2*) Kitaigorodskii (54, 55), and (*3*) Crowell (57). The potential of Crowell (57) (curve *3*) corresponds to eq. (2.6).

Hill and Bartell. At distances greater than 80% of the sum of the H atom van der Waals radii, the differences between these potentials are comparatively small. It should be noted that, contrary to the case of the potential of interaction between free H atoms, the potential of interaction between C—H bond H atoms describes correctly the intermolecular interactions in gaseous methane (56).*

The interactions between nonbonded carbon atoms (C···C) have been described by Crowell (57) and Kitaigorodskii (54,55) in terms of the potentials, which have the form of eq. (2.6) with constants given in Table 2.1, as well as of potentials of the form

$$U(r) = (A/r^{12}) - (B/r^6) \tag{2.7}$$

where, according to Crowell (57), $A = 5.2 \times 10^5$ kcal/mole-Å^{12}, $B = 340$ kcal/mole-Å^6, while according to Bartell (53), $A = 3.0 \times 10^5$ kcal/mole-Å^{12}, $B = 320$ kcal/mole-Å^6. All these potentials have been obtained from crystallochemical and thermodynamic data. As can be seen from Figure

*The potential of Hill(52) was used by Borisova and Volkenshtein (56) for calculating the interactions between C—H bond H atoms.

2.5 they are quite similar and agree to within 10% when distances between the centers of the C atoms are greater than 80% of the sum of their van der Waals radii.

The interaction potential between nonbonded C···H atoms may be obtained by combining the potentials of the C···C and H···H interactions with the use of the combination rule (58–60), according to which each term of the potential of interaction between nonidentical atoms is given by the geometric mean of the corresponding terms of the potentials of interaction between identical atoms. Treatment of the

TABLE 2.1
Values of Constants in the Interaction Potentials of Nonbonded H and C Atoms and CH_3 Groups

Interacting atoms	$K \times 10^{-3}$, kcal/mole	K', kcal/mole-Å^6	a, Å^{-1}	References
H. . .H	35	18	5.7	52
	66	49	4.1	53
	30	43	5.0	54,55
C. . .C	~40	350	3.6	57
	37	330	3.6	54,55
CH_3. . .CH_3 ($r \geq 3.2$ Å)	270	2900	3.3	36

potential of the C···H interaction in the form of eq. (2.6) gives $K_{C\cdots H} = \sqrt{K_{C\cdots C}K_{H\cdots H}}$, $K'_{C\cdots H} = \sqrt{K'_{C\cdots C}K'_{H\cdots H}}$, and $a_{C\cdots H} = {}^1/_2(a_{C\cdots C} + a_{H\cdots H})$.

It should be pointed out that H···H, C···C and C···H interaction potentials have been proposed by Kitaigorodskii (54,55) in the form

$$U = [U_{2/3}/[11.4 - (6/\alpha)e^{\alpha/3})]\left(\frac{1}{z^6} - \frac{6}{\alpha}e^{\alpha(1-z)}\right) \tag{2.8}$$

This is the result of a rearrangement of eq. (2.6). Here $z = r/r_0$ is the ratio of the distance r between the atoms to their equilibrium distance r_0; $U_{2/3}$ is the energy of interaction between atoms located at a distance $r = {}^2/_3 r_0$, and $\alpha = ar_0$, where a is the constant in eq. (2.6). Assuming that $U_{2/3}$ and α are identical for C···C, H···H, and C···H, and equal to 3.5, and 13 kcal/mole, respectively, Kitaigorodskii calculated the curves of eq. (2.8) for H···H, C···C, and C···H in the general form

$$U = 3.5[-(0.04/z^6) + 8.6 \times 10^3 e^{-13z}] \tag{2.9}$$

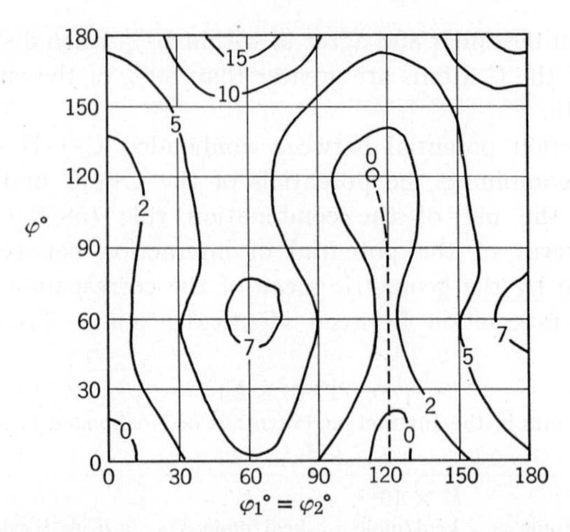

Fig. 2.6. Dependence of the internal rotation energy in *n*-butane on the angles of rotation. The numbers on the curves are energies in kcal/mole. The path of isomerization is shown by the dotted line.

Setting r_0 = 2.6, 3.8, and 3.15 Å for H···H, C···C, and C···H, respectively, results in the curves for the H···H and C···C interactions given in Table 2.1 and the corresponding curve for the C···H interaction.

The potentials presented above cannot be applied at distances considerably smaller than the sum of the van der Waals radii of the atoms, since they are based on experiments in which the atoms do not approach each other too closely. Pedley (61) has calculated recently the potentials of the H···H and C···C interactions at very short distances. For H···H, $U(r) = 78/r^4$ kcal/mole at 1.4 Å $\leq r \leq$ 1.9 Å; for C···C, $U(r) = 370/r^4$ kcal/mole at $r \leq$ 2.55 Å (here, as above, r is expressed in Å).

In calculations of the potential energy of hydrocarbon molecules, according to eq. (2.5), it becomes possible, in a number of cases, to consider carbon atoms together with the hydrogen atoms linked to them as single groups and to talk about an interaction potential between these groups. In the quoted study of Mason and Kreevoy (36) replacement of the interaction potential of CH_3 groups by the interaction potential of a methane molecule (36,62) was proposed. At distances between C atoms $r \geqslant$ 3.2 Å this potential has the form given by eq. (2.6) with constants listed in Table 2.1, while at 2.47 Å $\leqslant r \leqslant$ 3.2 Å, this takes on the form $U(r) = 2.39 \times 10^4/r^{7.37}$ kcal/mole [see eq. (2.4)].

The potential energy of internal rotation in the simplest hydrocarbon molecules, propane and *n*-butane, has been calculated in the studies of

Borisova and Volkenshtein (63) on the basis of eq. (2.5) with the C···C potential of Kitaigorodskii (54,57), and the H...H potential of Hill (52). These calculations showed that, in both molecules, the potential energy minimum corresponds to the *trans* conformation of the C—C bonds. Steric interaction makes a relatively small contribution to the potential barrier of propane ($\approx$250 cal/mole); this is in good agreement with the experimental value of this barrier, 3300 cal/mole, which is only 300 cal/mole greater than that in ethane. The energy difference between the *gauche* and *trans* isomers in *n*-butane is determined by the steric interaction between the methyl group C atoms and, in particular, by the interaction between one pair of H atoms of these groups. Assuming that the *gauche* isomer has an internal rotation angle $\varphi = 120°$, this energy difference ΔU becomes approximately equal to 900 cal/mole, which is close to the experimental value. If the potential energy minimum is at an angle slightly different from 120°, the effect of bond orientation, as well makes a contribution to the energy difference between the rotational isomers; if realistic values of U_{or} are used (close to U_0 of ethane), the quantity ΔU remains close to the experimental value in this case as well, i.e., close to $\approx$800 cal/mole. Inclusion of steric interactions and of the bond orientation effect determines the rather flat bottom of the potential wells of the *trans* and *gauche* isomers of *n*-butane; this results in the presence of torsional oscillations with an amplitude of $\approx$10–15°.

Figure 2.6 shows curves of the potential surface obtained for *n*-butane by Borisova and Volkenshtein (63) as a function of the angle of rotation φ about the "internal" bond, —CH_2—CH_2—, and of the angles of rotation (equal to each other) $\varphi_1 = \varphi_2$ about the "external" bonds, —CH_2—CH_3. As can be seen from Figure 2.6, the potential energy minima are at angles $\varphi = 0$ and 120° and φ_1 and φ_2 close to 0 and 120°. Transition from a *trans* isomer ($\varphi = 0°$) to a *gauche* isomer ($\varphi = 120°$) requires the overcoming of a potential barrier of about 3 kcal/mole; this is due principally to the effect of bond orientations.

The potential barriers of compounds which contain oxygen atoms (65) and C=C double bonds (65) have been calculated in similar manner on the basis of eq. (2.5) in the investigations of Borisova and Birshtein (64) and Borisova (65). The potential barrier of rotation about the C—O bond in methanol, CH_3—OH, which is equal to 1 kcal/mole (66), is due almost entirely to the bond orientation effect (since the steric interaction between the H atoms is negligibly small, just as in ethane). As a result, for rotation about a C—O bond U_{or} of eq. (2.5) is equal to 1 kcal/mole. Using this value of U_{or} together with an estimate of the contribution of steric interaction to the potential barrier of dimethyl ether, $CH_3—O—CH_3$, Borisova and Birshtein (64) obtained a value of 2.5–3.0 kcal/mole for this barrier; this is in good agreement with the experimental value of ≈2.7 kcal/mole (67,68). The potential barriers during rotation about C—C bonds have been calculated (65) for propylene $CH_3CH{=}CH_2$, and the derivatives methylallene, $CH_3CH{=}C{=}CH_2$; *trans*- and *cis*-2-butene, $CH_3CH{=}CH—CH_3$); and isobutene, $(CH_3)_2C{=}CH_2$. In this calculation, it was assumed that the potential energy minimum corresponds to the *trans* position of single bonds, i.e., to the *cis* position of the methyl group CH bonds relative to the C=C bond [see, for example, (69,70)]. The contribution of the steric interactions of the H and C atoms is negligibly small in all cases (except for *cis*-2-butene); in the case of *cis*-2-butene it is equal to 1.5 kcal/mole. Therefore, according to eq. (2.5), the potential barriers of all these compounds, except for *cis*-2-butene, must be equal, while that of *cis*-2-butene must be smaller by 1.5 kcal/mole. This prediction of the theory is in excellent agreement with the experimental data on the barriers of propylene and its derivatives: in propylene, methylallene, and *trans*-2-butene the height of the barrier is ≈2.0 kcal/mole (4), in isobutene it is ≈2.4 kcal/mole (71), and in *cis*-2-butene it is ≈0.5 kcal/mole (71,72).

Notwithstanding the fact that the calculations cited above are rough, it can be remarked that the intramolecular interactions in simple hydrocarbons are described quite adequately by the semiempirical potentials of the C and H atom interactions obtained from data on the intermolecular interactions of these molecules, when these are combined with a potential which takes into account approximately the effect of bond orientation; these potentials permit the prediction of the most probable conformations of these molecules and even the evaluation of the energy differences between them. As has been noted above, the most probable conformations of most molecules can be predicted qualitatively in an even simpler manner; namely, these conformations must be such that any pair of nonbonded atoms or atomic groups would not approach each other to distances considerably shorter than the sums of their van der Waals radii.

References

1. Mizushima, S., *Stroenie Molekul i Vnutrennee Vrashchenie,* IL, Moscow, 1958, originally published as *Structure of Molecules* Academic, New York (1954).
2. Volkenshtein, M. V., *Konfiguratsionnaya Statistika Polimernykh Tsepei,* Izdatel'stvo Akad. Nauk SSSR, Moscow, 1959 (published in translation as *Configurational Statistics of Polymeric Chains,* Interscience, New York, 1963).
3. Lin, C. C., and J. D. Swalen, *Rev. Mod. Phys.*, **31,** 841 (1959).
4. Wilson, E. B., Jr., *Adv. Chem. Phys.*, **3,** 367 (1959).

5. Sheppard, N., *Adv. Spectr.*, **1**, 288 (1959).
6. Gordi, V., Smit, and R. Trambarulo, *Radiospektroskopiya*, GTTI, Moscow, 1955, originally published as *Microwave Spectroscopy*.
7. Tauns, C., and A. Shavlov, *Radiospektroskopiya*, IL, Moscow, 1957.
8. Endryu, E., *Yadernyi Magnitnyi Resonans*, IL, Moscow, 1957.
9. Jackman, L. M., *Applications of Nuclear Magnetic Resonance Spectroscopy in Organic Chemistry*, Pergamon Press, London–New York, 1959.
10. Pople, J. A., W. G. Shneider, and H. J. Bernstein, *Spektry Yadernogo Magnitnogo Resonansa Vysokogo Razresheniya*, IL, Moscow, 1962 (originally published as *High Resolution Nuclear Magnetic Resonance*, McGraw-Hill, New York, 1959).
11. Herschbach, D. R., and L. C. Krisher, *J. Chem. Phys.*, **28**, 728 (1958).
12. Kilb, R. W., and L. Pierce, *J. Chem. Phys.*, **27**, 108 (1957).
13. Kilb, R. W., C. C. Lin, and E. B. Wilson, *J. Chem. Phys.*, **26**, 1695 (1957).
14. Herschbach, D. R., and J. D. Swalen, *J. Chem. Phys.*, **29**, 761 (1958).
15. Tannenbaum, E., R. J. Myers, and W. D. Gwinn, *J. Chem. Phys.*, **25**, 42 (1956).
16. Naylor, R. E., and E. B. Wilson, Jr., *J. Chem. Phys.*, **26**, 1057 (1957).
17. Kohlrausch, K. W. F., *Z. Physik. Chem.*, **B18**, 61 (1932).
18. Checkland, P. B., and W. H. T. Davison, *Trans. Faraday Soc.*, **52**, 151 (1956).
19. Mizushima, S., T. Shimanouchi, K. Nakamura, M. Hayashi, and S. Tsuchiya, *J. Chem. Phys.*, **26**, 970 (1957).
20. Mizushima, S., T. Shimanouchi, I. Nakagawa, and A. Miyake, *J. Chem. Phys.*, **21**, 215 (1953).
21. Mukhtarov, I. A., Dokl. Akad. Nauk *SSSR*, **115**, 486 (1957); *Izv. Akad. Nauk SSSR, Otd. Khim Nauk*, **22**, 1154 (1958).
22. Volkenshtein, M. V., and V. T. Brevdo, *Zhur. Fiz. Khim.*, **28**, 313 (1954).
23. Mizushima, S., and Y. Morino, *J. Chem. Phys.*, **18**, 1516 (1950).
24. Wada, A., *J. Chem. Phys.*, **22**, 198, 1217 (1954).
25. Eyring, H., *J. Am. Chem. Soc.*, **54**, 3191 (1932).
26. Gorin, E., J. Waiter, and H. Eyring, *J. Am. Chem. Soc.*, **61**, 1876 (1939).
27. Wilson, E. B., Jr., *Proc. Natl. Acad. Sci., U.S.*, **43**, 816 (1957).
28. Eucken, A., and K. Schaffer, *Naturwissenschaften*, **27**, 122 (1939).
29. Pauling, L., *Proc. Natl. Acad. Sci., U.S.*, **44**, 211 (1958).
30. Harris, G. M., and F. E. Harris, *J. Chem. Phys.*, **31**, 1450 (1959).
31. Bischoff, C., *Berichte*, **24**, 1085 (1891).
32. Aston, J. G., S. Isserow, G. J. Szasz, and R. M. Kennedy, *J. Chem. Phys.*, **12**, 336 (1944).
33. Freuch, F. A., and R. S. Rasmussen, *J. Chem. Phys.*, **14**, 389 (1946).
34. van Dranen, J., *J. Chem. Phys.*, **20**, 1982 (1952).
35. Mizushima, S., Y. Morino, and T. Shimanouchi, *J. Phys. Chem.*, **56**, 324 (1952).
36. Mason, E. A., and M. M. Kreevoy, *J. Am. Chem. Soc.*, **77**, 5808 (1955).
37. Lassettre, E. N., and L. B. Dean, Jr., *J. Chem. Phys.*, **16**, 151, 553 (1948).
38. Lassettre, E. N., and L. B. Dean, Jr., *J. Chem. Phys.*, **17**, 317 (1949).
39. Oosterhoff, L. J., *Discussions Faraday Soc.*, **10**, 79 (1951).
40. Au, Chin-Tang, *J. Chinese Chem. Soc.*, **18**, 1 (1951); *ibid.*, **19**, 33 (1952); *Sci. Sinica*, **3**, 279 (1954).
41. Smith, W. V., and R. Howard, *Phys. Rev.*, **79**, 132 (1950).
42. Hecht, H. G., D. M. Grant, and H. Eyring, *Mol. Phys.*, **3**, 577 (1960).
43. Bunn, C. W., *Proc. Roy. Soc. (London)*, **A180**, 67 (1942).

44. Bunn, C. W., and D. R. Holmes, *Discussions Faraday Soc.*, **25,** 95 (1958).
45. Kreevoy, M. M., and E. A. Mason, *J. Am. Chem. Soc.*, **79,** 4851 (1957).
46. Kitaigorodskii, A. I., *Usp. Khim. Tekhnol. Polimerov Sb.*, **2,** 191 (1957).
47. Kitaigorodskii, A. I., *Dokl. Akad. Nauk SSSR*, **124,** 1267 (1959); *Tetrahedron*, **9,** 183 (1960).
48. Fordham, J. W. L., *J. Polymer Sci.*, **39,** 321 (1959).
49. Lennard-Jones, J. E., *Physica*, **4,** 941 (1937).
50. Hirschfelder, J. O., and J. W. Linnet, *J. Chem. Phys.*, **18,** 130 (1950).
51. Müller, A., *Proc. Roy. Soc. (London)*, **A154,** 624 (1936); *ibid.*, **A178,** 227 (1941).
52. Hill, T. L., *J. Chem. Phys.*, **16,** 399, 938 (1948).
53. Bartell, L. S., *J. Chem. Phys.*, **32,** 827 (1960).
54. Kitaigorodskii, A. I., *Dokl. Akad. Nauk SSSR*, **137,** 116 (1961).
55. Kitaigorodskii, A. I., and K. V. Mirskaya, *Kristallografiya*, **6,** 507 (1961).
56. Borisova, N. P., and M. V. Volkenshtein, *Zh. Strukt. Khim.*, **2,** 346 (1961).
57. Crowell, A. D., *J. Chem. Phys.*, **29,** 446 (1958).
58. Mason, E. A., and W. E. Rice, *J. Chem. Phys.*, **22,** 522 (1954).
59. Amdur, I., E. A. Mason, and A. L. Harkness, *J. Chem. Phys.*, **22,** 1071 (1954).
60. Mason, E. A., *J. Chem. Phys.*, **23,** 49 (1955).
61. Pedley, J. B., *Trans. Faraday Soc.*, **57,** 1492 (1951).
62. Mason, E. A., and W. E. Rice, *J. Chem. Phys.*, **22,** 843 (1954).
63. Borisova, N. P., and V. M. Volkenshtein, *Zh. Strukt. Khim.*, **2,** 469 (1961).
64. Borisova, N. P., and T. M. Birshtein, *Vysokomol. Soedin.*, **5,** 279 (1963).
65. Borisova, N. P., *Vysokomol. Soedin., Sb. Karbotsepniye* Soedin carbochain compounds **71** (1963).
66. Ivash, E. V., and D. M. Dennison, *J. Chem. Phys.*, **21,** 1804 (1953).
67. Lide, D. R., Jr., *J. Chem. Phys.*, **27,** 343 (1957).
68. Kivelson, D., and D. R. Lide, Jr., *J. Chem. Phys.*, **27,** 353 (1957).
69. Lennard-Jones, J., and J. A. Pople, *Discussions Faraday Soc.*, **10,** 19 (1951).
70. Pauling, L., *Proc. Natl. Acad. Sci., U.S.*, **44,** 211 (1958).
71. Kilpatrick, J. E., and K. S. Pitzer, *J. Res. Natl. Bur. Std.*, **37,** 163 (1946).
72. Luft, N. W., *Z. Elektrochem.*, **59,** 46 (1955).
73. Maier, W., *Pure Appl. Chem.*, **4,** 157 (1962).
74. Herschbach, D., *International Symposium on Molecular Structure and Spectroscopy, Tokyo*, **1962,** Butterworths, London, 1963, S. 1. S. a, C401/1–C401/8.
75. Pitzer, K. S., *Discussions Faraday Soc.*, **10,** 66 (1951).
76. Swick, D. A., and I. L. Karle, *J. Chem. Phys.*, **23,** 1499 (1955).
77. Kilb, R. W., and L. Pierce, *J. Chem. Phys.*, **27,** 108 (1957).
78. Lide, D. R., Jr., and D. Kivelson, *J. Chem. Phys.*, **23,** 2191 (1955).

Chapter 3

CONFORMATIONS OF MACROMOLECULES AND MECHANISM OF THEIR FLEXIBILITY

3.1. Crystal Structures of Typical Macromolecules

In order to treat the flexibility of macromolecules in a quantitative manner it is necessary to determine, first the one-dimensional short-range order, i.e., the conformations of monomer units, and, second, the mechanism by which this order is disturbed. At the present time, there are no direct, reliable methods for determining the conformations of macromolecules in solutions. X-ray analysis, however, gives us detailed information on their conformations in the crystalline state; it permits us to judge whether the structure of the main chain is flat or helical, and to determine the identity period, the number of monomer units and turns of the helix in the period, and even the conformations of side groups with internal degrees of freedom (147).

Chain molecules can form a three-dimensional crystal only in the presence of a regular sequence of the various *stereoisomeric configurations of monomer units* along the chain, i.e., if such molecules are *stereoregular.*

Let us consider macromolecules with the general structure $(—M_1—M_2—)_n$, built on the "head-to-tail" principle and containing two bonds of the main chain in each monomer unit. We shall limit ourselves to the investigation of such molecules in which group M_1 is symmetric with respect to the plane which passes through two neighboring bonds of the main chain. This class contains polyvinyl molecules of type $(—CH_2—CRR'—)_n$, including $(—CH_2—CHR—)_n$, polyaldehydes $(—O—CRR'—)_n$, polysiloxanes $(—O—SiRR'—)_n$, etc. In the case that group M_2 is also symmetric with respect to the plane which passes through two neighboring bonds of the main chain, only a single stereoisomeric form can exist in the molecules; in this form, the plane of the stretched *trans* chain of the molecule is also the plane of symmetry. The polymers under consideration, such as polyethylene $(—CH_2—CH_2—)_n$, polyisobutylene $[—CH_2—C(CH_3)_2—]_n$, poly(vinyledene chloride) $(—CH_2—CCl_2—)_n$, polytetrafluoroethylene $(—CF_2—CF_2—)_n$, polydimethylsiloxane $[—O—Si(CH_3)_2—]_n$, and others, are always stereoregular, and, therefore, at least in principle, are always capable of crystallization.

If group M_2 is not symmetric, two stereoisomeric configurations of each monomer unit are possible; these differ in the spatial distribution of bonds attached to that atom of group M_2 which belongs to the main chain. Thus, for molecules of type $(—CH_2—CHR—)_n$, stereoisomeric configurations are determined by the distribution of four bonds: C— (beginning of the chain), C— (end of the chain), and the C—H and C—R bonds attached to the C atom of the —CHR— group. If the carbon bonds at the beginning of the

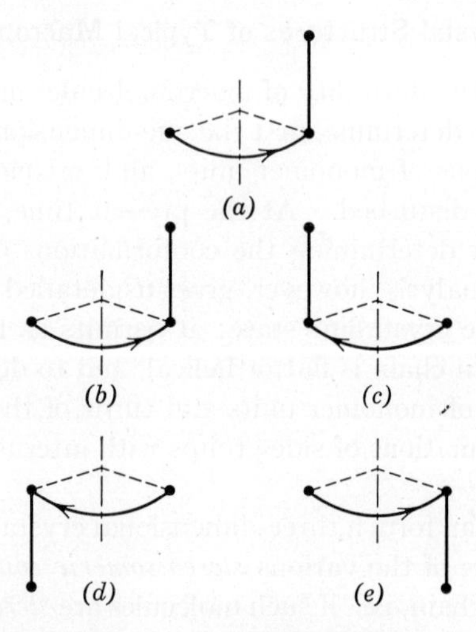

Fig. 3.1. Schematic representation of structural units: (*a*) equivalent starting unit; (*b*) isomorphous isoclined, (*c*) enantiomorphous isoclined; (*d*) isomorphous anticlined; (*e*) enantiomorphous anticlined.

chain and end of the chain are placed in the plane of a schematic drawing, then in the two stereoisomeric forms, designated by symbols *d* and *l*, the C—R bonds will project out of the plane of the drawing in opposite directions.

In the case under consideration, namely that of a chain of type $(—M_1—M_2—)_n$ with an asymmetric group M_2, two types of stereoregular chains capable of crystallization are possible: isotactic and syndiotactic. In *isotactic* chains all monomer units have identical configurations (all *d* or all *l*); in *syndiotactic* chains, *d* and *l* configurations of monomer units alternate. Stereoregular molecules of type $(—CH_2—CHR—)_n$ are shown in Figure 1.1 (see section 1.2). *Atactic* polymers, in which different stereoisomeric configurations of monomer units are positioned irregularly along the chain, are not capable of crystallization.

It should be pointed out that, even though each C atom of the CHR group is, strictly speaking, asymmetric because its two side groups, namely of the beginning and end of the chain, are not equal, an isotactic molecule is not optically active,* since (ignoring end effects) it has a plane of symmetry which passes through the middle of the chain. Furthermore, the C atoms of the —CHR— groups are actually not truly asymmetric, since optical activity arises only if symmetry is absent in the immediate environment of the C atom; this environment is practically symmetric for each CHR group (with the exception of those nearest to the ends of the chain). This does not apply, of course, to macromolecules which have truly asymmetric carbon atoms in their side groups.

In their studies of the crystal structures of a large number of stereoregular polymers by the x-ray method, Natta and Corradini found that, in all cases studied, the repeating structural units of a crystalline chain occupied geometrically equivalent positions with respect to the chain axis. They summarized these results (1,2,127) in the form of a *postulate of equivalence* of the geometric positions of structural units. From the stereochemical structure of the macromolecule, the equivalence postulate permits prediction of the symmetry type of a crystalline chain and the possible conformations of monomer units.

In order to determine the conditions of equivalence of structural units of a crystalline macromolecule, let us introduce into this molecule a system of cylindrical coordinates (ρ, ϑ, ζ) where the ζ axis is coincident with the chain axis. In that case, if the coordinates of the ith atom of a given structural unit are $(\rho_i, \vartheta_i, \zeta_i)$, then those chain units for which the coordinates of the ith atoms are $(\rho_i, \Theta \pm \vartheta_i, Z \pm \zeta_i)$, where $i = 1, 2 \ldots m$, will be equivalent to it with respect to the chain axis. m is the number of atoms in a structural unit, while Θ and Z are functions of the distance along the chain between the units under examination; Θ and Z may be set equal to zero, if in passing from one unit to another the origin of measurement of ϑ and ζ is transformed in the appropriate manner.

Equivalent structural units, the corresponding atoms of which differ (with a precision up to translocation of the origin of measurement) by the sign of one of the coordinates ϑ_i or ζ_i, can be transformed into each other simply by reflection (*enantiomorphous* structural units). If the corresponding atoms of equivalent units have (with a precision up to the translation of the origin of measurement) identical coordinates, these units are called *isomorphous*. Structural units which differ in signs of both coordinates ϑ_i and ζ_i are also isomorphous, since they can be transformed into each other by rotation about a line perpendicular to the axis of the molecule. Following Natta and Corradini (1,2,127) we will call *isoclined* those structural units, of which the corresponding atoms (with a

* We are neglecting here the possibility that a macromolecule may be optically active as a result of its helical conformation (see below).

precision up to the translation of the origin of measurement) do not differ in the sign of ζ_i; we term *anticlined* those structural units of which the corresponding atoms differ in the sign of ζ_i. Then, if the coordinates of the ith atom of some structural unit are $(\rho_i, \vartheta_i, \zeta_i)$, the structural unit with coordinates of the ith atom $(\rho_i, \Theta + \vartheta_i, Z + \zeta_i)$ is isomorphous isoclined, while that with coordinates $(\rho_i, \Theta - \vartheta_i, Z + \zeta_i)$ is enantiomorphous isoclined, that with coordinates $(\rho_i, \Theta - \vartheta_i, Z - \zeta_i)$ is isomorphous anticlined, and that with coordinates $(\rho_i, \Theta + \vartheta_i, Z - \zeta_i)$ is enantiomorphous anticlined (Fig. 3.1)

The symmetry type of the structural units of the chain is determined by the chemical and stereochemical structures of the chain. Thus, if the two possible directions of the chain are not equivalent in a macromolecule, all the structural units of these molecules are isoclined. Such polymers are represented, for example, by polyamides $[—(CH_2)_m—NH—CO—]_n$, polypeptides $(—CHR—NH—CO—)_n$, and 1,4-polyisoprene $[—CH_2—CH{=}CH—CH(CH_3)—]_n$; in these, the structural units are monomer units. In polypeptide and polyamide molecules, which contain in each monomer unit an asymmetric carbon atom in the same *d*- or *l*- configuration, all monomer units must be isomorphous. For molecules of the type $(—M_1—M_2)_n$, both directions of the chain and, consequently both directions of each monomer unit are absolutely equivalent (with the exception of the endgroups); therefore, in these molecules, the monomer units, which are simultaneously structural units, can be both isoclined and anticlined. In isotactic molecules of this type, neighboring monomer units can be isomorphous isoclined or enantiomorphous isoclined; in syndiotactic molecules, they can be isomorphous anticlined or enantiomorphous isoclined.

On the other hand, the symmetry type of the neighboring structural units determines the symmetry of the chain in the crystal. In fact, Natta and Corradini have shown (1,2,127) that a regular sequence of equivalent structural units in a molecule may be obtained in the following ways.

1. A sequence of isoclined isomorphous units is obtained by the operations of translation of a structural unit along the chain axis by a distance $d = c/p$, with simultaneous rotation by an angle $\vartheta = 2\pi q/p$ in the plane perpendicular to this axis. In this manner a p_q helix is formed; it contains p monomer units and q turns in an identity period of length c.

2. A sequence of isomorphous, pairwise-anticlined units forms a helix which has dyad axes of symmetry perpendicular to the helix axis.

3. A sequence of isoclined, pairwise-enantiomorphous units is obtained by the translation of the structural unit by a distance $c/2$, with a simultaneous reflection in the plane which passes through the chain axis and is, therefore, the glide plane of the system under examination.

4. A sequence of enantiomorphous, anticlined units is obtained by means of translation of the structural unit in the presence of either a plane of symmetry perpendicular to the chain axis or of a center of symmetry.

The fact that the symmetry of neighboring monomer units, on one hand, depends on the chemical and stereochemical structure of the chain and, on the other hand, determines the symmetry of the crystalline form of the chain as a whole, permits one to establish the relation between the crystal structure of the chain and its chemical and stereochemical structures. In particular, from what has been said above it follows that molecules of polypeptides and polyamides can crystallize only as helices, while 1,4-polyisoprene must crystallize either in the form of a helix or in the form of a structure that has a glide plane. Figure 3.2 presents typical examples of crystalline chains of different

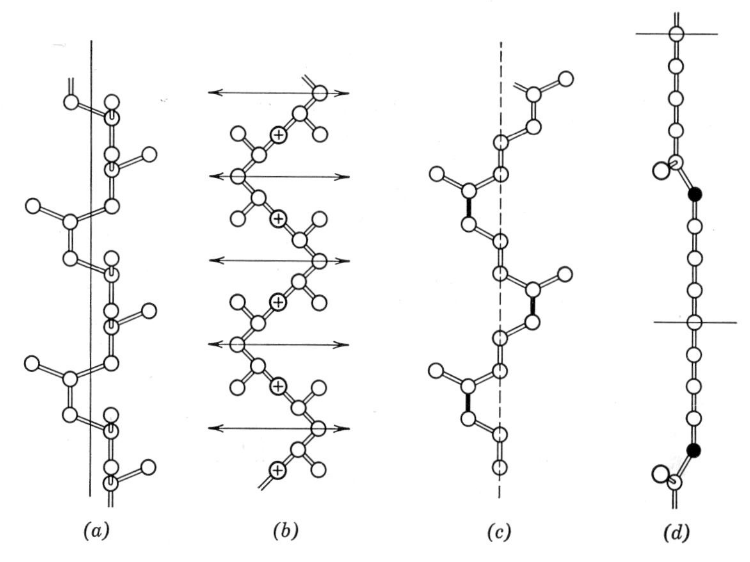

Fig. 3.2. Various types of conformations of crystalline chains: (*a*) isotactic polypropylene; (*b*) syndiotactic polypropylene; (*c*) *cis*-1,4-polyisoprene; (*d*) nylon 77.

symmetries which have been studied by x-ray analysis. In isotactic polypropylene the sequence of isomorphous isoclined units forms a 3_1 helix. Syndiotactic polypropylene consists of isomorphous, alternating anticlined monomer units, which form a helix with dyad axes of symmetry with respect to pairs of monomer units; furthermore, a dyad axis perpendicular to the helix axis passes through every methylene group of the chain. The crystal structure of *cis*-1,4-polyisoprene molecules, which consist of isoclined alternating enantiomorphous monomer units, is an example of a structure that possesses a glide plane. In the crystalline form of the nylon 77 chain, neighboring structural units, which consist of two halves of adjacent monomer units, are enantiomorphous and anticlined and are related by a plane of symmetry.

Let us examine now in greater detail the crystal structures of stereoregular polymers of type $(\text{—}M_1\text{—}M_2\text{—})_n$. From now on, in order to be specific, we shall speak of polyvinyl molecules of type $(\text{—}CH_2\text{—}CRR'\text{—})_n$, and, in particular, of molecules of type $(\text{—}CH_2\text{—}CHR\text{—})_n$; however, the results obtained below are, of course, valid as well for other molecules of the indicated structure, for example, for polyaldehydes $(\text{—}O\text{—}CRR'\text{—})_n$ and polysiloxanes $(\text{—}O\text{—}SiRR'\text{—})_n$, etc.

In accordance with what has been said above, isotactic molecules of type $(\text{—}CH_2\text{—}CRR'\text{—})_n$ may crystallize in the form of helices. The helices of isotactic molecules can be either right-handed or left-handed. Let us examine the right-handed helix of an isotactic molecule in which all the

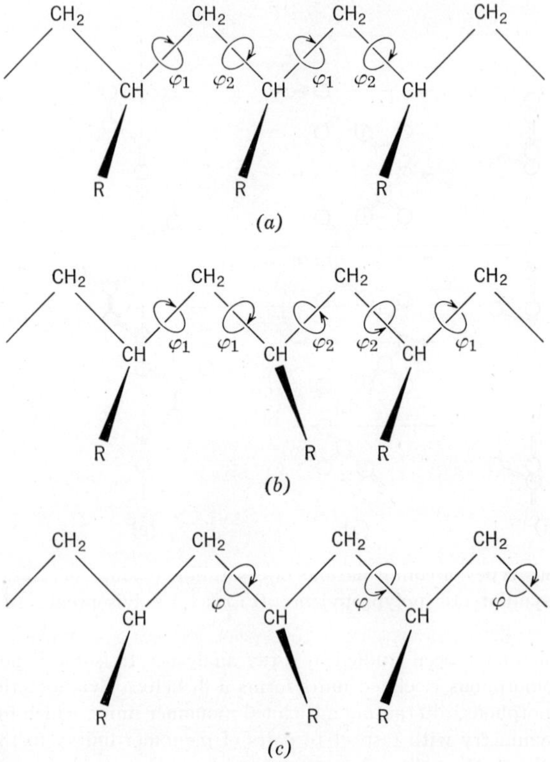

(a)

(b)

(c)

Fig. 3.3. Angles of internal rotation in (*a*) isotactic and (*b*) syndiotactic molecules of the type (—CH_2—CHR—)$_n$, corresponding to helical crystalline conformations, and (*c*) angles of internal rotation in syndiotactic molecules of the type (—CH_2—CHR—)$_n$, which correspond to the conformation having a glide plane.

Bonds of the main chain (thin line) are in the plane of the drawing. The heavy lines protrude on both sides of this plane and are drawn in perspective. The arrow indicates the direction of measurement of angles φ.

monomer units have the *d* configuration. If, using the equivalence of the two directions in a molecule, we reverse the direction of the chain axis ζ, we obtain again a right-handed helix but now of an *l*-isotactic molecule, since reversal of the direction of the chain causes the *d* configuration of a monomer unit to change into the *l* configuration. These two right-handed helices are isomorphous and anticlined. Furthermore, since reflection in a plane parallel to the axis of the molecule transforms the *d* configuration of a monomer unit into an *l* configuration, it follows that the anticlined left-handed helices of *l*- and *d*-isotactic molecules correspond to the anticlined right-handed helices of *d*- and *l*-isotactic molecules; the two sets of helices are mutually enantiomorphous. These helices, which are related to each other by symmetry transformations, have an identical mutual arrangement of all the atoms of the chain, differing only in the spatial arrangement of the atoms, and are, therefore, isoenergetic. On the other hand, their interactions with each other depend on the type of helix and, in particular, the condition of the best packing in a crystalline polymer requires that the nearest neighbors of right-handed helices be enantiomorphous left-handed helices and vice versa.

Let us point out that right- and left-handed helical molecules must have optical activity, due to the helical structure of the chain, while the polymer, as a whole, is not optically active (if, of course, it does not contain truly asymmetric C atoms in the side groups), as long as it contains an equal amount of mutually enantiomorphous right- and left-handed helices. If the side groups of an isotactic molecule contain truly asymmetric atoms in identical configurations, the right-handed and left-handed helices of such a molecule become energetically nonequivalent, and the polymer as a whole must have an excess optical activity, which is determined by the preponderance of helices of one sign.

Let us characterize the conformation of a molecule of type ($—CH_2—CRR'—)_n$ by the sequence of pairs of angles of internal rotation of the $—CH_2—CRR'—$ and $—CRR'—CH_2—$ bonds of monomer units about the preceding $—CRR'—CH_2—$ and $—CH_2—CRR'—$ bonds, respectively. These pairs of angles determine the relative position of neighboring —CRR'— groups, i.e., the conformations of the monomer units. The helical, crystalline conformation of an isotactic molecule, in which the monomer units must be isomorphous and isoclined, is described by the expression $(\varphi_1, \varphi_2)_n$, where φ_1 and φ_2 are the angles of internal rotation of the $—CH_2—CRR'—$ and $—CRR'—CH_2—$ bonds (3,127) (see Fig. 3.3). Here $\varphi_2 \neq -\varphi_1$* except the case $\varphi_1 = \varphi_2 = 0$.† In the examination of the conformations of chains with asymmetric side groups, it is convenient to link the direction of measurement of the angles of internal rotation in the chains with the stereochemistry of the monomer units, i.e., to measure the angles in *d*- and *l*-isotactic molecules in opposite directions. Thus, if a right-handed helix of a *d*-isotactic molecule is characterized by the internal rotation angles $(\varphi_1, \varphi_2)_n$, then the enantiomorphous isoclined left-handed helix

* Let us recall that, as was pointed out in section 1.2, we measure the angles of internal rotation always from a *trans* conformation of the main chain bonds.

† A $(\varphi_1, -\varphi_1)_n$ helix with $\varphi_1 \neq 0$ would have an identity period equal to zero [see below eq. (3.4)], i.e., such a helix cannot exist for steric reasons.

of the *l*-isotactic molecule which is obtained from the initial molecule by reflection in the plane parallel to the molecular axis is characterized by the same internal rotation angles $(\varphi_1, \varphi_2)_n$. The right-handed helix of the *l*-isotactic molecule is anticlined and isomorphous with the initial one and can be obtained from it by changing the direction of the molecular axis; this helix is characterized by angles of internal rotation $(-\varphi_2, -\varphi_1)_n$. (When the direction of the axis of a molecule is changed, the $—CH_2—CRR'—$ bond of a monomer unit must be considered as a $—CRR'—CH_2$ bond, and vice versa.) The same angles of internal rotation characterize as well the left-handed helix of the *d*-isotactic molecule.

Thus, the angles of internal rotation $(\varphi_1, \varphi_2)_n$ and $(-\varphi_2, -\varphi_1)_n$ correspond to the enantiomorphous helices of both *d*- and *l*-isotactic molecules. It should be pointed out that, from the equivalence of the $(\varphi_1, \varphi_2)_n$ and $(-\varphi_2, -\varphi_1)_n$ helices, it follows that, in isotactic chains with asymmetric side groups, $\varphi_2 \neq \varphi_1$ (with the exception of the case $\varphi_1 = \varphi_2 = 0$), since for $\varphi_1 = \varphi_2 \neq 0$ we would have obtained symmetry with respect to the direction of turning of the helix in the given molecule; this can take place only in chains which have symmetric side groups.

It has been pointed out above that isotactic molecules of the type $(—CH_2—CRR'—)_n$ can consist of anticlined enantiomorphous units in the crystal also. In this case, the crystalline chain must be symmetric with respect to planes perpendicular to the axis of the chain, or possess a number of centers of symmetry. It is evident that a center of symmetry relating neighboring monomer units cannot exist in isotactic molecules, while a plane of symmetry can exist only for a flat chain structure. Such a flat structure is also the limiting case of the helical structure considered above in accordance with the condition that $\varphi_1 = \varphi_2 = 0$.

Let us examine now syndiotactic molecules of the type $(—CH_2—CRR'—)_n$, where the repeating chain element is a pair of monomer units. From the postulate of the equivalence of monomer units with respect to the helix axis (1,2,127) it follows that, in this case, the following conformations of the chain can exist:

1. In the case of enantiomorphous, pairwise-isoclined monomer units, which are repeated along a glide plane, the crystalline conformation of the chain must be described by the expression $(0, \varphi)_n$.* A change of direction of the axis in such a chain results in an isomorphous, anticlined conformation $(\varphi, 0)_n$, while reflection in the plane parallel to the chain axis, which is,

* Since we have related the direction of measurement of angles of internal rotation to the stereochemistry of monomer units, the angles of rotation in neighboring monomer units of syndiotactic chains are measured in opposite directions (see Fig. 3.3).

therefore, the glide plane (with a precision up to translation by one monomer unit), preserves, of course, the initial conformation.

2. In the case of isomorphous, pairwise-anticlined monomer units which are repeated along the helix (and in which, in addition, there are dyad axes perpendicular to the chain axis which pass through the methylene groups of the chain), the crystalline conformation of the chain is described by the expression $[(\varphi_1, \varphi_1)(\varphi_2, \varphi_2)]_{n/2}$, where pairs of angles, (φ_1, φ_1) and (φ_2, φ_2), characterize the conformations of neighboring monomer units and are measured in opposite directions (see Fig. 3.3). Moreover, $\varphi_1 \neq \varphi_2$ (with the exception of $\varphi_1 = \varphi_2 = 0$), since for $\varphi_1 = \varphi_2$ the helical structure obtained has an identity period equal to zero [eq. (3.5)].

Reflection of the right-handed helix $[(\varphi_1, \varphi_1)(\varphi_2, \varphi_2)]_{n/2}$ of a *dl*-syndiotactic molecule in the plane parallel to the axis of the helix transforms it into the enantiomorphous left-handed helix $[(\varphi_1, \varphi_1)(\varphi_2, \varphi_2)]_{n/2}$ of a *ld*-syndiotactic molecule; moreover, in the right-handed helix all the *d* monomer units will have (φ_1, φ_1) conformations, while all the *l* units will have (φ_2, φ_2) conformations; in the left-handed helix all the *d* monomer units will have (φ_2, φ_2) conformations, while all the *l* units will have (φ_1, φ_1) conformations. When the direction of the axis of such a helix is changed, the initial structure is preserved, of course, since it is symmetric with respect to the plane perpendicular to the helix axis.

Molecules with symmetric side groups of type $(—CH_2—CR_2—)_n$ are a particular case both of isotactic and syndiotactic molecules of type $(—CH_2—CRR'—)_n$, with $R = R'$. Therefore, in principle, these molecules can have those crystal structures which are possible for both types of stereoregular polymers, i.e., they can have both helical conformations and conformations characterized by a glide plane. Let us examine the helical crystalline conformation of molecules of type $(—CH_2—CR_2—)_n$, which is described by angles of internal rotation $(\varphi_1, \varphi_2)_n$. As long as such molecules do not have different *d* and *l* configurations, the direction of measurement of the angles of internal rotation cannot be related to the stereochemistry of a monomer unit, as has been done before; we shall measure these angles in an arbitrary but identical manner in all the molecules that are being examined simultaneously. It is obvious that the reflection of a right-handed helix $(\varphi_1, \varphi_2)_n$ in the plane parallel to its axis will result in an enantiomorphous isoclined left-handed helix, $(-\varphi_1, -\varphi_2)_n$, whereas a change in the direction of the axis will result in an isomorphous anticlined right-handed helix $(\varphi_2, \varphi_1)_n$. Thus, in such molecules, it is possible to have anticlined right-handed helices, $(\varphi_1, \varphi_2)_n$ and $(\varphi_2, \varphi_1)_n$, and their enantiomorphous left-handed helices, $(-\varphi_1, -\varphi_2)_n$ and $(-\varphi_2, -\varphi_1)_n$.

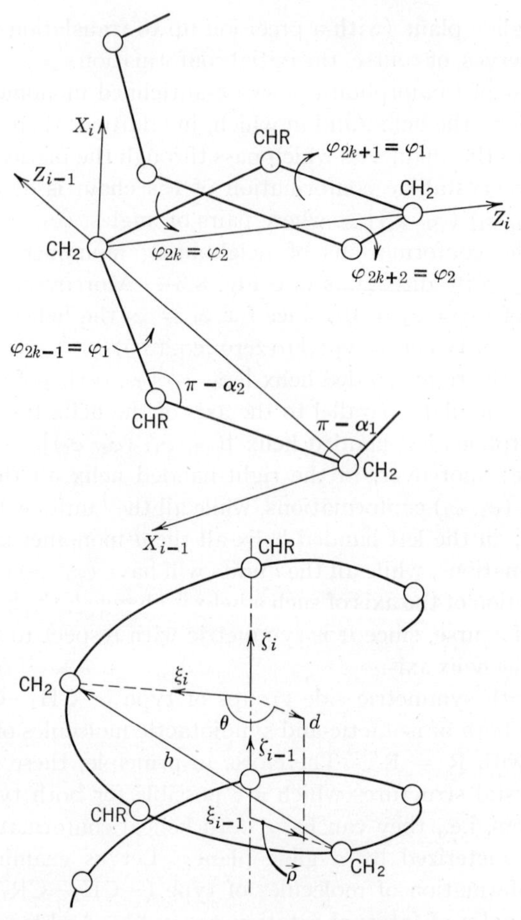

Fig. 3.4. Two sets of coordinate systems in a helical macromolecule of the type $(—CH_2—CHR—)_n$.

The crystalline conformation of molecules with symmetric side groups, which possesses a glide plane, is described by the expression $[(0, \varphi)\ (0, —\varphi)]_{n/2}$ (since, in this case, the angles of internal rotation are measured in neighboring monomer units in the same direction, and not in opposite directions, as is done in syndiotactic molecules). The anticlined conformation has the form $[(—\varphi, 0)\ (\varphi, 0)]_{n/2}$.

At the beginning of section 3.1 we stated that x-ray analysis gives information on the crystal structure of the chains, making possible the determination, first, of the nature of their symmetry, the size of the identity period of the chain, and the number of monomer units and turns of the helix within a period. From these data, it is possible to determine also the values of the angles of internal rotation which characterize the crystalline conformation of the chain.* The general method of determination of molecular parameters from known crystallographic data has been developed by Shimanouchi and Mizushima (4) [see also Hughes and Lauer (5)] for chains of any structure. Let us introduce two sets of n Cartesian systems of coordinates (n being the number of repeating units in the chain): a set of molecular systems of coordinates, linked to the molecular parameters (bond lengths, valence angles, angles of internal rotation) and a set of systems of coordinates of the helix, linked to the helix parameters (angle of the turn and step along the helix axis per repeating unit of the chain). Let us link the local molecular systems of coordinates, X_i, Y_i, Z_i in identical manner with the repeating units of the chain. The local systems of coordinates of the helix (ξ_i, η_i, ζ_i) will be selected as follows. The origins of all the systems of coordinates lie on the helix axis on perpendicular lines dropped on this axis from the origins of the molecular systems of coordinates. Furthermore, axes ζ_i are directed along the helix axis, while axes ξ_i are directed toward the origins of the local molecular systems of coordinates X_i, Y_i, Z_i (Fig. 3.4).

Writing an arbitrary vector in the coordinate system (ξ_i, η_i, ζ_i) and passing over to the system (ξ_{i-1}, η_{i-1}, ζ_{i-1}) directly, as well as by means of systems (X_i, Y_i, Z_i) and (X_{i-1}, Y_{i-1}, Z_{i-1}), we obtain

$$N = T^{-1}ST$$

$$\mathbf{d} = (I - T^{-1}ST)\boldsymbol{\varrho} + T^{-1}\mathbf{b} \tag{3.1}$$

where

$$N = \begin{pmatrix} \cos\vartheta & -\sin\vartheta & 0 \\ \sin\vartheta & \cos\vartheta & 0 \\ 0 & 0 & 1 \end{pmatrix} \tag{3.2}$$

is the matrix of rotation from the system of coordinates (ξ_i, η_i, ζ_i) to system (ξ_{i-1}, η_{i-1}, ζ_{i-1}), ϑ is the angle of turn about the helix axis per repeating unit of the chain, S is the matrix of rotation from system (X_i, Y_i, Z_i) to system (X_{i-1}, Y_{i-1}, Z_{i-1}), the elements of which are functions of the angles of internal rotation and of the valence angles of the chain, T is the matrix of rotation from the helical system (ξ_i, η_i, ζ_i) to the molecular system (X_i, Y_i,

* In a number of cases a detailed x-ray analysis has made it possible to determine the coordinates of all the atoms of a chain and, in this manner, to find directly all the molecular parameters (bond lengths, valence angles, angles of internal rotation).

Z_i), $\mathbf{d} = d\mathbf{e}_\zeta$ is the step along the helix axis per repeating unit of the chain, $\mathbf{b}(b_1b_2b_3)$ and $\boldsymbol{\rho} = \rho\mathbf{e}_\xi$ are vectors which determine the position of the origin of coordinate system (X_i, Y_i, Z_i) in systems (X_{i-1}, Y_{i-1}, Z_{i-1}) and (ξ_i, η_i, ζ_i), and I is a unit matrix. Equating the sums of the diagonal components of matrices N and S and calculating the component of vector **d**, we obtain from eqs. (3.1) and (3.2)

$$\cos \vartheta = {}^1/_2 (\mathrm{Sp}\, S - 1)$$

$$2d^2(1 - \cos \vartheta) = \frac{[b_1(S_{13} + S_{31}) + b_2(S_{23} + S_{32}) + b_3(1 - S_{11} - S_{22} + S_{33})]^2}{1 - S_{11} - S_{22} + S_{33}}$$

$$2\rho^2(1 - \cos \vartheta) + d^2 = b_1{}^2 + b_2{}^2 + b_3{}^2 \qquad (3.3)$$

where S_{ik} are elements of matrix S.*

The stereochemical structure of the chain must be accounted for in the transition from the matrix eqs. (3.3), which are valid for any polymer chains, to equations which relate the helix parameters d, ϑ, and ρ to the characteristics of the conformations of monomer units in actual macromolecules. Let us examine isotactic chains of type $(\text{—CH}_2\text{—CRR}'\text{—})_n$ (including chains with symmetric side groups, for which R = R′), which crystallize in the form of helices, characterized by angles of internal rotation $(\varphi_1, \varphi_2)_n$.

Let us link the local systems of coordinates (X_i, Y_i, Z_i) to monomer units, as is shown in Figure 3.4. The Z_i axis of the ith system of coordinates is directed along the vector of the monomer unit length, the X_i axis lies in the plane of the bonds of the main chain; the directions of the X_i and Y_i axes are chosen in such a way that the magnitude of the projections of the C—R bonds on these axes would be positive. (In the case of a molecule with symmetric side groups, the selection of the direction of the Y_i axis is arbitrary; but, it is essential that all the local systems of coordinates be either right- or left-handed.) The origin of the system of coordinates is placed in the C atom of the $\text{—CH}_2\text{—}$ group. It is evident that coordinate systems selected in such manner will all be right- or left-handed, depending on whether we are dealing with d- or l-type molecules.

In the case under consideration, $\mathbf{b} = 2l \cos(\alpha_2/2)\, \mathbf{e}_z$, where l is the length of a bond in the main chain, $\pi - \alpha_2$ is the valence angle C—CRR′—C.

* *Translator's note:* Sp is the trace of the matrix.

Introducing into eq. (3.3) the expression for the components of vector **b** and matrix S [see eq. (6.5)], we obtain (6–8):

$$\pm\cos(\vartheta/2) = \cos\varphi\cos(\alpha_1/2)\cos(\alpha_2/2) + \cos\Delta\varphi\sin(\alpha_1/2)\sin(\alpha_2/2)$$

$$\pm(d/2l)\sin(\vartheta/2) = \sin\varphi\cos(\alpha_1/2)\cos(\alpha_2/2) \quad (3.4)$$

where

$$\varphi = (\varphi_1 + \varphi_2)/2$$

$$\Delta\varphi = (\varphi_1 - \varphi_2)/2$$

while $\pi - \alpha_1$ is the valence angle C—CH_2—C. If angles (φ_1, φ_2) satisfy eqs. (3.4), then angles $(-\varphi_1, -\varphi_2)$ and $\pm(\varphi_2, \varphi_1)$ also satisfy them. The corresponding helices are equivalent in the sense of the distribution of elements in the main chain; in the case of molecules with asymmetric side groups, however, they differ with respect to the mutual distribution of the side groups; the choice between these helices may be made on the basis of the real stereochemical structure of the chain. In those cases, in which only the general structure of the helix (3_1, 4_1, etc.) and the identity period are known, it is necessary to determine four parameters: α_1, α_2, φ_1 and φ_2, from eqs. (3.4); thus, for a unique solution it is necessary to have information, e.g., on valence angles, from independent sources.

Equations (3.3) may be used also for determining the relation between the parameters of the helix and those of the molecule in the case of syndiotactic molecules of type $(—CH_2—CRR'—)_n$. In doing this, angle ϑ and period d must be related to pairs of monomer units, which are the repeating elements of the chain. Miyazawa (7) has recently solved the matrix equations, eqs. (3.3), for the helical conformation of syndiotactic molecules, which corresponds to alternating angles (φ_1, φ_1) and (φ_2, φ_2) measured in opposite directions (isomorphous pairwise-anticlined monomer units):

$$\begin{aligned}\pm\cos(\vartheta/2) &= \cos(\varphi_1 - \varphi_2)\cos^2(\alpha_1/2)\cos^2(\alpha_2/2)\\ &+ 2(\cos\varphi_1 + \cos\varphi_2)\sin(\alpha_1/2)\cos(\alpha_1/2)\sin(\alpha_2/2)\cos(\alpha_2/2)\\ &+\sin^2(\alpha_1/2)[\sin^2(\alpha_2/2) - \cos^2\alpha_2/2] - \cos(\varphi_1 + \varphi_2)\cos^2(\alpha_1/2)\sin^2(\alpha_2/2)\end{aligned}$$

$$\begin{aligned}\pm(d/4l)\sin(\vartheta/2) &= \sin(\varphi_1 - \varphi_2)\cos^2(\alpha_1/2)\cos^2(\alpha_2/2) + (\sin\varphi_1 - \sin\varphi_2)\\ &\times \sin(\alpha_1/2)\cos(\alpha_1/2)\sin(\alpha_2/2)\cos(\alpha_2/2) \quad (3.5)\end{aligned}$$

Miyazawa (7) derived equations which relate the crystallographic and molecular parameters of chains, the repeating units of which consist of three, five, and six atoms. The question of the determination of molecular parameters from known d and ϑ, in particular as it applies to polypeptide

TABLE 3.1. Parameters Characterizing the Crystal Structure of Macromolecules

Polymer	Repeating unit	Identity period, Å	Helix type[a]	Valence angles, degrees	Angles of internal rotation, degrees	Ref.
A. Polymers with Symmetric Side Groups						
Polyethylene	$-CH_2-CH_2-$[c]	2.53	1_1	110	0, 0	13,14
Polytetrafluoroethylene	$-CF_2-CF_2-$	16.8	$6.5_{1/2}$[b]	112–115	16, 16	15
Polyisobutylene	$-CH_2-C(CH_3)_2-$	18.63	8_5	114 $\angle CH_2 \cdot 126$ $\angle C(CH_3)_2 \cdot 107$	82, 82 102.5 51	16,17 18
B. Isotactic Polymers[c]						
Polypropylene	$-CH_2-CH(CH_3)-$	6.49–6.51	3_1	114	0, 120	10,12, 19–22
Poly-1-butene	$-CH_2-CH(CH_2-CH_3)-$	6.50	3_1	114	0, 120	12,23,24
Poly-5-methyl-1-hexene	$-CH_2-CH[(CH_2)_2-CH(CH_3)_2]-$	6.50	3_1	114	0, 120	12,25
Poly-5-methyl-1-heptene	$-CH_2-CH[(CH_2)_2-CH(CH_3)-CH_2-CH_3]-$	6.40	3_1	113	0, 120	12
Poly-1,2-butadiene	$-CH_2-CH(CH{=}CH_2)-$	6.50	3_1	114	0, 120	26

Polystyrene	$-CH_2-CH-$ C_6H_5	6.65	3_1	116	0, 120	10,12,27
Poly-3-phenyl-1-propene	$-CH_2-CH-$ CH_2 C_6H_5	6.40	3_1	113	0, 120	12
Poly-4-phenyl-1-butene	$-CH_2-CH-$ $(CH_2)_2$ C_6H_5	6.55	3_1	115	0, 120	12
Poly-*o*-fluorostyrene	$-CH_2-CH-$ C_6H_4F	6.63–6.65	3_1	116	0, 120	12,28–31
Polyvinylcyclopentane	$-CH_2-CH-$ C_5H_9	6.6	3_1			32
Poly(vinyl methyl ether)	$-CH_2-CH-$ O CH_3	6.50	3_1			12
Poly(vinyl *n*-butyl ether)	$-CH_2-CH-$ O $(CH_2)_3$ CH_3	6.5	3_1			33

(*continued*)

TABLE 3.1 (*continued*)

Polymer	Repeating unit	Identity period, Å	Helix type[a]	Valence angles, degrees	Angles of internal rotation, degrees	Ref.
Poly(vinyl isobutyl ether)	—CH_2—CH—(O—CH_2—CH—$(CH_3)_2$)	6.50	3_1			12,34,35
Poly(vinyl neopentyl ether)	—CH_2—CH—(O—CH_2—C—$(CH_3)_3$)	6.40	3_1			12
Poly(vinyl formate)	—CH_2—CH—(O—C(=O)—H)	6.55				125
Poly(isopropyl acrylate)	—CH_2—CH—(C(=O)—O—CH—(CH_3))	6.50	3_1			12

Poly(isobutyl acrylate)	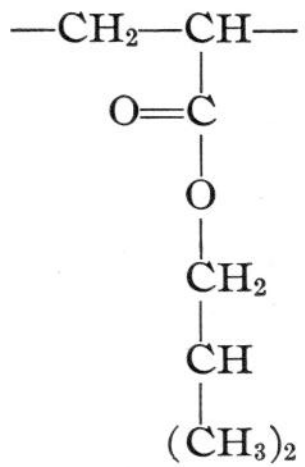 $-CH_2-CH(-C(=O)-O-CH_2-CH-(CH_3)_2)-$	6.42	3_1		36
Poly(*sec*-butyl acrylate)	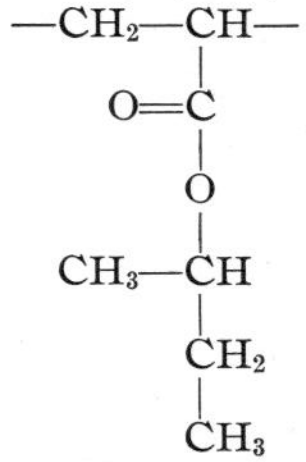 $-CH_2-CH(-C(=O)-O-CH(CH_3)-CH_2-CH_3)-$	6.49	3_1		36
Poly(*tert*-butyl acrylate)	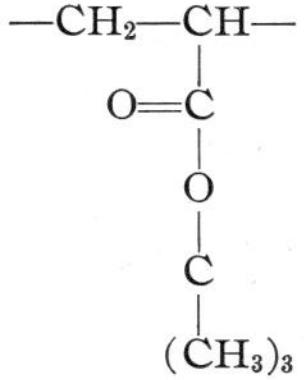 $-CH_2-CH(-C(=O)-O-C-(CH_3)_3)-$	6.45–6.48	3_1		12,36
Poly-2-vinylpyridine	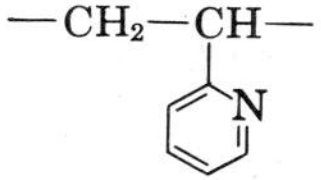 $-CH_2-CH(C_5H_4N)-$ (2-pyridyl)	6.7			37

(continued)

TABLE 3.1 (*continued*)

Polymer	Repeating unit	Identity period, Å	Helix type[a]	Valence angles, degrees	Angles of internal rotation, degrees	Ref.
Poly-*N*,*N*-dibutylacrylamide	$-CH_2-CH(-C(=O)-N((CH_2)_3CH_3)_2)-$	6.30	3_1			38
Polyallylsilane	$-CH_2-CH(-CH_2-SiH_3)-$	6.45	3_1			12,29,39
Polyallyltrimethylsilane	$-CH_2-CH(-CH_2-Si(CH_3)_3)-$	6.50	3_1			12,29,39
Poly-5-trimethylsilyl-1-pentene	$-CH_2-CH(-(CH_2)_3-Si(CH_3)_3)-$	6.55	3_1			12,29
Poly-*p*-trimethylsilylstyrene	$-CH_2-CH(-C_6H_4-Si(CH_3)_3)-$	60.4–60.6	29_9			40,41

Polyallylcyclohexane	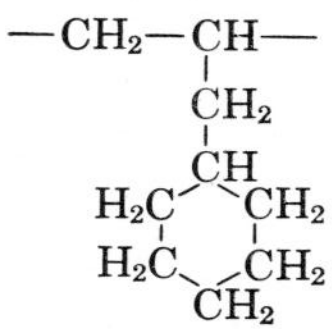 $—CH_2—CH(CH_2C_6H_{11})—$ (side chain: CH_2–CH of cyclohexane ring H_2C, CH_2, H_2C, CH_2, CH_2)		10_3			43
Poly-*p*-methylstyrene	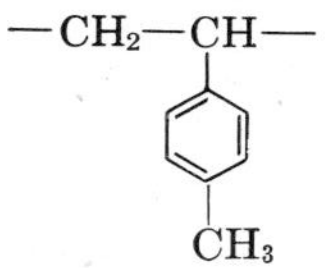 $—CH_2—CH(C_6H_4—CH_3)—$	12.9				40
Poly-4-methyl-1-pentene	$—CH_2—CH(CH_2—CH(CH_3)_2)—$	13.80–13.85	7_2	110	−13, 110	12,42
Poly-4-methyl-1-hexene	$—CH_2—CH(CH_2—CH(CH_3)—CH_2—CH_3)—$	14.00	7_2	111	−13, 110	12,25
Poly-*m*-methylstyrene	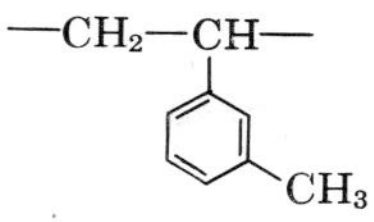 $—CH_2—CH(C_6H_4—CH_3)—$	21.74	11_3	114	−16, 104	12,43
		57.0–57.1	29_8			40,41,44
Poly-3-methyl-1-butene	$—CH_2—CH(CH(CH_3)_2)—$	6.84	4_1	110	−24, 96	25,45

(continued)

TABLE 3.1 (*continued*)

Polymer	Repeating unit	Identity period, Å	Helix type[a]	Valence angles, degrees	Angles of internal rotation, degrees	Ref.
Polyvinylcyclohexane	$-CH_2-CH-$ (cyclohexyl: CH, H_2C, CH_2, H_2C, CH_2, CH_2)	6.5–6.6	4_1		−29, 97	12,32,45
Poly-α-vinylnaphthalene	$-CH_2-CH-$ (α-naphthyl)	8.10–8.20	4_1	110	0, 90	12,29,46
Poly-*o*-methylstyrene	$-CH_2-CH-$ (phenyl, CH_3)	8.10	4_1	110	0, 90	12,29,47
Poly-*p*-fluorostyrene	$-CH_2-CH-$ (phenyl, F)	8.30	4_1		0, 90	12,29,30
Poly-*o*-methyl-*p*-fluorostyrene	$-CH_2-CH-$ (phenyl, CH_3, F)	8.05	4_1		0, 90	12,29,30
Poly-2,5-dimethylstyrene	$-CH_2-CH-$ (phenyl, CH_3, CH_3)	8.1	4_1		0, 90	48

Polyacetaldehyde	$-O-CH(CH_3)-$	4.8	4_1	110	−45, 95	48–50
Polypropionaldehyde	$-O-CH(CH_2CH_3)-$	4.8	4_1	110	−45, 95	48,49,51
Poly-*n*-butyraldehyde	$-O-CH((CH_2)_2CH_3)-$	4.8	4_1	110	−45, 95	48,49,51
Polyisobutyraldehyde	$-O-CH(CH(CH_3)_2)-$	5.2	4_1	110	−35, 97	48,51
Polyisovaleraldehyde	$-O-CH(CH_2CH(CH_3)_2)-$	5.2	4_1	110	−35, 97	51
Poly(methyl methacrylate)	$-CH_2-C(CH_3)(C(=O)OCH_3)-$	10.55	5_2			52
C. Syndiotactic Polymers						
Poly-1,2-butadiene	$-CH_2-CH(CH=CH_2)-$	5.14	2_2	113	0.0, 0.0	53,54

(continued)

TABLE 3.1 (*continued*)

Polymer	Repeating unit	Identity period, Å	Helix type[a]	Valence angles, degrees	Angles of internal rotation, degrees	Ref.
Poly(vinyl chloride)[d]	—CH₂—CH(—Cl)— ($-CH_2-CH(Cl)-$)	5.10–5.20	2_2		0.0, 0.0	53–56
Poly(vinyl formate)	$-CH_2-CH(-O-C(=O)-H)-$	5.0	2_2		0.0, 0.0	125
Polyacrylonitrile[d]	$-CH_2-CH(-C\equiv N)-$	5.0	2_2		0.0, 0.0	57
Polypropylene	$-CH_2-CH(-CH_3)-$	7.3			0.0, −120, −120	12
Poly(methyl methacrylate)	$-CH_2-C(CH_3)(-C(=O)-O-CH_3)-$	21.1	10_4			58
Polyacetaldehyde[e]	$-O-CH(-CH_3)-$	3.9			0.180, 0.180	59
D. Atactic Polymers[f]						
Poly(vinyl fluoride)	$-CH_2-CH(-F)-$	2.53	1_1		0.0, 0.0	60

Poly(vinyl alcohol)	$—CH_2—CH(OH)—$	2.52	1_1		0.0, 0.0	61–63
E. Polyoxides						
Poly(methylene oxide)[g]	$—CH_2—O—$	17.30	9_5			64,135
Poly(ethylene oxide)	$—CH_2—CH_2—O—$	12.0				65,66
		19.25	7_2		0, 120, 0	144
Poly(trimethylene oxide)	$—(CH_2)_3—O—$			1_1		18
Poly(tetramethylene oxide)	$—(CH_2)_4—O—$			1_1		18
Poly(D,L-propylene oxide)	$—CH(CH_3)—CH_2—O—$	6.92		1_1		67–69

[a] The helical structures of macromolecules are denoted by the symbols p_q, where p is the number of monomer units in the identity period, and q is the number of turns of the helix per period.

[b] This indicates 13 CF_2 groups and $^1/_2$ turn per period.

[c] Data for isotactic polymers of type $(—CH_2—CHR—)_n$ and $(—O—CHR—)_n$, *i.e.*, for all the isotactic polymers cited, with the exception of poly(methyl methacrylate), are given in increasing order of number of monomer units per turn of the helix; in helices 3_1, 29_9, 10_3, 7_2, 29_8, 11_3, and 4_1 there are per turn 3, $3^2/_9$, $3^1/_3$, $3^1/_2$, $3^5/_8$, $3^2/_3$, and 4 monomer units, respectively.

[d] The data are for atactic polymers; however, the identity period refers to a planar *trans* conformation of a syndiotactic chain, so that, in this case, an atactic chain has a structure which is close to syndiotactic.

[e] The crystal structure of polyacetaldehyde is characterized by a glide plane (see p. 58).

[f] The identity periods of ≈2.5 Å are evidence for a flat structure for the chains under investigation, since they coincide with the length per monomer unit in a planar *trans* chain. For chains which are able to crystallize only when the distribution of side groups is regular, such an identity period would indicate an isotactic structure for the chains (since, in this case only, the monomer unit would be the repeating unit of the chain). It seems, however, that the polymers under investigation can crystallize also with a nonregular distribution of side groups, since the van der Waals radii of F atoms and OH groups are relatively small, and these side groups can replace H atoms in the crystal lattice. This is confirmed, for example, by the crystallinity of copolymers of polyethylene and poly(vinyl alcohol) (132). A detailed investigation of the x-ray diagrams of poly(vinyl alcohol) points to the random placement of *d* and *l* positions of the OH groups (62).

[g] Strictly speaking, polyformaldehyde $(—CH_2—O—)_n$ is not a polyoxide, but it represents formally the first member of the homologous series of poly(methylene oxides).

chains (the repeating unit of which consists of three atoms), has been studied in detail by Nagai and Kobayashi (9).

The crystallographic data on the structure of a number of macromolecules in the crystal state are summarized in Table 3.1. A more or less complete compilation of such data, published prior to 1961, is given in the paper of Miller and Nielsen (10), while earlier compilations, pertaining mainly to isotactic polymers, are given in the papers of Natta (11,12). The identity period and the types of helices,* i.e., the number of monomer units and helix turns per period, are given in Table 3.1, which does not claim to be comprehensive. (It contains only those data which will be necessary for further discussion.) In those cases in which it was possible, the valence angles and the angles of internal rotation† are also given; these were determined from crystallographic data according to eqs. (3.4) and (3.5) or were found directly by determining from x-ray diagrams the coordinates of all the atoms of the chain.

3.2. Crystal Structures of Polymers and Intramolecular Interactions

Table 3.1 in the preceding section contains information on the crystal structures of a large number of different macromolecules. The question arises: how can these structures be interpreted, by relating them to the chemical structure of the corresponding polymers? Ptitsyn and Sharonov (6) have expressed the hypothesis that the crystalline conformations of macromolecules, in the majority of cases, are determined not only by intramolecular but also by intermolecular interactions. This hypothesis was based originally on the fact, pointed out above (see Chapter 2), that the crystalline conformations of small molecules are identical with their most stable conformations in the gas phase. Later, the question of the crystalline conformations in macromolecules was analyzed in detail by Bunn and Holmes (18) [see also (1,2,127)]. Bunn and Holmes pointed out that, although the crystal structure of macromolecules must be determined not only by intramolecular but also by intermolecular interactions, i.e., by the closest packing of chains (14), the maximal differences between the densities

* A planar *trans* chain is considered as a particular case of a helix, with one monomer unit and one turn per period (1_1) if the repeating unit of the chain contains one monomer residue (for example, in polyethylene), and with two monomer units and two turns per period (2_2), if the repeating unit contains two monomer residues (for example, in syndiotactic vinyl polymers).

† We shall measure the angles φ in such manner that rotation in the positive direction about the CHR—CH_2 bond would occur from the *trans* position of units of the main chain in the direction of the C—R bond. The direction of rotation about a CH_2—CHR bond is selected in the same manner as for the preceding CHR—CH_2 bond (see Fig. 9).

of the different packings in hydrocarbon polymers are associated with energy differences of only 300 cal/mole per unit. Therefore, intermolecular interactions can determine the crystal structure only of sufficiently flexible polymers, in which the various regular conformations differ by energies smaller than 300 cal/mole, while the crystal structures of most polymers must be determined by intramolecular interactions.

In Chapter 2, we considered briefly the problems of internal rotation and rotational isomerism in small molecules and came to the conclusion that the most probable conformations of a majority of molecules can be predicted relatively easily, by using the principle of staggered bonds and the principle of the best intramolecular packing (according to which a pair of nonbonded atoms cannot approach each other to a distance significantly smaller than the sum of their van der Waals radii). Let us prove that these simple considerations, together with the hypothesis that the crystal structures of polymer chains are determined by intramolecular interactions, are sufficient to interpret the crystalline conformations of a majority of macromolecules.

It is easy to see, for example, that the molecules of polyethylene, the side groups of which (hydrogen atoms) have a van der Waals radius of approximately 1.2 Å, must crystallize in the form of planar *trans* chains, since, in this structure, the distance between neighboring H atoms is equal to 2.5 Å, i.e., it is larger than the sum of their van der Waals radii. Rotation about any single bond from the *trans* to the *gauche* position causes some pair of nonbonded atoms to approach each other and increases the energy by ≈ 800 cal/mole (see Chapter 2). At the same time, replacement of all the H atoms by F atoms (which leads to molecules of polytetrafluoroethylene) renders the flat *trans* structure unfavorable, since the van der Waals radius of an F atom is equal to 1.4 Å and the distance between neighboring atoms in this case is less than the sum of their van der Waals radii. Therefore, molecules of polytetrafluoroethylene crystallize in the form of helices of low pitch with 13 CF_2 groups and $^1/_2$ turn per period, which is equal to 16.8 Å. In this helix (the valence angles are opened slightly to 115°), the distance between neighboring F atoms reaches 2.7 Å, i.e., it is almost equal to the sum of their van der Waal radii.

We can interpret in a similar way the crystal structures of isotactic and syndiotactic vinyl chains (18,71,72); we shall consider these in greater detail, since it is just the structure and flexibility of such chains which shall be examined in detail in this book.*

From the data of Table 3.1 it can be seen that the majority of isotactic

* A detailed survey of data on methods of preparation of stereoregular polymers and on their physical properties can be found in the monograph by Gaylord and Mark (74).

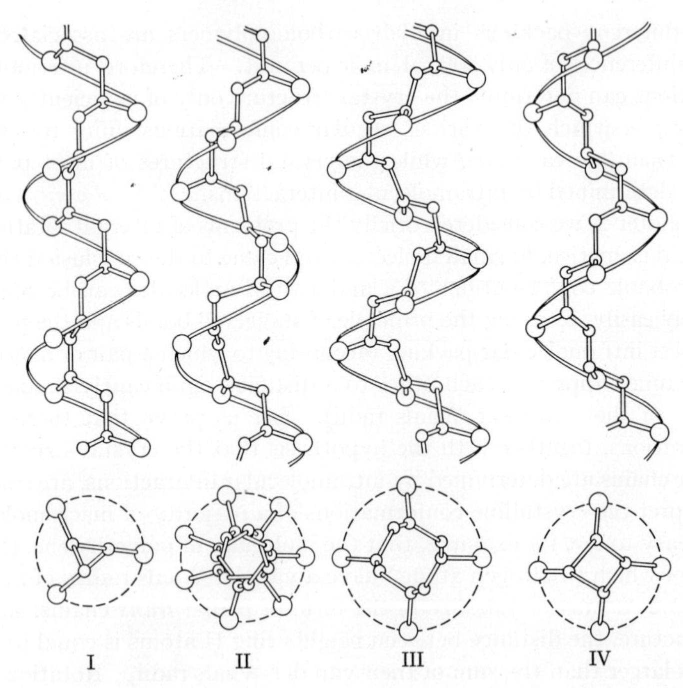

Fig. 3.5. Isotactic helices of various types: (I) 3_1; (II) 7_2; (III); and (IV) 4_1.

polymers of the type $(-CH_2-CHR-)_n$ crystallize in the form of a 3_1 helix (having three monomer units and one turn per period); this corresponds to alternating *trans* and *gauche* positions ($\varphi_1 = 0°$, $\varphi_2 = 120°$); in this case the principle of staggered bonds is fulfilled. A side group with branching close to the main chain as in poly-3-methyl-1-butene, leads to a 4_1 helix ($\varphi_1 = -24°$, $\varphi_2 = 96°$), while branching at the second atom of the side chain, as in poly-4-methyl-1-pentene, poly-4-methyl-1-hexene, leads to the "intermediate" 7_2 helix ($\varphi_1 = -13°$, $\varphi_2 = 110°$). Finally, if the branching is located at the third atom of the side group, e.g., poly-5-methyl-1-hexene, poly-5-methyl-1-heptene, poly(vinyl isobutyl ether), poly(vinyl neopentyl ether), poly(isopropyl acrylate), poly(*sec*-butyl acrylate), poly(*tert*-butyl acrylate) or at the fourth atom of the side group, as in poly(isobutyl acrylate), poly-5-trimethylsilyl-1-pentene,* and also if the side group is an unbranched, long chain, as in poly(vinyl *n*-butyl ether), the helix assumes again a 3_1 structure. A similar situation exists also in polymers which con-

* In some cases (poly-*N,N*-di-n-butylacrylamide, polyallyltrimethylsilane), structure 3_1 is formed even when branching occurs at the second atom of the side group chain.

tain cyclic groups in their side groups. If a phenyl or cyclopentyl group is attached to the chain, directly or through an aliphatic bridge, the chain has a 3_1 structure, e.g., polystyrene, poly-3-phenyl-1-propene, poly-4-phenyl-1-butene, polyvinylcyclopentane. The presence of a bulky substituent in the phenyl ring close to the main chain, i.e., in the *ortho* position, as in poly-*o*-methylstyrene, poly-*o*-methyl-*p*-fluorostyrene, or poly-2,5-dimethylstyrene, or an increase in the size of the side group, e.g., poly-α-vinylnaphthalene, polyvinylcyclohexane, leads to a 4_1 helix; on the other hand, the presence of a substituent which is relatively remote from the main chain (in the *meta* position) leads to the "intermediate" 11_3 helix ($\varphi_1 = -16°$, $\varphi_2 = 104°$) or to the closely related 29_8 helix, e.g., poly-*m*-methylstyrene. Finally, if the substituent is far from the main chain, i.e., in the *para* position, as in poly-*p*-trimethylsilylstyrene and possibly also poly-*p*-methylstyrene, or if the bulky cyclic side group is not directly attached to the chain, as in polyallylcyclohexane, the chain has the structure of a 29_9 or a 10_3 helix; these are closer to a 3_1 helix than a 29_8 or 11_3 helix.* Figure 3.5 shows the 3_1, 4_1, and 7_2 helices.†

We see that the conformations of isotactic chains are essentially independent of the total dimensions of the side group, but are determined by their structure in the immediate vicinity of the main chain. This fact in itself indicates that the conformations of isotactic chains are determined by intramolecular interactions and not by the requirements of intermolecular packing; if the contrary were true, the conformation of helices would have changed in a regular manner with an increase in the length of the side group and would have been correlated with the density of crystalline polymers; this does not happen.

Syndiotactic polymers of type $(\text{—CH}_2\text{—CHR—})_n$ crystallize either in the form of planar *trans* chains, e.g., poly-1,2-butadiene, poly(vinyl chloride), polyacrylonitrile, or in the form of a helix which corresponds to the alternation of angles $\varphi_1 = \varphi_1' = 0°$ and $\varphi_2 = \varphi_2' = -120°$ e.g., polypropylene.

* An odd exception is found in the fluoro-substituted polystyrenes, among which poly-*p*-fluorostyrene has structure 4_1, poly-*o*-fluorostyrene structure 3_1, while poly-*m*-fluorostyrene has an identity period of 2.5 Å (73). The structure of polyaldehydes, which fits perfectly into the proposed scheme, will be discussed below.

† As can be seen from Table 3.1, two types of 4_1 helices are encountered in isotactic polymers: (*a*) a helix of type (φ_1, φ_2), where $\varphi_1 = -24°$ (poly-3-methyl-1-butene), $-29°$ (polyvinylcyclohexane), $-35°$ (polyaldehydes with branched side groups) or $-45°$ (polyaldehydes with linear side groups), while $\varphi_2 = 95$–$97°$, and (*b*) a helix of type (0°, 90°) (poly-α-vinylnaphthalene and a number of substituted polystyrenes). Both types of 4_1 helices are shown in Figure 3.5.

Let us analyze all the possible conformations of monomer units of isotactic and syndiotactic polymers of type (—CH_2—CHR—)$_n$ from the point of view of the intramolecular interactions of atoms and groups which are separated by one or two units of the main chain (the so-called first- and second-order interactions.)* It follows from Chapter 2 that such an analysis may be carried out, even without knowledge of the exact potential energy of interaction between the H and C atoms, on the basis of a simple comparison of the distances between all possible pairs of atoms and groups in different conformations of monomer units with the sum of the van der Waals radii (taking into consideration the principle of staggered bonds).

Since the van der Waals radius of —CH_2— and CH_3— groups is equal to 2.0 Å, and the half-thickness of a benzene ring is 1.85 Å, all conformations in which these groups approach each other to a distance less than 3.5 Å, may be considered as prohibited. Having verified (at intervals of 30°) the values of angles φ_1 and φ_2, and having excluded those which are prohibited (in the sense indicated above) by second-order interactions, we obtain the sets of conformations of monomer units shown in Table 3.2. The minimal distances $r_{\min}$ between the bulky groups in the corresponding conformations are also given.

Conformations (−60°, 60°) in isotactic and (−60°, −60°) in syndiotactic polymers, which are permitted by second-order interactions, are essentially prohibited, however, by first-order interactions and by the repulsion of the electron clouds of the bonds (principle of staggered bonds). The rest of the conformations of monomer units are more or less close to conformations which satisfy the principle of staggered bonds: in isotactic chains, they are close to conformations (0°, 120°) or (−120°, 0°), which are related by symmetry conditions and correspond to right-handed and left-handed 3_1 helices, while in syndiotactic chains they are close to conformations (0°, 0°) and (−120°, −120°).

It is clear from Figure 3.6 that, of all the possible staggered or similar conformations of chains of type (—CH_2—CHR—)$_n$ only such chains are actually realized in which no pair of bulky groups (including among them also "tails" of the chain) is located on the same side of the plane of the drawing. The conformations (0°, 120°) and (−120°, 0°) in isotactic chains and conformations (0°, 0°) and (−120°, −120°) in syndiotactic chains, although less favorable from the point of view of second-order interactions than those listed in Table 3.2, are not totally prohibited

* By an interaction of the mth order is understood an interaction of atoms or groups separated by m units of the main chain. Consequently, this interaction is a function of m angles of internal rotation, $\varphi_i, \varphi_{i+1}, \ldots, \varphi_{i+m-1}$.

TABLE 3.2
Conformations of Monomer Units

φ_1, degrees	φ_2, degrees	r_{min}, Å
	A. Isotactic Polymers	
−30	90	
−90	30	4.3
0	90	
−90	0	4.0
−30	120	
−120	30	4.0
−60	60	4.2
	B. Syndiotactic Polymers	
0	−30	4.0
−30	0	
−90	−120	4.0
−120	−90	
−60	−60	4.2
−30	−30	4.3
−90	−90	4.3

(the minimal distance between interacting groups being 3.5 Å). Consequently, in isotactic chains a compromise between the principle of staggered bonds and second-order interactions leads to energetically equivalent conformations of monomer units $(-\Delta_1,\ 120° - \Delta_2)$ and $(-120° + \Delta_2,\ -\Delta_1)$, where $0° \leqslant \Delta_{1,2} \leqslant 30°$; Δ_1 and Δ_2 are the greater the stronger the second-order interactions, i.e., the bulkier the side groups. This completely explains the crystal structures of isotactic polymers which vary from a 3_1 helix (0°, 120°) to a 4_1 helix (−24°, 96°) or (0°, 90°) with an increase in the repulsion between side groups.*

The crystal structures of molecules of isotactic polyaldehydes are interesting from this point of view; they differ from analogous molecules of the vinyl series only by the replacement in the main chain of a —CH_2— group by an —O— atom. Such a replacement corresponds to a decrease in the number of bonds attached to the axis of rotation from three to one; this

* Since the energy differences between the conformations of the indicated type, which differ by the values of Δ_1 and Δ_2, are probably not very great, intermolecular interaction can also play a role in the selection of any one of these conformations. In fact, poly-1-butene crystallizes in the form of both 3_1 and 4_1 helices; moreover, the 4_1 helix, which is formed during rapid crystallization, is less stable and, with time, changes into a 3_1 helix (2).

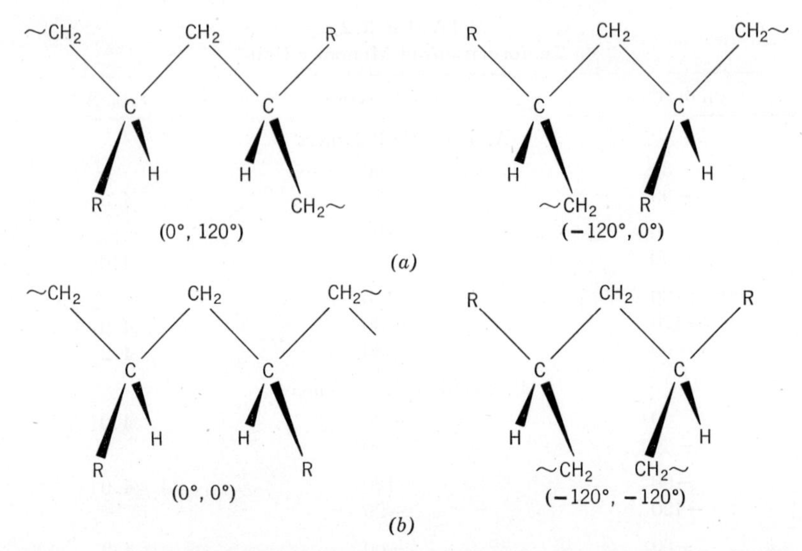

Fig. 3.6. Conformations of monomer units of macromolecules of type $(\text{—CH}_2\text{—CHR—})_n$; (*a*) isotactic; (*b*) syndiotactic. The thin lines lie in the plane of the drawing, while the heavy lines protrude on both sides of this plane and are drawn in perspective.

leads to a decrease in the role of the interactions of the electron clouds of these bonds. As a result, as has been pointed out in section 2.3, the potential barrier in a molecule of methyl alcohol decreases by a factor of three relative to the potential barrier in ethane, i.e., from 3000 to 1000 cal/mole (75). Accordingly, molecules of polyaldehydes, which contain both linear and branched side groups, crystallize in the form of 4_1 helices, which are determined principally by the repulsion of the bulky side groups.

To the contrary, in poly(propylene oxide), where the bulky side groups are separated from each other not only by a methylene group, but also by ethereal oxygen, the interactions of side groups are of little importance, and the molecules of the polymer crystallize in the form of planar *trans* chains.

In syndiotactic chains of the type $(\text{—CH}_2\text{—CHR—})_n$, the compromise between the principle of staggered bonds and the interactions of bulky groups results in the state that the most stable conformations are $(-\Delta_1, -\Delta_1)$ and $(-120° + \Delta_2, -120° + \Delta_2)$, where $0° \leqslant \Delta_{1,2} \leqslant 30°$. In fact, syndiotactic or almost syndiotactic poly-1,2-butadiene, poly(vinyl chloride), and polyacrylonitrile crystallize in a form which is very close to flat *trans* chains ($\varphi_1, \varphi_2 \approx 0°$), while syndiotactic polypropylene crystallizes in the form of a helix, in which *trans* conformations (0°, 0°) and *gauche* conformations (−120°, −120°) alternate. The formation of a helix in which all the monomer units would have conformations close to (−120°, −120°), must be considered as impossible, both in view of the equivalence postulate of Natta and Corradini (see section 3.1), and also, as has been shown by an investigation of models, because a sequence of two monomer units in the coiled conformation is prohibited by steric, high-order interactions. At the same time, the *gauche* conformation of syndiotactic chain monomer units has itself (i.e., from the point of view of first- and second-order interactions) almost the same free energy as the *trans* conformation.

The results presented above, which have been obtained by a simple comparison of the distances between different pairs of atoms in the chain with the sum of their van der Waals radii, are also confirmed by more detailed calculations based on various semiempirical potentials of interaction between nonbonded atoms of the chain (see section 2.3). Such calculations were carried out by Natta, Corradini, and Ganis (81,127) for isotactic and syndiotactic polypropylene, by Borisova and Birshtein for isotactic poly-α-olefins and polyaldehydes (76) and syndiotactic polypropylene and poly-1,2-butadiene (126), by De Santis, Giglio, Liquori, and Ripamonti (84) for polyethylene, polytetrafluoroethylene, polyisobutylene, poly(vinyl chloride), polyoxymethylene, and isotactic polyolefins, by Iwasaki (143) for polytetrafluoroethylene and by Borisova for polyethylene (128). In some studies (81,84,127) the first-order interactions between the C atoms (together with the H atoms attached to them) were considered to be the same as in 1,1-dimethylpropane (134):

$$V(\varphi) = {}^3/_2(1 - \cos 3\varphi) + {}^2/_3\left[2 - \cos\varphi - \cos\left(\varphi + \frac{2\pi}{3}\right)\right]$$

while the higher-order interactions were calculated with the help of the semiempirical potentials of Mason and Kreevoy (133) (see sections 2.2, 2.3). In the studies of Borisova and Birshtein (76,126,128), the calculations were carried out with the help of eq. (2.5), which gives the potential energy of interaction in the form of the sum of the bond orientation energy and the energy of interaction between nonbonded atoms of the chain. In this, U_{or} (the fraction of the potential barrier due to bond orientation) was set equal to 3000 cal/mole for rotation about a C—C bond and to 1000 cal/mole for rotation about a C—O bond, and the potentials of interaction used were those proposed by Bartell (77) and Kitaigorodskii (78,124) for C···C interactions, and those proposed by Bartell (77), Kitaigorodskii (78,124), and Hill (79) for H···H interactions (see section 2.3).

In all cases, the results of the calculations indicate, regardless of the potentials used, that *the crystal structures of the chains correspond to the*

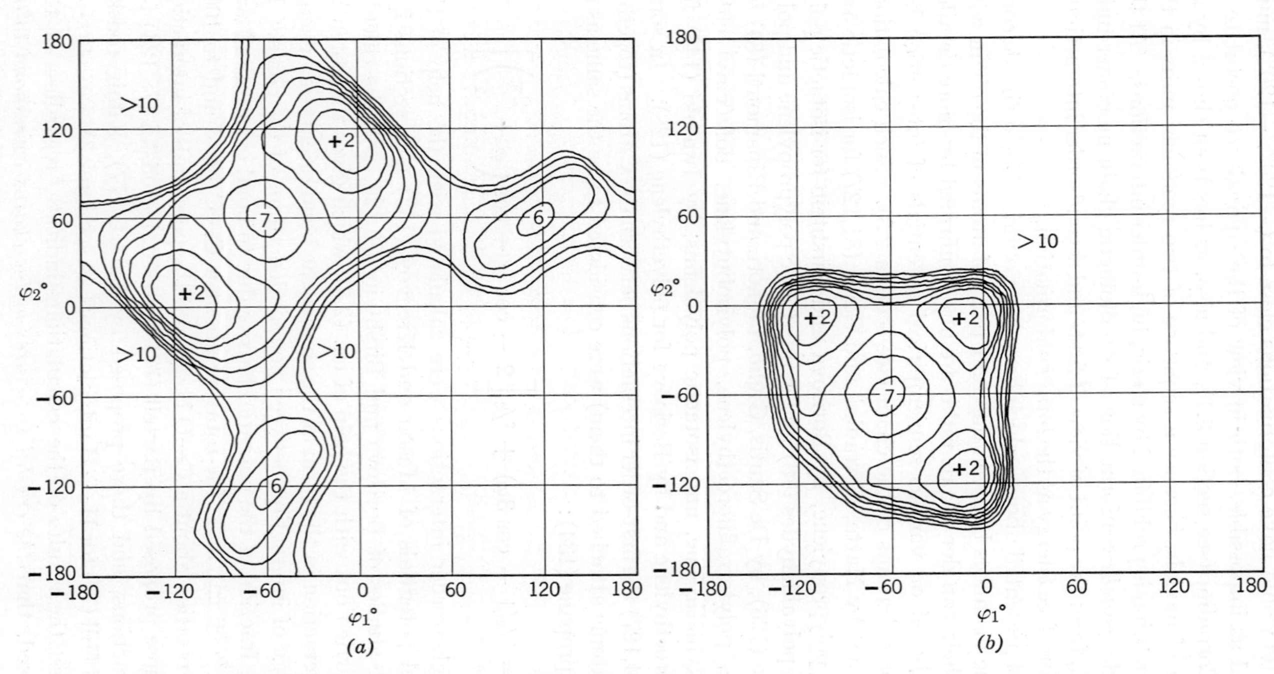

Fig. 3.7. Potential surfaces in polypropylene molecules: (*a*) dependence of the energy of the monomer unit of isotactic polypropylene on the angles of internal rotation (φ_1, φ_2); (*b*) dependence of the energy of a pair of monomer units of syndiotactic polypropylene on the angles of internal rotation (φ_1, φ_1); (φ_2, φ_2). Numbers on curves are values of the energy in kcal/mole of monomer units. The valence angles in the main chain are 112°.

minimum of the energy of intramolecular interaction. As an illustration, let us show (Fig. 3.7) the potential surfaces of the monomer units of isotactic polypropylene and of pairs of monomer units of syndiotactic polypropylene, as calculated by Natta, Corradini, and Ganis (3,127). It is evident from Figure 3.7 that in isotactic polypropylene the energy minimum corresponds to monomer unit conformations (0°, 120°) and (−120°, 0°), i.e., to right-handed and left-handed 3_1 helices, while in syndiotactic polypropylene it corresponds to monomer unit pair conformations (0°, 0°, 0°, 0°), (0°, 0°, −120°, −120°) and (−120°, −120°, 0°, 0°), i.e., to flat *trans* chains or right-handed or left-handed helices. The minimum corresponding to the flat structure of a syndiotactic polypropylene chain is also obtained in the investigation of conformations characterized by a glide plane.

More detailed calculations of the conformations of isotactic chains of the type $(\text{—CH}_2\text{—CHR—})_n$ carried out by Borisova and Birshtein (76), have shown that, when the valence angles are tetrahedral, the more stable conformation of an isolated polypropylene chain corresponds to internal rotation angles $\varphi_1 = -20°$, $\varphi_2 = 100°$, whereas, if the experimental values of the valence angles (114°) are used, this corresponds to angles $\varphi_1 = 0°$, $\varphi_2 = 120°$. On the other hand, for isolated chains containing branching in the side groups, the most stable conformation corresponds to angles $\varphi_1 = -25°$, $\varphi_2 = 100°$ if the branching is located at the first atom of the side group (poly-3-methyl-1-butene) and to angles $\varphi_1 = -15°$, $\varphi_2 = 110°$ if the branching is located at the second atom of the side group (poly-4-methyl-1-propylene, poly-4-methyl-1-hexene). As we see, the most stable conformations of these polymers, calculated for individual macromolecules, coincide almost exactly with their conformations determined experimentally in the crystalline state (see Table 3.1).

Borisova and Birshtein have also calculated the most stable conformations of molecules of isotactic polyaldehydes (76). The calculation was carried out as before by using eq. (2.5), where the potentials of the C···O and H···O interactions were taken as equal to the potentials of the C···C and H···C interactions, respectively. The last assumption cannot lead to serious errors, since the van der Waals radii of C (1.85 Å) and O (1.60 Å) atoms are not very much different. An evaluation of the contribution of dipole–dipole interactions has shown it to be relatively small. The (0°, 120°) conformation is highly unfavorable in this case even for polyacetaldehyde (which is an analog of polypropylene), because of the decrease in the role of the interactions of electron clouds, while the intramolecular energy minimum corresponds to conformation (−30°, 100°), which is close to the experimental value (see Table 3.1). Calculations have shown that in the case of polyaldehydes, the presence of branching in side groups should not affect the conformations of monomer units of the chain.

A detailed calculation of the conformations of syndiotactic macromolecules of the type $(—CH_2—CHR—)_n$ carried out by Borisova and Birshtein (126) has given the following results. As has been pointed out in section 2.3, the energy difference between *gauche* and *trans* isomers in *n*-butane is due to first-order interactions, C···C, and especially to third-order interactions, H···H, of one pair of hydrogens of the methyl group. Similarly, in syndiotactic polypropylene, the interactions between one of the hydrogen atoms of the methyl group and an H atom of the neighboring group, $—CH(CH_3)$, are important, as well as the third-order interactions between the H atoms which are directly linked to the main chain. As a result, the energy of a monomer unit in the conformation (−120°, −120°), which is located between monomer units in conformations (0°, 0°), is found to be approximately 1 kcal/mole smaller than the energy of a planar monomer unit in conformation (0°, 0°). This energy difference is due to the fact that, in the transition from a planar to a coiled conformation of one monomer unit, two junctions are formed between the planar and coiled monomer units. At each junction, the disappearance of the interaction between the methyl group and the H atoms of one of the neighboring $—CH(CH_3)$ groups is compensated for by the appearance of third-order interactions between the indicated H atom and a methylene group of the main chain, while the interaction between the methyl group with an H atom of the second neighboring $—CH(CH_3)$ group decreases by 0.5 kcal/mole, because the methyl group can rotate about the C—C bond. The situation is that which would exist if the methyl groups, CH_3, repelled each other more strongly than the methylene groups, $—CH_2—$, which form the continuation of the main chain. As a result, the conformation (−120°, −120°), which corresponds to the maximal separation of methyl groups (see Fig. 3.6b), is more favorable than conformation (0°, 0°), which corresponds to the maximal separation of methylene groups.

The situation is different in syndiotactic poly-1,2-butadiene, in which the side groups, $—CH{=}CH_2$, interact weakly with each other and with the H atoms of the main chain. Therefore, during transition from a flat to a coiled conformation in this case, the energy of the chain increases by the energy of the third-order interaction between the H atoms of the main chain, which is equal to ≈1.0 kcal/mole. The situation is as if the $—CH{=}CH_2$ groups of side chains which are attached to the main chain repelled each other less strongly than methylene groups. Let us note that, in poly-1,2-butadiene, calculation points to some deformation of the structure of those monomer units which are adjacent to monomer units in coiled conformations.

In complete agreement with these theoretical predictions, syndiotactic polypropylene crystallizes in the form of helices, with an alternation of conformations (0°, 0°) and (−120°, −120°), while syndiotactic poly-1,2-butadiene crystallizes in the form of flat chains, i.e. conformations (0°, 0°). In the case of syndiotactic polymers with polar side groups, e.g., poly(vinyl chloride), the difference in the electrostatic interaction energies of C—Cl bonds between conformations (−120°, −120°) and (0°, 0°) amounts to more than 1.5 kcal/mole, as estimated by Fordham (131); this explains the flat structure of these chains in the crystalline state.

The polymer chains of type $(\text{—CH}_2\text{—CHR—})_n$, considered above, contain such staggered, or similar, conformations in which the distances between all bulky groups are sufficiently large. Evidently, this is not possible for chains of the types $(\text{—CH}_2\text{—CR}_2\text{—})_n$ or $(\text{—CH}_2\text{—CRR}'\text{—})_n$, which contain two bulky groups of each alternate carbon atom of the main chain. In such chains, any staggered conformation leads to the superposition of bulky groups, so that these chains must exist in a state of extreme strain.* Therefore, it is not possible to carry out a simple qualitative analysis (18,83) of conformations of polymer types $(\text{—CH}_2\text{—CR}_2\text{—})_n$ and $(\text{—CH}_2\text{—CRR}'\text{—})_n$. On the other hand, a theoretical evaluation of the conformation energies of these chains on the basis of semiempirical interaction potentials encounters considerable difficulties, since, for all conformations, the distances between any pairs of atoms or atomic groups is found to be smaller than the sum of their van der Waals radii, and the semiempirical expressions for the potential energy of interaction at such small distances are *a priori* inexact. Nevertheless, a successful attempt at calculation of the energies of various conformations of polyisobutylene has been undertaken in the recent study of Liquori and his co-workers (84). As is shown in this study, the minimum of the energy of intermolecular interaction in polyisobutylene is found at angles of internal rotation $\varphi_1 = \varphi_2 = 95°$, which is very close to the internal rotation angles $\varphi_1 = \varphi_2 = 82°$, characteristic of the crystal structure of the chain, namely an 8_5 helix (see Table 3.1). Let us point out that, according to the calculations of Liquori, each monomer unit of polyisobutylene can have two other conformations, (135°, 25°) and (25°, 135°),

* It can be expected that the strained state of such chains will be partly mitigated by the opening of the valence angles. This effect has been observed, actually, with polyisobutylene and poly(methyl methacrylate), both by the method of x-ray analysis (for polyisobutylene, see Table 3.1) and from the optical anisotropy, determined from the dynamic birefringence (80,81) or from the photoelastic effect (82).

related by the symmetry conditions; these have energies a little larger than the energy of conformation (95°, 95°).*

The potential of internal rotation in the polytetrafluoroethylene molecule was calculated by Iwasaki (143); in this study, he took into consideration both the steric and the electrostatic interactions (the energy of bond orientation was not taken into account). It was shown that the dependence of the steric interaction energy on the angle of internal rotation is related, essentially, to the interaction between F atoms separated by one or two bonds of the main chain. These interactions were calculated by means of the semiempirical potential of Mason and Kreevoy (133) (see sections 2.2 and 2.3). The calculated energy of steric interaction has two minima at $\pm 17°30'$, separated by a maximum with a height of ≈ 0.5 kcal/mole at 0°. The energy increases sharply in the region of angles greater in absolute value than $\approx 20°$. When dipole–dipole interactions of C—F bonds are taken into account, the minima are displaced to $\approx 19°$, and the potential barrier which separates them is increased to ≈ 1 kcal/mole. The results obtained are in very good agreement with the crystal structure of chains of polytetrafluoroethylene (see Table 3.1); this structure is characterized by the internal rotation angles (16°, 16°).

On the basis of similar considerations which take into account only the intramolecular interactions of the chains, Bunn and Holmes (18) have interpreted the crystal structure of molecules of rubber hydrochloride $[—CH_2—CH_2—CH_2—C(CH_3)Cl—]_n$, which is a helix with a period of 8.95 Å and internal rotation angles $\varphi_1 = \varphi_2 = \varphi_3 = 0°$, $\varphi_4 = 120°$, $\varphi_5 = \varphi_6 = \varphi_7 = 0°$, $\varphi_8 = -120°$ (85), and Borisova (86) has interpreted the crystal structure of natural rubber and gutta-percha molecules.

3.3. Short-Range Order in Free Macromolecules and the Mechanism of Their Flexibility

As has been shown in the preceding section, the crystal structures of practically all of the polymers studied, such as polyethylene, polytetrafluoroethylene, isotactic and syndiotactic polymers of type $(—CH_2—CHR—)_n$, polyisobutylene, polyoxymethylene, and others correspond to the minimum of intramolecular energy. This fact leads to the necessary logical conclusion that *the most probable conformations of monomer units of macromolecules in solution or in a high elastic bulk state are identical with their crystalline conformations.* Of course, this should not be understood

* It is evident, furthermore, that, in chains with symmetric side groups such as polyisobutylene, each conformation (φ_1, φ_2) has a corresponding isoenergetic conformation $(-\varphi_1, -\varphi_2)$.

in the sense, that, for example, isotactic macromolecules are present in solution in the form of rigid helices, while syndiotactic ones are in the form of rigid *trans* chains. In order to maintain long-range one-dimensional order in a free macromolecule, it is necessary to have intramolecular forces which can withstand the disorienting action of thermal motion. Hydrogen bonds are such forces; they secure the rigid helical structure of free molecules of synthetic polypeptides (87). Evidently, forces of steric repulsion between groups cannot by themselves rigidly fix the positions of elements of the main chain and cannot resist the coiling of the macromolecule into a statistical coil. It is possible to assert only that, although a macromolecule in solution or in the high elastic block state is devoid of one-dimensional long range order, its *short-range one-dimensional order, in a majority of cases, is similar to the long-range one-dimensional order in the crystal state.*

This thesis, which forms the basis of the theory of the physical properties of macromolecules in solution presented in the following chapters, was first expressed by Ptitsyn and Sharonov (6) in the form of a hypothesis. Since then it has been supported by the calculations, presented above, of the intramolecular potential energy in typical macromolecules, from which it follows that the most stable conformations calculated for individual macromolecules coincide almost completely with the conformations determined experimentally in the crystal state.

This thesis has been confirmed in recent years also by spectroscopic studies of short-range order in macromolecules in solution and in the amorphous, bulk state. The studies of Japanese investigators have shown that bands characteristic of the helical crystal structure of isotactic chains (3_1 helix) are preserved in the infrared absorption spectra of amorphous, annealed isotactic polystyrene (83) and also of isotactic polystyrene in melt and in CCl_4 solution (90,91); these bands are absent in the case of atactic samples. Similar results were obtained for amorphous, annealed poly-*p*-deuterostyrene (88) and melted poly-*p*-fluorostyrene (90,91). Recently, the presence of one-dimensional short-range order in free macromolecules was demonstrated spectroscopically by Volchek for the case of isotactic polypropylene. In this study (93) it was shown that the 974 cm^{-1} band, which is present in the spectrum of crystalline isotactic polypropylene, is characteristic of intrachain short-range order (the helical conformation of the chain). In contrast to the 997 cm^{-1} band,* which is characteristic of intermolecular short-range order and which disappears upon melting or dissolution of polypropylene, the 974 cm^{-1} band undergoes practically no

* Both the 974 and 997 cm^{-1} bands are absent from atactic polymers.

change during the melting of the polypropylene; it is present with the same intensity in the spectrum of an annealed sample and decreases by only 20% when the polypropylene is dissolved. This indicates clearly that, even when intermolecular order disappears completely in polypropylene chains, short-range one-dimensional order is preserved; the latter is similar to the one-dimensional order in the crystal state.

Particularly effective proofs of the preservation of short-range order in free isotactic molecules can be found in the papers of Pino and his co-workers (94,95,136,137) and of other authors (138,139) on the investigation of the optical activity of isotactic polymers. In these studies a number of polymers of optically active α-olefins, i.e., polymers of the type $(—CH_2—CHR—)_n$, (where R is an optically active side group containing an asymmetric carbon atom) were synthesized and investigated. It was found that molecules of the isotactic fractions of such polymers possess a quite large optical activity: the molecular rotatory power $[M]$ of these polymers (i.e., the angles of rotation of the plane of polarization per mole of monomer units of the rotating substance) exceeds in absolute value the molecular rotatory power of similar low molecular compounds by more than one order of magnitude (see Table 3.3). The sign of the optical activity of the poly-

TABLE 3.3

Comparison of the Optical Activities of the Most Atactic and the Most Isotactic Fractions of Some Poly-α-olefins with the Optical Activities of Low Molecular Weight Paraffins of Similar Structure[a]

Low molecular weight paraffin	$[M]_D^{25}$, degrees	Polymer	$[M]_D^{25}$, degrees[b]: Amorphous or very weakly crystalline fraction	$[M]_D^{25}$, degrees[b]: Highly crystalline fraction
S-2,3-Dimethylpentane	−11.4	Poly-(S)-3-methyl-1-pentene	+29.4	+161
S-2,4-Dimethylhexane	+21.3	Poly-(S)-4-methyl-1-hexene	+11.6	+288
S-2,5-Dimethylheptane	+11.7	Poly-(S)-5-methyl-1-heptene	+13.1	+68[c]
S-3-methyloctane	+13.3	Poly-(S)-6-methyl-1-octene	+12.8	+20[c]
S-2,6-Dimethyloctane	+14.4	Poly-(R)-3,7-dimethyl-1-octene	−20.6	−154

[a] Data of Pino et al. (137).

[b] These data pertain to the most isotactic of the fractions obtained; these are not, however, highly crystalline, i.e., they possess only a low degree of stereoregularity.

[c] $[M]_D^{25}$ is the molecular rotatory power at 25°C for the sodium D line.

α-olefins studied is determined by the absolute configuration of the asymmetric carbon atom of the monomer: all the polymers of (S)-α-olefins are characterized by positive rotation, while polymers of (R)-α-olefins by negative rotation.

The observed effect was explained in the study of Pino and his coworkers (137) on the basis of the concepts, presented above, that there is helical short-range order in macromolecules of isotactic polymers. It is evident that, in chains of optically active poly-α-olefins, containing an asymmetric carbon atom in the side group, right-handed and left-handed helices are not equivalent, since, for a given conformation of the asymmetric carbon atom, different sets of side-group conformations and different energies of these conformations exist in the right-handed and left-handed helices. In the study of Pino et al. (137), a rough evaluation is given of the numbers of the most probable rotational isomers of side groups for monomer units

TABLE 3.4
Comparison of Calculated and Experimental Values of the Optical Activity of Poly-α-Olefins for Right-Handed and Left-Handed Helices

Polymer	Number of conformations of side groups		Free energy difference of monomer units in right-handed and left-handed helices, cal/mole[a]	Molecular rotatory power $[M]_D^{25}$, degrees		
	Left-handed helix τ_{left}	Right-handed helix τ_{right}		Left-handed helix	Right-handed helix	Experimental value
Poly-(S)-3-methyl-1-pentene	2	1	400	+180	−240	+161
Poly-(S)-4-methyl-1-hexene	2	1	400	+240	−300	+288
Poly-(S)-5-methyl-1-heptene	5	4	100	+228	−225	+68
Poly-(S)-6-methyl-1-octene	11	10	60	+240	−192	+20
Poly-(R)-3,7-dimethyl-1-octene	7	14	−400	+282	−180	−154

[a] $\Delta F = -kT \ln (\tau_{right}/\tau_{left})$.

present in segments of right-handed and left-handed 3_1 helices. By using the semiempirical method proposed by Brewster (140), values of $[M]$ were calculated for all these rotational isomers, and then the values of $[M]$ were calculated for monomer units present in right-handed and left-handed 3_1 helices by averaging over sets of rotational isomers (which, for the sake of simplicity, were considered to be isoenergetic). The results of these calculations are given in Table 3.4, where the experimental values of $[M]$ are also given for the most isotactic fractions of the investigated polymers.

We see that, in all cases, the observed optical activity corresponds in sign to the value calculated for that helix which corresponds to the largest number of rotational isomers in the side group, i.e., to the smallest free energy. Comparison of calculated and observed $[M]$ values for poly(*S*)-3-methyl-1-pentene, poly-(*S*)-4-methyl-1-hexene, and poly-(*R*)-3,7-dimethyl-1-octene shows that they are all quite close, i.e., in these polymers, an overwhelming majority of monomer units must be in conformations which correspond to helices of a single direction of turning. In poly-(*S*)-5-methyl-1-heptene and, especially, in poly-(*S*)-6-methyl-1-octene, the observed values are considerably smaller than those calculated for completely helical structures. Although this discrepancy can be explained partly by the relatively low degree of stereoregularity of these polymers (see footnotes in Table 3.3), it can be compared with the fact that in these polymers the numbers of side group conformations in right-handed and left-handed helices are much less different than in the other three polymers (the free energy difference is 100 and 60 cal/mole, respectively, and not 400 cal/mole).

The question arises as to whether the free energy difference of monomer units in right-handed and left-handed helices of optically active poly-α-olefins is sufficient to explain the observed values of $[M]$. In the three cases cited above, these values are practically identical with those calculated for a helix of one sign. The answer to this question was given recently by Birshtein and Luizi (141), who showed that, in macromolecules in which short-range order extends over several adjacent monomer units, even a small difference in the free energies of right-handed and left-handed helices leads to a large excess of the more favorable helical conformation (see section 7.1).

In this manner, as a result of the spectroscopic and polarimetric investigations presented above, the existence of short-range one-dimensional order in free polymeric chains can be considered as completely proven.

The next question which must be solved in order to develop a quantitative theory of polymer molecules is: what is the mechanism of breaking of one-dimensional order in macromolecules or, in other words, *what is the mechanism of flexibility of polymer chains?* Two answers to this question have been proposed. Bresler and Frenkel (96), who were the first to examine the restriction of internal rotation in macromolecules, started from *torsional oscillations* about the *trans* conformations of monomer units, i.e., they believed that the potential curve has the form

$$U(\varphi) = (U_0/2)(1 - \cos \varphi) \tag{3.6}$$

Generalizing this point of view, Nagai (97), Rossi and Magnasco (98,99), Mori (100), and other investigators have expressed the hypothesis that internal rotation in macromolecules consists of torsional oscillations about the crystalline conformation of the chain.

There is no doubt that, in all real macromolecules, torsional oscillations do exist and make a contribution to chain flexibility. From experimental data on low molecular compounds (see section 2.1), however, it follows that internal rotation in molecules with single bonds, cannot be reduced entirely, as a rule, to torsional oscillations about some single conformation. Such molecules usually have several possible conformations, rotational isomers, and the internal rotation includes jumps over potential barriers which separate these conformations (see Fig. 2.1). That is why, in 1951, Volkenshtein (101,102), starting from the similarity between the internal rotations in low and high molecular weight compounds, proposed a new approach to the flexibility of macromolecules, namely, *the rotational-isomeric model of a polymer chain.* According to this model, a macromolecule is regarded as an equilibrium mixture of rotational isomers, while internal rotation in the chain is considered as. . . rotational isomerization" (i.e., jumps between the various rotational isomers). Even earlier, H. Kuhn (103) and Taylor (104) took into account the presence in polymer chains, as well as in low molecular compounds, of the relatively stable *gauche* conformations, along with the stable *trans* conformations; they proposed for the potential energy the equation

$$U(\varphi) = A(1 - \cos \varphi) + B(1 - \cos 3\varphi) \tag{3.7}$$

Volkenshtein has proposed that the continuous $U(\varphi)$ curve, which possesses several minima of different depths, be replaced by a discontinuous function, containing a series (with respect to the number of minima) of infinitely narrow crevaces (Fig. 3.8). Quite evidently, the rotational-isomeric model does not deny existence of torsional oscillations in each potential well, but it starts from the assumption that chain flexibility is determined mainly not by these oscillations but by rotational isomerism, i.e., by jumps between wells.

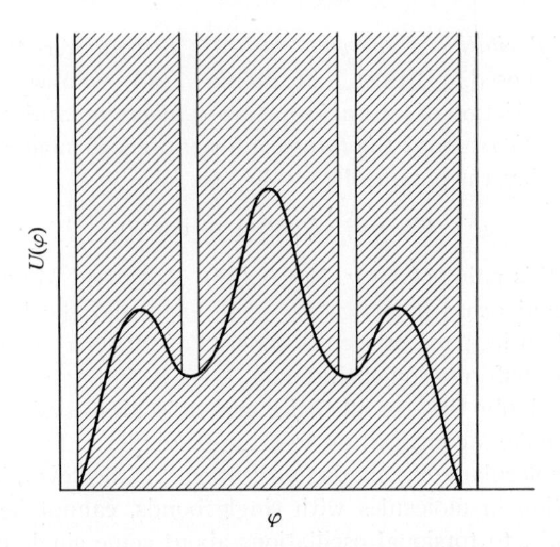

Fig. 3.8. Rotational isomeric model.

In the rotational-isomeric approximation, the averaging of the trigonometric functions of the angle of internal rotation φ over all the possible conformations of the molecule with a potential energy $U(\varphi)$ is replaced by summation over all the rotational isomers, taking into account their statistical weights. For example,

$$\eta = \overline{\cos \varphi} = \sum_{\alpha} \cos \varphi^{(\alpha)} e^{-F^{(\alpha)}/kT} \Big/ \sum_{\alpha} e^{-F^{(\alpha)}/kT}$$
$$= \sum_{\alpha} \cos \varphi^{(\alpha)} e^{-\Delta F^{(\alpha)}/kT} \Big/ \sum_{\alpha} e^{-\Delta F^{(\alpha)}/kT} \quad (3.8)$$

where $\varphi^{(\alpha)}$ are angles corresponding to the rotational isomers, $F^{(\alpha)}$ are the free energies of the rotational isomers, $g^{(\alpha)} = \exp\left\{-F^{(\alpha)}/kT\right\}$ are their statistical weights, while $\Delta F^{(\alpha)} = F^{(\alpha)} - F^{(1)}$. From eq. (3.8), according to which the equilibrium properties of macromolecules are determined by the difference in the free energies of rotational isomers,* it follows that, if the axis of rotation is also an axis of symmetry of the second or higher order, $\overline{\cos \varphi}$, $\overline{\sin \varphi}$, etc. are equal to zero, and all the equilibrium properties of the molecule are the same as with free rotation (see section 1.2).

The question which of the two mechanisms of macromolecule flexibility, torsional oscillation or rotational isomerism, is the predominant one is, of

* Generally, this does not mean that the equilibrium properties of molecules are absolutely independent of the height of potential barriers, since they can affect to some extent entropy differences between rotational isomers.

course, subject to experimental and theoretical investigation in each individual case. The existence of rotational isomerism in macromolecules is confirmed by a number of spectroscopic data (compare section 2.1). Novak (105,106) has investigated the temperature dependence of infrared absorption spectral bands for polyethylene; he detected rotational isomerism in this polymer and evaluated the energy difference between the rotational isomers to be 700–800 cal/mole; this is close to results obtained with low molecular weight paraffins (107). Identification of the frequencies of the valence oscillations of C—Cl, which are characteristic of rotational isomers of chlorine-substituted isoparaffins, has permitted the detection of rotational isomerism in poly(vinyl chloride) and rubber hydrochloride (108–110). In the case of poly(vinyl chloride), the dependence of the absorption intensities of *trans* and *gauche* isomers on polymerization conditions has been observed: the intensity of the band characteristic for the *trans* isomer increased with a decrease of the temperature of polymerization when the chain structure approached a syndiotactic one (108). This is consistent with the conformations of monomer units of syndiotactic polymers discussed above. Rotational isomerism has been studied spectroscopically also for poly(ethylene terephthalate) (111,112) and poly(ethylene glycol) (113). Boitsov and Gotlib (146) have developed the theory of the effect of rotational isomerism on the infrared spectra of poly(vinyl chloride) (145) and poly(ethylene terephthalate) (146).

Volchek and Nikitin (93,114–117) have obtained convincing evidence for the presence of rotational isomerism in polymers. Using polarized light, they observed changes in the intensities of the infrared absorption bands, which correspond to different rotational isomers, during the stretching of poly(vinyl acetate), polyethylene, natural rubber, gutta-percha, and polypropylene. This phenomenon is explained by the displacement of the equilibrium between the rotational isomers during stretching; this was predicted theoretically by Volkenshtein and Ptitsyn (118–120) [see Chapter 8, where the theory of the influence of this effect on infrared spectra developed by Ptitsyn (121) is presented]. In the case of natural rubber (115), it was possible to show that during stretching, there is an increase in the amount of that isomer which appears with a decrease in temperature, while in the case of gutta-percha there was found (116) a transition from the less stretched crystalline α-modification to the more stretched β-modification. (The α and β forms of gutta-percha are simply two rotational isomers which are stabilized by intermolecular interactions.) Mizushima and his coworkers (109) have shown that, during the stretching of poly(vinyl chloride), the intensity of the 693 cm^{-1} band is decreased; according to their analysis of the spectrum, this band corresponds to the valence oscillation of a C—Cl *gauche* isomer. A complete table of the results of various studies (93,109,114–117) is presented in Chapter 8.

These spectroscopic data prove the existence of different conformations (rotational isomers) in a number of typical macromolecules. Therefore, it is necessary to find out to what extent the flexibility of such chains may be termed rotational isomerization and to what extent, torsional oscillations. In order to answer this question it is necessary first to work out a quantitative approach to rotational isomerism in macromolecules. As we have seen above, the conformations of monomer units of polymers of types $(—CH_2—CR_2—)_n$ and $(—CH_2—CHR—)_n$ are determined predominantly by the interactions of bulky R groups. Therefore, in such polymers, it is essentially useless to speak of *trans* or *gauche* isomers that arise during rotation about separate bonds, but, as has been suggested by Ptitsyn and Sharonov (6), one should consider the rotational isomers of monomer units, which are characterized by two angles of internal rotation.

Following Ptitsyn and Sharonov (122) we shall establish the rotational isomers of monomer units of free macromolecules from the crystalline conformations of chains using *the hypothesis of the identity of conformations of monomer units in the crystal and amorphous state.* Above (see section 3.1), symmetry conditions were formulated, according to which macromolecules in the crystal state can form different enantiomorphous isoenergetic structures (right-handed and left-handed helices). For chains with symmetric side groups, four helical structures: $(\varphi_1, \varphi_2)_n$, $(-\varphi_1, -\varphi_2)_n$, $(\varphi_2, \varphi_1)_n$, $(-\varphi_2, -\varphi_1)_n$ are possible; these differ in the signs and sequences of the angles of internal rotation. For isotactic chains, two helical structures $(\varphi_1, \varphi_2)_n$ and $(-\varphi_2, -\varphi_1)_n$, are possible; they are obtained from each other by the simultaneous change in signs and sequences of angles. In these cases, all the monomer units have identical conformations in every polymer chain of a given helical structure. The hypothesis of the identity of monomer units in the crystal and amorphous states in the absence of long-range order in free macromolecules means that, *in free macromolecules, the indicated structures coexist within the same polymer chain.* In other words, each monomer unit of a given macromolecule, which is characterized in the crystal state by one rotational isomer that corresponds to a definite helical structure, has, in the free state, several rotational isomers that correspond to different crystal helical structures.

Formally, a somewhat different, but essentially analogous situation exists in helical syndiotactic chains, where the crystal structures have the forms $(\varphi_1, \varphi_1;\ \varphi_2, \varphi_2)_n$ and $(\varphi_2, \varphi_2;\ \varphi_1, \varphi_1)_n$, i.e., they differ only in the sequence of the angles of internal rotation (see section 3.1). In this case, the even and odd monomer units of the polymer chain of a given structure have different conformations (except for the values $\varphi_1 = \varphi_2 = 0$), but in the crystal state each given monomer unit exists, as before, in one fixed conformation. Moreover, in free macromolecules, each monomer unit can have any of the "crystalline" conformations (φ_1, φ_1) or (φ_2, φ_2). This is illustrated in Table 3.5, which makes it possible to obtain *a set of rotational isomers of monomer units of free macromolecules,* starting from their crystalline conformations. It is only in special cases, when $\varphi_1 = \varphi_2 = 0$, that a single conformation of the monomer unit in a free macromolecule corresponds to the crystalline conformation of the chain.

TABLE 3.5
Rotational Isomers of Monomer Units of a Chain in the Crystalline State and in Free Macromolecules

	State	
Polymer type	Crystalline	Free
$(—CH_2—CR_2—)_n$	(φ_1, φ_2)	$(\varphi_1, \varphi_2), (-\varphi_1, -\varphi_2),$ $(\varphi_2, \varphi_1), (-\varphi_2, -\varphi_1)$
$(—CH_2—CRR'—)_n$		
isotactic	(φ_1, φ_2)	$(\varphi_1, \varphi_2), (-\varphi_2, -\varphi_1)$
syndiotactic	$(\varphi_1, \varphi_1;\ \varphi_2, \varphi_2)$	$(\varphi_1, \varphi_1), (\varphi_2, \varphi_2)$

The hypothesis was put forward by Ptitsyn and Sharonov (6) that all the other rotational isomers of monomer units, i.e., those which do not conform to the crystalline conformations and to the conditions of symmetry, are much less probable and can be neglected. The analysis of intramolecular interactions in isotactic chains of type $(—CH_2—CHR—)_n$ cited above, fully confirms the validity of this hypothesis for such chains, since it is shown that all other rotational isomers, except for the two which correspond to right-handed and left-handed helices, have a very large energy and thus are virtually not formed. For syndiotactic chains of the type $(—CH_2—CHR—)_n$, it follows also from this analysis that rotational isomers, other than those which are formed in the various possible crystalline conformations of these chains, are not possible.

On the other hand, in the case of a number of other polymers, analysis of intramolecular interactions clearly points to the existence of conformations of monomer units which are not found in their crystal structures, but which are close in energies to the crystalline conformations. For example, the calculations of Liquori and co-workers (84) have shown (see section 3.4) that in polyisobutylene, $[-CH_2-C(CH_3)_2-]_n$, each monomer unit can have six almost isoenergetic conformations, of which only two correspond to the crystal structure of the chain.

Polyethylene, $(-CH_2-CH_2-)_n$, occupies a special place; it does not have bulky side groups and, therefore, in this case it is more correct to consider those rotational isomers which arise as a result of rotations about individual bonds, rather than the rotational isomers of monomer units. Considering the similarity between the structures of polyethylene and *n*-butane molecules, it can be expected that three rotational isomers are possible as a result of rotation about each unit of the polyethylene chain: a *trans* isomer, and right and left *gauche* isomers. This is confirmed by the detailed calculations of Borisova (128) of intramolecular interactions in the polyethylene chain, as well as by spectroscopic data (105,106,114).

Above, we have examined those conformations of monomer units in macromolecules which characterize the short-range one-dimensional order in polymer chains and its breaking, i.e., the flexibility of the chains. Quantitatively, the flexibility of macromolecules is determined by the energy difference between the different conformations and also by the amplitudes of torsional oscillations.

From the data presented, (see section 3.4), it follows that the conformations of monomer units of chains of the type $(-CH_2-CR_2-)_n$ and $(-CH_2-CRR'-)_n$ are determined primarily by second-order interactions between bulky groups, as well as by the effect of staggered bonds and by other first-order interactions. Therefore, in calculating the potential energy of the chain, as a first approximation, it is possible to limit oneself to a consideration of only these interactions, as has been suggested by Gotlib and Ptitsyn and Sharonov (6). Since the first-order interactions depend on one angle of internal rotation, while the second-order interactions between bulky groups depend on the angles of internal rotation about two units of the main chain that separate the CR_2 and CRR' groups (angles φ_{2k-1} and φ_{2k} on Fig. 3.4), the potential energy of the chain, in this approximation, is decomposed into the sum of independent terms

$$U(\varphi_1, \varphi_2 \ldots, \varphi_N) = \sum_{k=1}^{n} U(\varphi_{2k-1}, \varphi_{2k}) = \sum_{k=1}^{n} U(\Omega_k) \qquad (3.9)$$

where Ω_k is the conformation of the kth monomer unit, determined by angles φ_{2k-1}, φ_{2k}, while $n = N/2$ is the degree of polymerization. Expression (3.9) indicates that the polymer molecule is considered as a sum of monomer units, the conformations of which are independent of each other.

In the present approximation, the flexibility of a macromolecule is characterized by the energy difference between the conformations of individual monomer units and by the amplitudes of torsional oscillations in these conformations. For example, the rotational isomers listed in the last column of Table 3.5 are formed in isotactic chains of type $(—CH_2—CHR—)_n$; these have equal energies and consequently equal probabilities. In syndiotactic chains of type $(—CH_2—CHR—)_n$ the rotational isomers listed in Table 3.5 are also formed; these, however, are no longer isoenergetic, so that the probabilities of their formation are essentially different. As has been pointed out above, in polyisobutylene, there are six almost isoenergetic conformations of each monomer unit.

For many polymer chains, approximation (3.9) is not valid, since in them interactions of higher order are important. For example, for chains of type $(—CH_2—CR_2—)_n$ and $(—CH_2—CRR'—)_n$ this approximation does not take into account second-order interactions between methylene groups, third-order interactions between methylene and $—CR_2—$ or $—CRR'—$ groups and (what is particularly important) fourth-order interactions between nearest nonadjacent bulky groups. These interactions are determined by two $(\varphi_{2k}, \varphi_{2k+1})$, three $(\varphi_{2k-1}, \varphi_{2k}, \varphi_{2k+1})$ or $(\varphi_{2k}, \varphi_{2k+1}, \varphi_{2k+2})$, or four $(\varphi_{2k-1}, \varphi_{2k}, \varphi_{2k+1}, \varphi_{2k+2})$ angles of internal rotation, i.e., they are a function of the conformations of two consecutive monomer units. Examination of molecular models shows that it is not valid to neglect these interactions (particularly the last ones). In reality, they can play an important role which leads to the interdependence of the conformations of neighboring monomer units; thus, the potential energy of the chain is expressed in the form

$$U(\varphi_1, \varphi_2 \ldots, \varphi_N) = \sum_{k=1}^{n} U(\Omega_{k-1}, \Omega_k) \tag{3.10}$$

For example, although *trans* and coiled isomers of the monomer units of syndiotactic chains by themselves have similar energies, a sequence of two monomer units in the coiled isomer form is essentially prohibited under these conditions, because of the fourth-order interactions between the bulky groups (see section 3.4). In isotactic chains, examination of molecular models also points to a strong repulsion of the nearest nonadjacent bulky groups in those conformations in which two neighboring monomer units are characterized by rotational isomers (0°, 120°) and (−120°, 0°). The distance between these groups is found to be only 2.5 Å instead of the 5.0 Å found in the regular conformation in which both monomer units are characterized by the same rotational isomers. Therefore, not every sequence of the rotational isomers examined above has the same probability, i.e., short-range one-dimensional order in macromolecules extends over more than one monomer unit. In these cases, the flexibility of a macromolecule is characterized, of course, not only by the energy differences between the various conformations of individual monomer units, but by the energy differences between different *sequences of conformations* of two neighboring monomer units.

The energy differences between the various conformations of macromolecules and the amplitudes of torsional oscillations have been evaluated in a number of theoretical studies, in which the same semiempirical potentials of interactions between nonbonded atoms were used as in the evaluation of the crystalline conformations of the chains (see section 3.4). The most detailed calculations have been carried out for isotactic polypropylene, $[—CH_2—CH(CH_3)—]_n$ (76,123). For this polymer, as well as for other isotactic polymers of the type $(—CH_2—CHR—)_n$, the flexibility of the chain is determined by the energy differences between different and identical conformations of neighboring monomer units, i.e., by the energy of breaking of a helical structure of a chain, and also of course, by the amplitudes of the torsional oscillations of the units. It appears that, in isotactic chains, two types of junctions are possible between segments of right-handed and left-handed helices, i.e., between sequences (0°, 120°) and (−120°, 0°). According to the calculations of Borisova and Birshtein (76), the energy of the first junction (−120°, 0°; 0°, 120°) exceeds only by 0.5 kcal/mole the energy of the regular sequence; however, the energy of the second junction (0°, 120°; −120°, 0°) is very large, due to the strong repulsion between the H atoms of the nearest nonadjacent $—CH(CH_3)$ groups. This repulsion, however, does not exclude junctions of the second type, since a relatively small change in the angles of internal rotation can result in a considerable decrease in energy, while breaking of the helical structure determines the increase in entropy of the chain. Taking into consideration the principle of staggered bonds and the potentials of the van der Waals interactions of C and H atoms, Borisova and Birshtein obtained the result that, for the valence angles of isotactic polypropylene (114°), the energy minimum at junctions of the second type corresponds to conformation (−5°, 95°; −95°, 5°); the energy of this conformation is only 3 kcal/mole larger than the energy of a regular sequence. If the valence angles at the junction are opened more (for example, to 120°), the most favorable conformation of the regular sequence can change to (−10°, 100°; −100°, 10°), and its energy can decrease by approximately an additional 0.5 kcal/mole. As a result, the mean energy of breaking of the helical structure,

$$\Delta U = {}^1/_2(U_{12} + U_{21} - U_{11} - U_{22}) \tag{3.11}$$

(where U_{12}, U_{21} is the energy of the junctions and U_{11}, U_{22} are the energies of regular sequences) is found to be equal to only ≈ 1.5 kcal/mole. This means (see section 7.1), that a regular helical segment of the chain of isotactic polypropylene contains about 10–12 monomer units.

Corradini and co-workers have arrived at similar conclusions (123,142); their calculations were based on somewhat different interaction potentials (see section 3.4). According to these authors, the energy minimum at junctions of the second type corresponds to conformations (0°, 60°, −120°, 0°) and (0°, 120°; −60°, 0°); their energy is only ≈ 2.7 kcal/mole greater than the energy of the regular sequence. Since, according to their calculations, the energy of junctions of the first type is close to the energy of the

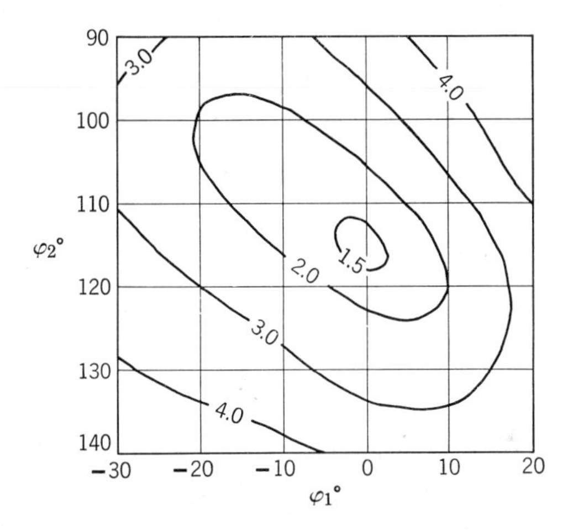

Fig. 3.9. Dependence of the energy of a monomer unit of isotactic polypropylene on the angles of internal rotation, φ_1, φ_2. The valence angles in the main chain are 114°.

regular sequence, the mean energy of breaking of the helical structure is equal to ≈ 1.4 kcal/mole; this is close to the results obtained by Borisova and Birshtein. This data of Borisova and Birshtein (76), as those of Corradini and co-workers (122, 142), show directly that the probability of "junctions" between segments of a right-handed and a left-handed 3_1 helix is sufficiently large to assume the presence of the rotational isomeric mechanism of chain flexibility in isotactic polypropylene. This refutes the opinion expressed by several authors (97–100) that, because of the very small probability of junctions, isotactic macromolecules in solution have almost completely the structures of enantiomorphous right-handed and left-handed 3_1 helices; in such a case their flexibility is related only to the torsional oscillations of the units.

On the other hand, Natta, Corradini, and Ganis (3) calculated the potential barriers between the rotational isomers of monomer units of isotactic polypropylene. It was shown in this study that transition between rotational isomers (0°, 120°) and (−120°, 0°) takes place via the conformation (−60°, 60°); this has a potential barrier of the order of 5 kcal/mole (see Fig. 3.7*a*), which is close to that of other polymers (for example, polyethylene). This refutes the earlier opinion of Natta that transitions between conformations that correspond to right-handed and left-handed 3_1 helices can be prohibited by unusually high potential barriers which separate them.

The effect of torsional oscillation on the flexibility of isotactic polypropylene chains is considered in the study of Borisova and Birshtein (76) cited above; in this study they investigated the shape of the potential curve near the energy minimum of a monomer unit. Furthermore, it was shown that, when the angles of internal rotation undergo a correlated change of ~20–30°, the energy of the monomer unit changes slightly (Fig. 3.9); thus, in this interval of angles, it is possible to expect almost free oscillations of the units.

In Chapter 7 we shall consider the relative contributions of the mechanism of rotational isomerization and torsional oscillation to the observed flexibility of the chains of isotactic polypropylene, and we shall show that rotational isomerization plays the principal role. Nevertheless, in isotactic macromolecules with very strongly repelling side groups (for example, in molecules which crystallize in the form of 4_1 helices), because the probability of junction between segments of right-handed and left-handed helices can be so small, a contribution of torsional oscillations of the units to chain flexibility similar to that of rotational isomerization, or even greater is not excluded.

According to the evaluation of Borisova and Birshtein (126) (see section 3.4), in the case of syndiotactic polymers, the energy difference between the coiled (−120°, −120°) and flat (0°, 0°) conformations of monomer units located between monomer units in flat conformations is −1.0 kcal/mole for polypropylene, and approximately +1.0 kcal/mole for poly-1,2-butadiene, i.e., it is relatively small. Consequently, the appearance of coiled conformations of monomer units close to *trans* conformations does not result in a large change in the chain energy, but raises its entropy considerably. This means that, for such chains, the rotational isomeric mechanism of flexibility also plays an important role. The appearance in syndiotactic polypropylene of two consecutive monomer units in the coiled conformations involves an additional energy of ≈ 2.5 kcal/mole (relative to the energy of the flat chain) (126); therefore, it is quite a rare occurrence. Estimates by eqs. (4.68) and (4.71) show that the probability of two consecutive coiled conformations of monomer units is only approximately 3% in this case, while the average number of consecutive coiled units is very close to unity, i.e., essentially in all cases coiled conformations appear only in the neighborhood of *trans* conformations. It is true that torsional oscillations of units also exit in syndiotactic polymers just as in isotactic ones; they determine a part of the observed chain flexibility. As shown by Borisova and Birshtein (126), the range of torsional oscillations in syndiotactic polypropylene for any of the examined conformations of monomer units is close to the range of torsional oscillations in isotactic polypropylene, i.e., it is equal to ≈ 20–$30°$.

Borisova (128) has also calculated the energies of the different conformations of monomer units of polyethylene molecules; in this, she has used the same potentials of interaction of C and H atoms as in another study (76) and has taken into account all the first-, second-, and third-order interactions of the C and H atoms. During rotation about each unit of the main chain, three rotational isomers are found to be possible: a *trans* isomer and two *gauche* isomers (right and left). Calculations showed that the *trans* isomer has an angle of internal rotation $\varphi = 0°$, while the *gauche* isomer has angles $\varphi = \pm 110°$. The energy of each *gauche* isomer that follows a *trans* isomer or a *gauche* isomer coiled in the same direction is found to be 0.6 kcal/mole (if the energy of the *trans* isomer is set equal to zero), while the energy of a *gauche* isomer following an isomer coiled in the opposite direction, is 2.1–2.4 kcal/mole.* Thus, the calculation of Borisova points to the presence of considerable correlation between the rotations about neighboring units of the main chain in polyethylene. On the other hand, according to this calculation, there is no direct correlation between rotations about more remote units in the case of the conformations examined above.

As was pointed out above, Liquori and co-workers (84) have calculated the energies of the different conformations of polyisobutylene molecules, $(\text{—}CH_2\text{—}C(CH_3)_2\text{—})_n$. These calculations showed that each monomer unit of polyisobutylene can have six almost isoenergetic conformations (95°, 95°), (−95°, −95°), (135°, 25°), (−135°, −25°), (25°, 135°), (−25°, −135°), separated by relatively small potential barriers; this assures the high flexibility of the chain, due to rotational isomerization.

* In this last case, the angles of internal rotation of *gauche* isomers are not 110°, but 100°.

Two of these conformations (+95°, +95°) and (−95°, −95°) correspond almost exactly to the crystal structure of the chain (see Table 3.1), while the others come into being during melting. It is interesting that in a polymer of similar structure, poly(vinylidene chloride), $(\text{—}CH_2\text{—}CCl_2\text{—})_n$, there is no such sixfold degeneracy (84), and only calculations show that the crystalline conformations are found in the free chain. It is possible (84) that this difference in conformations of the monomer units of polyisobutylene and poly(vinylidene chloride) accounts for the fact that the first one is rubberlike at room temperature, while the second one is not.

Finally, Borisova (86) has examined the flexibility of the molecules of 1,4-polydienes: *cis*- and *trans*-1,4-polyisoprenes, (natural rubber and gutta-percha, respectively):

$$(\text{—}CH{=}C(CH_3)\text{—}CH_2\text{—}CH_2\text{—})_n$$

and *cis*- and *trans*-1,4-polybutadiene:

$$(\text{—}CH{=}CH\text{—}CH_2\text{—}CH_2\text{—})_n$$

Calculations show that three rotational isomers can be formed during rotation about the $\text{—}CH_2\text{—}CH_2\text{—}$ bond in such chains, just as in polyethylene: a *trans* isomer, $\varphi = 0°$, and two *gauche* isomers, $\varphi = \pm 120°$.

A *trans* isomer relative to the $\text{—}CH_2\text{—}CH_2\text{—}$ bond has a very shallow potential well of torsional oscillations about both single bonds adjacent to the double bond. As a result, for example in gutta-percha and natural rubber, torsional oscillations in the interval from −120° to 120° are possible for the $=CH\text{—}CH_2\text{—}$ bond and from 60 to 180° (or from −60° to −180°) for the $=C(CH_3)\text{—}CH_2\text{—}$ bond. These torsional oscillations must obviously account for the major part of chain flexibility in 1,4-polydienes. Moreover, in molecules of natural rubber, a considerable role is played by correlations between internal rotations in neighboring monomer units, while they can be neglected in gutta-percha. This is what probably explains the fact that the dimensions of gutta-percha molecules in solution are closer to those calculated for free rotation than the dimensions of natural rubber molecules.

Thus, theoretical investigations of the energy of internal rotation in polymer chains has confirmed the presence of the rotational isomeric mechanism of the flexibility of macromolecules; these investigations also indicate the considerable role which can be played by torsional oscillations of units in the mechanism of flexibility. The presence of rotational isomerism in typical macromolecules is confirmed also by the spectroscopic investigations mentioned above. However, the real criterion of the validity of various concepts regarding the structure (short-range order) and mechanism of flexibility of macromolecules in solution and in the state of high elasticity must be agreement between the experiment and the quantitative theory of macromolecules based on these concepts.

In Chapters 4 to 6, the mathematical relations of such a theory are presented, while in Chapters 7 and 8, quantitative conclusions based on the comparison of this theory with experiments are drawn concerning the short-range order and mechanism of flexibility in molecules of a number of typical polymers. It would be shown, that the concepts developed above are in satisfactory qualitative, and, in a number of cases, also quantitative agreement with experimental data on the flexibility of the corresponding chains.

References

1. Natta, G., and P. Corradini, *J. Polymer Sci.*, **39**, 29 (1959).
2. Natta, G., and P. Corradini, *Nuovo Cimento (Suppl. 1)*, **15**, 9 (1960).
3. Natta, G., P. Corradini, and P. Ganis, *Makromol. Chem.*, **39**, 238 (1960).
4. Shimanouchi, T., and S. Mizushima, *J. Chem. Phys.*, **23**, 707 (1955); *Probl. Sovrem. Fiz.*, **No. 12**, 80 (1956).
5. Hughes, R. E., and J. L. Lauer, *J. Chem. Phys.*, **30**, 1165 (1959).
6. Ptitsyn, O. B., and Yu. A. Sharonov, *Zh. Tekhn. Fiz.*, **27**, 2762 (1957).
7. Miyazawa, T., *J. Polymer Sci.*, **55**, 215 (1961).
8. Birshtein, T. M., *Vysokomol. Soedin.*, **5**, 1675 (1963).
9. Nagai, K., and M. Kobayashi, *J. Chem. Phys.*, **36**, 1268 (1962).
10. Miller, R. L., and L. E. Nielsen, *J. Polymer Sci.*, **55**, 643 (1961).
11. Natta, G., *Angew. Chem.*, **68**, 393 (1956).
12. Natta, G., *Makromol. Chem.*, **35**, 94 (1960).
13. Bunn, C. W., *Trans. Faraday Soc.*, **35**, 482 (1939).
14. Walter, E. R., and F. P. Reding, *J. Polymer Sci.*, **21**, 561 (1956).
15. Bunn, C. W., and E. R. Howells, *Nature*, **174**, 549 (1954).
16. Fuller, C. S., C. J. Frosch, and N. R. Pape, *J. Am. Chem. Soc.*, **62**, 1905 (1940).
17. Liquori, A. M., *Acta Cryst.*, **8**, 345 (1955).
18. Bunn, C. W., and D. R. Holmes, *Discussions Faraday Soc.*, **25**, 95 (1958).
19. Natta, G., P. Corradini, and M. Cesari, *Atti Accad. Nazl. Lincei, Rend. Classe Sci. Fis. Mat. Nat.*, [8] **21**, 365 (1956).
20. Natta, G., and P. Corradini, *Nuovo Cimento (Suppl. 1)*, **15**, 40 (1960).
21. Wilchinsky, Z. W., *J. Appl. Phys.*, **31**, 1969 (1960).
22. Menčík, Z., *Chem. Prumysl*, **10**, 377 (1960).
23. Natta, G., P. Corradini, and I. W. Bassi, *Makromol. Chem.*, **21**, 240 (1956).
24. Natta, G., P. Corradini, and I. W. Bassi, *Nuovo Cimento (Suppl. 1)*, **15**, 52 (1960).
25. Natta, G., P. Corradini, and I. W. Bassi, *Atti Accad. Nazl. Lincei, Rend. Classe Sci. Fis. Mat. Nat*, [8] **19**, 404 (1955).
26. Natta, G., P. Corradini, and I. W. Bassi, *Atti Accad. Nazl. Lincei Rend. Classe Sci. Fis. Mat. Nat.*, [8] **23**, 363 (1957).
27. Natta, G., P. Corradini, and I. W. Bassi, *Nuovo Cimento, (Suppl. 1)*, **15**, 68 (1960).
28. Corradini, P., G. Natta, and I. W. Bassi, *Angew. Chem.*, **70**, 598 (1958).
29. Natta, G., P. Corradini, and I. W. Bassi, *Gazz. Chim. Ital.*, **89**, 784 (1959).

30. Sianesi, D., R. Serra, and F. Danusso, *Chim. Ind.* (*Milan*), **41,** 515 (1959).
31. Natta, G., P. Corradini, and I. W. Bassi, *Nuovo Cimento* (*Suppl. 1*), **15,** 83 (1960).
32. Overberger, C. G., A. E. Borchert, and A. Katchman, *J. Polymer Sci.*, **44,** 491 (1960).
33. Dall'Asta, G., and I. W. Bassi, *Chim. Ind.* (*Milan*), **43,** 999 (1961).
34. Natta, G., I. W. Bassi, and P. Corradini, *Makromol. Chem.*, **18–19,** 455 (1956).
35. Vandenberg, E. J., R. F. Heck, and D. S. Breslow, *J. Polymer Sci.*, **41,** 519 (1960).
36. Makimoto, T., T. Tsuruta, and J. Furukawa, *Makromol. Chem.*, **50,** 116 (1961).
37. Natta, G., G. Mazzanti, P. Longi, G. Dall'Asta, and F. Bernardini, *J. Polymer Sci.*, **51,** 487 (1961).
38. Badami, D. V., *Polymer,* **1,** 273 (1960).
39. Natta, G., G. Mazzanti, P. Longi, and F. Bernardini, *J. Polymer Sci.*, **31,** 181 (1958).
40. Murahashi, S., S. Nozakura, and H. Tadokoro, *Bull. Chem. Soc. Japan,* **32,** 534 (1959).
41. Nitta, I., Y. Chatani, and Y. Sakata, *Bull. Chem. Soc. Japan,* **33,** 125 (1960).
42. Corradini, P., and P. Ganis, *J. Polymer Sci.*, **43,** 311 (1960).
43. Frank, F. C., A. Keller, and A. O'Connor, *Phil. Mag.*, **4,** 200 (1959).
44. Chatani, Y., *J. Polymer Sci.*, **47,** 491 (1960).
45. Natta, G., P. Corradini, and I. W. Bassi, *Makromol. Chem.*, **33,** 247 (1959).
46. Corradini, P., and P. Ganis, *Nuovo Cimento* (*Suppl. 1*), **15,** 104 (1960).
47. Corradini, P., and P. Ganis, *Nuovo Cimento* (*Suppl. 1*), **15,** 96 (1960).
48. Natta, G., P. Corradini, and I. W. Bassi, *J. Polymer Sci.*, **51,** 505 (1961).
49. Natta, G., G. Mazzanti, P. Corradini, and I. W. Bassi, *Makromol. Chem.*, **37,** 156 (1960).
50. Natta, G., G. Mazzanti, P. Corradini, P. Chini, and I. W. Bassi, *Atti Accad. Nazl. Lincei Rend. Classe Sci. Fis. Mat. Nat.*, [8] **28,** 8 (1960).
51. Natta, G., G. Mazzanti, P. Corradini, A. Valvasori, and I. W. Bassi, *Atti Accad. Nazl. Lincei Rend. Classe Sci. Fis. Mat. Nat.*, [8] **28,** 18 (1960).
52. Stroupe, J. D., and R. E. Hughes, *J. Am. Chem. Soc.*, **80,** 2341 (1958).
53. Natta, G., and P. Corradini, *Atti Accad. Nazl. Lincei Rend. Classe Sci. Fis. Mat. Nat.*, [8] **19,** 229 (1955).
54. Natta, G., and P. Corradini, *J. Polymer Sci.*, **20,** 251 (1956).
55. Burleigh, P. H., *J. Am. Chem. Soc.*, **82,** 749 (1960).
56. Asahina, M., and K. Okuda, *Kobunshi Kagaku,* **17,** 607 (1960).
57. Stefani, R., M. Chevreton, J. Terrier, and C. Eyrand, *Compt. Rend.*, **248,** 2006 (1959).
58. Fox, T. G, B. S. Garrett, W. E. Goode, S. Gratch, J. F. Kincaid, A. Spell, and J. D. Stroupe, *J. Am. Chem. Soc.*, **80,** 1768 (1958).
59. Letort, M., and A. Richard, *J. Chim. Phys.*, **57,** 752 (1960).
60. Golike, R. C., *J. Polymer Sci.*, **42,** 583 (1960).
61. Mooney, R. C. L., *J. Am. Chem. Soc.*, **63,** 2828 (1941).
62. Bunn, C. W., *Nature,* **161,** 929 (1948).
63. Mochizuki, T., *Nippon Kagaku Zasshi,* **81,** 15 (1960).
64. Hammer, C. F., T. A. Koch, and J. F. Whitney, *J. Appl. Polymer Sci.*, **1,** 169 (1959).
65. Sauter, E., *Z. Physik. Chem.*, **B21,** 161 (1933).
66. Fuller, C. S., *Chem. Rev.*, **26,** 143 (1940).

67. Natta, G., P. Corradini, and G. Dall'Asta, *Atti Accad. Nazl. Lincei Rend. Classe Sci. Fis. Mat. Nat.*, [8] **20,** 408 (1956).
68. Shambelan, C., *Dissertation Abstr.*, **20,** 120 (1959).
69. Stanley, E., and M. Litt, *J. Polymer Sci.*, **43,** 453 (1960).
70. Kitaigorodskii, A. I., *Organicheskaya Kristallokhimiya* (Crystal Chemistry of Organic Compounds), Izdatel'stvo Akad. Nauk SSSR, Moscow, 1955.
71. Birshtein, T. M., and O. B. Ptitsyn, *Zh. Tekhn. Fiz.*, **29,** 1048 (1959); *Soviet Phys.-Tech. Phys.*, **4,** 954 (1959).
72. Birshtein, T. M., and O. B. Ptitsyn, *Vysokomol. Soedin.*, **2,** 628 (1960).
73. Wooten, W. C., and H. W. Cooper, Jr., *J. Polymer Sci.*, **37,** 560 (1959).
74. Gaylord, N. G., and H. F. Mark, *Lineinye Stereoregulyarnye Polimery*, IL, Moscow, 1962 (originally published as *Linear and Stereoregular Addition Polymers*, Interscience, New York, 1959).
75. Ivash, E. V., and D. M. Dennison, *J. Chem. Phys.*, **21,** 1804 (1953).
76. Borisova, N. P., and T. M. Birshtein, *Vysokomol. Soedin.*, **5,** 279 (1963).
77. Bartell, L. S., *J. Chem. Phys.*, **32,** 827 (1960).
78. Kitaigorodskii, A. I., *Dokl. Akad. Nauk SSSR*, **137,** 116 (1961).
79. Hill, T. L., *J. Chem. Phys.*, **16,** 399, 938 (1948).
80. Tsvetkov, V. N., V. E. Bychkova, S. M. Savvon, and N. K. Nekrasov, *Vysokomol. Soedin.*, **1,** 1407 (1959); *Polymer Sci. USSR*, **1,** 584 (1960) (abstract).
81. Tsvetkov, V. N., and N. N. Boitsova, *Vysokomol. Soedin.*, **2,** 1176 (1960).
82. Stein, R. S., F. H. Holmes, and A. V. Tobolsky, *J. Polymer Sci.*, **14,** 143 (1954).
83. Birshtein, T. M., O. B. Ptitsyn, and E. A. Sokolova, *Vysokomol. Soedin.*, **1,** 852 (1959).
84. De Santis, P., E. Giglio, A. M. Liquori, and A. Ripamonti, *Nuovo Cimento*, **26,** 616 (1962).
85. Bunn, C. W., and E. V. Garner, *J. Chem. Soc.*, **1942,** 654.
86. Borisova, N. P., *Vysokomol. Soedin.*, 74 (1963).
87. Doty, P., in *Problemy Sovremennoi Biofiziki* Vol. 1, IL, Moscow, 1962, p. 138 (originally published as *Biophysical Science: A Study Program*, J. L. Oncley, F. O. Schmitt, R. C. Williams, and M. D. Rosenberg, Eds., Wiley, New York, 1959).
88. Tadokoro, H., S. Nozakura, T. Kitazawa, Y. Yasuhara, and S. Murahashi, *Bull. Chem. Soc., Japan*, **32,** 313 (1959).
89. Tadokoro, H., N. Nishiyama, S. Nozakura, and S. Murahashi, *J. Polymer Sci.*, **36,** 553 (1959).
90. Takeda, M., K. Iimura, A. Yamada, and Y. Imamura, *Bull. Chem. Soc. Japan*, **32,** 1150 (1959).
91. Takeda, M., K. Iimura, A. Yamada, and Y. Imamura, *Bull. Chem. Soc. Japan*, **33,** 1219 (1960).
92. Kobayashi, M., K. Nagai, and E. Nagai, *Bull. Chem. Soc. Japan*, **33,** 1421 (1960).
93. Volchek, B. Z., *Vysokomol. Soedin.*, 260 (1963).
94. Pino, P., G. P. Lorenzi, and L. Lardicci, *Chim. Ind.* (*Milan*), **42,** 712 (1960).
95. Pino, P., and G. P. Lorenzi, *J. Am. Chem. Soc.*, **82,** 4745 (1960).
96. Bresler, S. E., and Ya. I. Frenkel, *Zh. Eksp. Teoret. Fiz.*, **9,** 1094 (1939).
97. Nagai, K., *Busseiron Kenkyu*, **4,** 65 (1958); *J. Chem. Phys.*, **30,** 660 (1959).
98. Magnasco, V., and C. Rossi, *J. Chem. Phys.*, **32,** 1881 (1960).
99. Rossi, C., and V. Magnasco, *Makromol. Chem.*, **41,** 45 (1960).

100. Mori, T., *Busseiron Kenkyu*, **8**, 175 (1960); *J. Phys. Soc. Japan*, **15**, 1482, 1638 (1960).
101. Volkenshtein, M. V., *Dokl. Akad. Nauk SSSR*, **78**, 879 (1951); *Zh. Fiz. Khim.*, **26**, 1072 (1952).
102. Volkenshtein, M. V., *Konfiguratsionnaya Statistika Polimernykh Tsepei*, Izdatel'stvo Akad. Nauk SSSR., Moscow, 1959 (published in translation as *Configurational Statistics of Polymeric Chains*, Interscience, New York, 1963.
103. Kuhn, H., *J. Chem. Phys.*, **15**, 843 (1947).
104. Taylor, W. J., *J. Chem. Phys.*, **16**, 257 (1948).
105. Novak, I. I., *Zh. Tekhn. Fiz.*, **24**, 18 (1954).
106. Novak, I. I., *Zh. Tekhn. Fiz.*, **25**, 1854 (1955).
107. Sheppard, N., and G. J. Szasz, *J. Chem. Phys.*, **17**, 86 (1949).
108. Mizushima, S., T. Shimanouchi, K. Nakamura, M. Hayashi, and S. Tsuchiya, *J. Chem. Phys.*, **26**, 970 (1957).
109. Shimanouchi, T., S. Tsuchiya, and S. Mizushima, *J. Chem. Phys.*, **30**, 1365 (1959).
110. Iimura, K., and M. Takeda, *J. Polymer Sci.*, **51**, S51 (1961).
111. Ward, I. M., *Chem. Ind.* (*London*), **1956**, No. 34, 905; *ibid.*, **1957**, No. 32, 1102.
112. Miyake, A., *J. Polymer Sci.*, **38**, 497 (1959).
113. Miyake, A., *J. Am. Chem. Soc.*, **82**, 3040 (1960).
114. Nikitin, V. N., M. V. Volkenshtein, and B. Z. Volchek, *Zh. Tekhn. Fiz.*, **25**, 2486 (1955).
115. Nikitin, V. N., B. Z. Volchek, and M. V. Volkenshtein, *Trudy 10-go Soveshchaniya po Spektroskopii* (Transactions of the 10th Conference on Spectroscopy), Izdatel'stvo Lvov Univ. 1957, Vol. 1, p. 411.
116. Volchek, B. Z., and V. N. Nikitin, *Zh. Tekhn. Fiz.*, **28**, 1753 (1958).
117. Volchek, B. Z., and Zh. N. Roberman, *Vysokomol. Soed.*, **2**, 1157 (1960).
118. Volkenshtein, M. V., and O. B. Ptitsyn, *Dokl. Akad. Nauk SSSR*, **91**, 1313 (1953).
119. Volkenshtein, M. V., and O. B. Ptitsyn, *Zh. Tekhn. Fiz.*, **25**, 649 (1955).
120. Volkenshtein, M. V., and O. B. Ptitsyn, *Zhur. Tekhn. Fiz.*, **25**, 662 (1955).
121. Ptitsyn, O. B., *Fiz. Tverd. Tela*, **1**, 923 (1959).
122. Ptitsyn, O. B., and Yu. A. Sharonov, *Zh. Tekhn. Fiz.*, **27**, 2744 (1957); *Soviet Phys.-Tech. Phys.*, **2**, 2544 (1957).
123. Corradini, P., and G. Allegra, *Atti Accad. Nazl. Lincei Classe Sci. Fis. Mat. Nat.*, [8] **30**, 516 (1961).
124. Kitaigorodskii, A. I., and K. V. Mirskaya, *Kristallografiya*, **6**, 507 (1961).
125. Fujii, K., T. Mochizuki, S. Imoto, J. Ukida, and M. Matsumoto, *Makromol. Chem.*, **51**, 225 (1962).
126. Borisova, N. P., and T. M. Birshtein, *Vysokomol. Soedin.*, **6**, 1234 (1964)
127. Natta, G., P. Corradini, and P. Ganis, *J. Polymer Sci.*, **58**, 1191 (1962).
128. Borisova, N. P., *Vysokomol. Soedin.*, **6**, 135 (1964)
129. Hoeve, C. A. J., *J. Chem. Phys.*, **35**, 1266 (1961).
130. Nagai, K., and T. Ishikawa, *J. Chem. Phys.*, **37**, 496 (1962).
131. Fordham, J. W. L., *J. Polymer Sci.*, **39**, 321 (1959).
132. Bunn, C. W., and H. S. Peiser, *Nature*, **159**, 161 (1947).
133. Mason, E. A., and M. M. Kreevoy, *J. Am. Chem. Soc.*, **77**, 5808 (1955).
134. Mizushima, S., and T. Simanouti, *J. Am. Chem. Soc.*, **71**, 1320 (1949).
135. Tadokoro, H., T. Yasumoto, S. Murahashi, and I. Nitta, *J. Polymer Sci.*, **44**, 266 (1960).

136. Pino, P., G. P. Lorenzi, L. Lardicci, and F. Chiardelli, *Vysokomol. Soedin.*, **3,** 1597 (1961).
137. Pino, P., F. Chiardelli, G. P. Lorenzi, and G. Montagnoli, *Makromol. Chem.*, **61,** 207 (1963).
138. Bailey, W. J., and E. T. Yates, *J. Org. Chem.*, **25,** 1800 (1960).
139. Nozakura, S., S. Takeuchi, H. Yuki, and S. Murahashi, *Bull. Chem. Soc. Japan*, **34,** 1673 (1961).
140. Brewster, J. H., *J. Am. Chem. Soc.*, **81,** 5475 (1959).
141. Birshtein, T. M., and P. L. Luizi, *Vysokomol. Soedin.*, **6,** 1238 (1964)
142. Allegra, G., P. Ganis, and P. Corradini, *Makromol. Chem.*, **61,** 225 (1963).
143. Iwasaki, M., *J. Polymer Sci.*, **A1,** 1099 (1963).
144. Miyazawa, T., K. Fukushima, and Y. Ideguchi, *J. Polymer Sci.*, **62,** S146 (1962).
145. Boitsov, V. G., and Yu. Ya. Gotlib, *Opt. Spektroskopiya Sb.*, **2,** 128 (1963).
146. Boitsov, V. G., and Yu. Ya. Gotlib, *Opt. Spektroskopiya*, **15,** 216 (1963).
147. Vainshtein, B. K., "Diffraction of X-Rays on Chain Molecules," *Izdatel'stvo Akad. Nauk SSSR*, Moscow, 1963.

Chapter 4

STATISTICS OF ONE-DIMENSIONAL COOPERATIVE SYSTEMS

4.1. Matrix Method of the One-Dimensional Ising Model

The mathematical methods of calculating the mean properties of macromolecules certainly would be quite simple if the energy of the macromolecule could be represented as the sum of the energies of the various monomer units

$$U(\Omega_1, \Omega_2, \ldots, \Omega_n) = \sum_{k=1}^{n} U(\Omega_k) \tag{4.1}$$

where Ω_k characterizes the conformation of the kth monomer unit.* As has been shown in the preceding chapter, however, the states (conformations) of neighboring monomer units of a macromolecule are mutually dependent; different sequences of neighboring monomer unit conformations have different energies. Therefore, in reality the energy of a macromolecule contains interlocking terms, which depend on conformations of at least two neighboring monomer units†

$$U(\Omega_1, \Omega_2, \ldots, \Omega_n) = \sum_{k=1}^{n} U(\Omega_{k-1}, \Omega_k) \tag{4.2}$$

Consequently, the macromolecule represents a statistical system which cannot be divided into elements with mutually independent states and, thus, it is a *cooperative system*. Furthermore, linear chain macromolecules are one of the few cases of *one-dimensional cooperative systems* that exist in nature (see Introduction); the coordination number of this system (i.e., the number of elements which are direct neighbors of a given

* Equation (4.1) and all subsequent equations neglect end effects, i.e., the specificity properties of the conformations of terminal monomer units in a macromolecule.

† The following discussions, with the proper changes (see below), are valid also for the case in which the energy of the macromolecule contains terms which depend on the conformations of any number m of neighboring monomer units (with the condition that $m \ll n$).

element) is two. This statement is valid only in those cases in which it is possible to neglect the effect of long-range interactions in the consideration of the physical properties of the macromolecule. Then, the number of elements with which each given element is interacting directly is much smaller than the total number n of elements in the system. Mathematical methods for the investigation of such one-dimensional cooperative systems have been developed by Ising (1) and Kramers and Wannier (2) [see also Montroll et al. (3–7)], and are quite applicable to macromolecules with short-range interactions. Furthermore, the same mathematical methods are applicable also to macromolecules in which long-range interactions are important, if these are ordered (as, for example, in the double helices of native or partly denatured DNA and synthetic polynucleotide molecules) (see Chapter 11). The effect of irregular long-range interactions (volume effects) on the physical properties of macromolecules can be excluded experimentally or taken into account by means of statistical methods; therefore, such interactions will not be considered here.

The model of a one-dimensional system, in which the interactions of all its units can be reduced to the interaction of nearest neighbors, has been proposed by Ising (1) in the theory of ferromagnetism. The nuclear spins in this model can occupy one of two discrete positions, so that the model is rotational-isomeric. Two methods for calculating the partition functions of the Ising model have been developed: the *combinatorial method or method of the largest term*, which was proposed by Ising (1) and the *matrix method*, proposed by Kramers and Wannier (2). We shall use the matrix method, which will allow us later to find the mean value of the scalar, vector, and tensor characteristics of macromolecules.

It is evident that the matrix method, as well as the combinatorial method, for calculating the partition function can be applied to a macromolecule only in the rotational-isomeric approximation, i.e., only with the condition that each monomer unit can have a finite number of conformations. The matrix method of Ising could, in principle, be generalized also to the case of an uninterrupted continuum of states of each monomer unit: in this case, the matrix equation would be replaced by integral equations. This, however, is not necessary from the practical point of view (even if the quantum nature of torsional oscillations is not taken into account), since a continuous internal rotation potential curve can be, with any *a priori* assigned degree of accuracy, divided into a finite number of separate regions in which the energy can be considered as constant. The extent of the regions introduced in this manner, which determine the entropy of the discrete states of a monomer unit, is evidently a function of the steepness of the potential curve at the given point. In connection with this, these discrete states of the system must be defined not by the energy but by the free energy, which, as before, we shall designate by the letter U.* It should be emphasized that, as a rule, the monomer units of macromolecules have in fact a finite (and usually quite small) number of discrete conformations (i.e., the rotational isomers), the energies of which are determined by the interactions of nonbonded atoms at the points of the relative minima of the potential curve; their entropies are determined by the steepness of the potential curve near these minima.

Let us note that the quantity U is equal to the energy (or free energy) of the macromolecule in a solvent, not in a vacuum, i.e., it is the result of averaging over the coordinates of all the solvent molecules which surround it. Therefore, it may be regarded as a potential of mean force, which is usually applied in the statistical physics of condensed media (11). As a result, the quantity U can be a function of the solvent, although, in most cases, this dependence seems to be small. This question is treated in detail by Lifson and Oppenheim (19).

In the rotational-isomeric approximation, the conformational partition function (the sum of the statistical weights of the conformational states) of an individual chain which is not under the action of any external forces, has the form

$$Z = \sum_{\Omega_1} \sum_{\Omega_2} \cdots \sum_{\Omega_n} e^{-U(\Omega_1, \Omega_2, \cdots \Omega_n)/kT} \tag{4.3}$$

In this, summation is carried out over all f rotational isomers of each monomer unit. If the free energy of the macromolecule has the form of eq. (4.2), then

$$Z = \sum_{\Omega_1} \sum_{\Omega_2} \cdots \sum_{\Omega_n} \prod_{k=1}^{n} g(\Omega_{k-1}, \Omega_k) \tag{4.4}$$

where†

$$g(\Omega_{k-1}, \Omega_k) = e^{-U(\Omega_{k-1}, \Omega_k)/kT} \tag{4.5}$$

In homopolymers, i.e., polymers which consist of identical monomer units, all the monomer units have identical sets of conformations $\Omega^{(1)}$,

* Strictly speaking, it is not the energy and free energy which should be considered, but the enthalpy and the thermodynamic potential; in onr case, however, these are practically the same.

† It is necessary to add to the beginning of the chain an additional (zero-th) monomer unit so that the quantity $g(\Omega_{k-1}, \Omega_k)$ would have a meaning for $k = 1$. For $n \gg 1$, the addition of one extra monomer unit and any assumption about its conformation can obviously have no effect on the physical properties of the chain.

$\Omega^{(2)}, \ldots, \Omega^{(f)}$ for any values of k. Therefore, all the quantities $g(\Omega_{k-1}, \Omega_k)$ assume identical values of $g(\Omega^{(\alpha)}, \Omega^{(\beta)})$, which are independent of k (where $\alpha, \beta = 1, 2, \ldots, f$), and, thus, may be regarded as the elements of a certain matrix,

$$G = \begin{bmatrix} g(\Omega^{(1)}, \Omega^{(1)}) & \ldots & g(\Omega^{(1)}, \Omega^{(f)}) \\ g(\Omega^{(f)}, \Omega^{(1)}) & \ldots & g(\Omega^{(f)}, \Omega^{(f)}) \end{bmatrix} \tag{4.6}$$

of order f, with elements

$$g(\Omega_{k-1}^{(\alpha)}, \Omega_k^{(\beta)}) = G_{\Omega_{k-1}^{(\alpha)}, \Omega_k^{(\beta)}} = g_{\alpha, \beta} \tag{4.7}$$

Using the rule of multiplication of matrices, $\sum\limits_q G_{pq}G_{qr} = (G^2)_{pr}$, we obtain from eqs. (4.4) and (4.7)

$$Z = \sum_{\Omega_1}\sum_{\Omega_2} \ldots \sum_{\Omega_n} G_{\Omega_0\Omega_1} G_{\Omega_1\Omega_2} G_{\Omega_2\Omega_3} \ldots G_{\Omega_{n-1}\Omega_n} = \sum_{\Omega_n} (G^n)_{\Omega_0\Omega_n} \tag{4.8}$$

Introducing, for convenience, cyclic conditions, i.e., setting $\Omega_0 = \Omega_n$, we find that Z is equal to the sum of the diagonal elements of matrix G^n:

$$Z = \mathrm{Sp}\, G^n = \lambda_1^n + \lambda_2^n + \ldots + \lambda_f^n \tag{4.9}$$

where $\lambda_1, \lambda_2, \ldots, \lambda_f$ are the eigenvalues of matrix G. Since all the elements of matrix G are positive, then, in accordance with the theorem of Frobenius (8), it has a largest eigenvalue $\lambda \equiv \lambda_1 > |\lambda_\beta|$ ($\beta = 2, 3, \ldots, f$), which is real, positive and nondegenerate. Then, for $n \gg 1$

$$Z \approx \lambda^n \tag{4.10}$$

The conformational partition function of the system under consideration, eq. (4.3), (4.4), or (4.10), gives complete information on its thermodynamic functions and conformational structure. Using standard expressions for the free energy F, entropy S, and energy E of the system, we obtain from eq. (4.10)

$$\begin{aligned} F &= -kT \ln Z = -nkT \ln \lambda \\ S &= k \ln Z + kT(\partial \ln Z/\partial T) = nk \ln \lambda + nkT(\partial \ln \lambda/\partial T) \\ E &= kT^2(\partial \ln Z/\partial T) = nkT^2(\partial \ln \lambda/\partial T) \end{aligned} \tag{4.11}$$

For the simplest case of a one-dimensional cooperative system, with an energy represented by eq. (4.2), the conformational structure is completely characterized by a binary distribution function, i.e., by the mean fraction of neighboring monomer unit pairs which have conformations $\Omega^{(\alpha)}, \Omega^{(\beta)}$ $(\alpha, \beta = 1, 2, \ldots, f)$:*

$$w(\Omega^{(\alpha)}, \Omega^{(\beta)}) = w(\Omega_{k-1}^{(\alpha)}, \Omega_k^{(\beta)})$$

$$= \frac{1}{Z} \sum_{\Omega_1} \cdots \sum_{\Omega_{k-2}} \prod_{i=1}^{k-2} g(\Omega_{i-1}, \Omega_i) g(\Omega_{k-2}, \Omega_{k-1}^{(\alpha)}) g(\Omega_{k-1}^{(\alpha)}, \Omega_k^{(\beta)})$$

$$\sum_{\Omega_{k+1}} \cdots \sum_{\Omega_n} g(\Omega_k^{(\beta)}, \Omega_{k+1}) \prod_{i=k+2}^{n} g(\Omega_{i-1}, \Omega_i) \quad (4.12)$$

The first-order distribution function (the average fraction of monomer units with conformation $\Omega^{(\alpha)}$)

$$w(\Omega^{(\alpha)}) = w(\Omega_k^{(\alpha)}) = \frac{1}{Z} \sum_{\Omega_1} \cdots \sum_{\Omega_{k-1}} \prod_{i=1}^{k-1} g(\Omega_{i-1}, \Omega_i) g(\Omega_{k-1}, \Omega_k^{(\alpha)})$$

$$\sum_{\Omega_{k+1}} \cdots \sum_{\Omega_n} g(\Omega_k^{(\alpha)}, \Omega_{k+1}) \prod_{i=k+2}^{n} g(\Omega_{i-1}, \Omega_i) \quad (4.13)$$

is evidently equal to

$$w(\Omega^{(\alpha)}) = \sum_{\Omega_{k-1}} w(\Omega_{k-1}, \Omega_k^{(\alpha)}) \quad (4.14)$$

Higher-order distribution functions are expressed through second-order and first-order distribution functions in the case of a one-dimensional cooperative system. For example, if the expression of the third-order distribution function, i.e., of the average fraction of groups of three neighboring units with conformations $\Omega^{(\alpha)}, \Omega^{(\beta)}, \Omega^{(\gamma)}$

$$w(\Omega^{(\alpha)}, \Omega^{(\beta)}, \Omega^{(\gamma)}) = w(\Omega_{k-1}^{(\alpha)}, \Omega_k^{(\beta)}, \Omega_{k+1}^{(\gamma)})$$

$$= \frac{1}{Z} \sum_{\Omega_1} \cdots \sum_{\Omega_{k-2}} \prod_{i=1}^{k-2} g(\Omega_{i-1}, \Omega_i) g(\Omega_{k-2}, \Omega_{k-1}^{(\alpha)}) g(\Omega_{k-1}^{(\alpha)}, \Omega_k^{(\beta)})$$

$$g(\Omega_k^{(\beta)}, \Omega_{k+1}^{(\gamma)}) \sum_{\Omega_{k+2}} \cdots \sum_{\Omega_n} g(\Omega_{k+1}^{(\gamma)}, \Omega_{k+2}) \prod_{i=k+3}^{n} g(\Omega_{i-1}, \Omega_i) \quad (4.15)$$

is compared with eqs. (4.12) and (4.13), it is easy to become convinced that

$$w(\Omega^{(\alpha)}, \Omega^{(\beta)}, \Omega^{(\gamma)}) = w(\Omega^{(\alpha)}, \Omega^{(\beta)}) w(\Omega^{(\beta)}, \Omega^{(\gamma)}) / w(\Omega^{(\beta)}) \quad (4.16)$$

* If end effects are neglected, $w(\Omega^{(\alpha)}, \Omega^{(\beta)})$, and all other quantities examined below are obviously, independent of k.

Equation (4.16) is similar to the so-called "superposition approximation" (9), normally used in the statistical physics of condensed media (i.e., of three-dimensional cooperative systems) (10,11), and it shows that this approximation is rigorously fulfilled in the case of one-dimensional cooperative systems.

There are a number of ways of calculating the second-order distribution function of the one-dimensional cooperative system described by eq. (4.2). Apparently, the simplest method consists in representing the conformational partition function of the chain by

$$Z = \sum_{s=0}^{n} C_{\alpha\beta}(s) g_{\alpha\beta}^{s} \tag{4.17}$$

where $C_{\alpha\beta}(s)g_{\alpha\beta}^{s}$ is the conformational partition function of the chain with the condition that s pairs of neighboring monomer units have conformations $\Omega^{(\alpha)}\Omega^{(\beta)}$. Then

$$w(\Omega^{(\alpha)}, \Omega^{(\beta)}) = \overline{s_{\alpha\beta}}/n = (1/n) \sum_{s=0}^{n} s C_{\alpha\beta}(s) g_{\alpha\beta}^{s}/Z \tag{4.18}$$

$$= (1/n)(\partial \ln Z/\partial \ln g_{\alpha\beta}) = \partial \ln \lambda/\partial \ln g_{\alpha\beta}$$

and

$$w(\Omega^{(\alpha)}) = w(\Omega_k^{(\alpha)}) = \sum_{\Omega_{k-1}} w(\Omega_{k-1}, \Omega_k^{(\alpha)}) = \sum_{\nu=1} \partial \ln \lambda/\partial \ln g_{\nu\alpha} \tag{4.19}$$

The average number of monomer units in a regular α-region of the chain, which consists of monomer units in conformations $\Omega^{(\alpha)}$, is equal to the ratio of the total number of units in that conformation to the number of transitions to monomer units in conformation $\Omega^{(\alpha)}$ from monomer units in any other conformation:

$$\nu(\Omega^{(\alpha)}) = \frac{w(\Omega^{(\alpha)})}{\sum\limits_{\Omega_{k-1} \neq \Omega^{(\alpha)}} w(\Omega_{k-1}, \Omega_k^{(\alpha)})}$$

$$= \frac{\sum\limits_{\nu=1}^{f} (\partial \ln \lambda/\partial \ln g_{\nu\alpha})}{\sum\limits_{\substack{\nu=1 \\ (\nu\neq\alpha)}}^{f} (\partial \ln \lambda/\partial \ln g_{\nu\alpha})} \tag{4.20}$$

$$= \frac{1}{1 - \dfrac{(\partial \ln \lambda/\partial \ln g_{\alpha\alpha})}{\sum\limits_{\nu=1}^{f} (\partial \ln \lambda/\partial \ln g_{\nu\alpha})}}$$

The derivatives $\partial\lambda/\partial g_{\alpha\beta}$, which occur in eqs. (4.18)–(4.20), may be expressed by the right-hand and left-hand eigenvectors of matrix G. The right-hand eigenvectors, columns $\boldsymbol{v}(\lambda_\alpha)$* ($\lambda_\alpha$ is one of the eigenvalues of matrix G), are the columns of matrix V, while the left-hand eigenvectors-rows $\tilde{\boldsymbol{u}}(\lambda_\alpha)$, are the rows of matrix U; furthermore, matrices V and U are defined by

$$GV = V\Lambda \tag{4.21}$$

$$UG = \Lambda U$$

where Λ is a diagonal matrix, the elements of which are the eigenvalues λ_α of matrix G, and

$$[(\boldsymbol{u}\lambda_\alpha),\ \boldsymbol{v}(\lambda_\beta)] = \delta_{\alpha\beta} \tag{4.22}$$

Here $\delta_{\alpha\beta}$ is the Kronecker delta ($\delta_{\alpha\beta} = 1$ for $\alpha = \beta$ and 0 for $\alpha \neq \beta$), α, $\beta = 1, 2, \ldots, f'$, where f' is the number of different eigenvalues of matrix $G(f' \leqslant f$, since there can be multiples among the eigenvalues of matrix $G)$.

In the calculation of the values of $\partial\lambda/\partial g_{\alpha\beta}$, let us note that the largest eigenvalue $\lambda = \lambda_1$ of matrix G (which is nondegenerate) is equal to element 1,1 of matrix UGV. In fact, multiplying the left-hand side of eq. (4.21) by matrix U and using eq. (4.22), we obtain

$$(UGV)_{11} = \sum_{\mu,\ \nu=1}^{f} u_{1\mu} g_{\mu\nu} v_{\nu 1} = \sum_{\mu=1}^{f} u_{1\mu} v_{\mu 1}\lambda = \lambda$$

Differentiation of both sides of this equation with respect to $g_{\alpha\beta}$ gives

$$\partial\lambda/\partial g_{\alpha\beta} = u_{1\alpha} v_{\beta 1} + \sum_{\mu,\ \nu=1}^{f} g_{\mu\nu} \frac{\partial}{\partial g_{\alpha\beta}} (u_{1\mu} v_{\nu 1})$$

Starting with eq. (4.21), we obtain

$$\sum_{\mu,\ \nu=1}^{f} g_{\mu\nu} \frac{\partial}{\partial g_{\alpha\beta}} (u_{1\mu} v_{\nu 1}) = \lambda \sum_{\mu,\ \nu=1}^{f} \left(\frac{\partial u_{1\mu}}{\partial g_{\alpha\beta}} v_{\mu 1} + u_{1\nu} \frac{\partial v_{\nu 1}}{\partial g_{\alpha\beta}} \right)$$

$$= \lambda \sum_{\mu=1}^{f} \frac{\partial}{\partial g_{\alpha\beta}} (u_{1\mu} v_{\mu 1}) = 0$$

from which

$$\partial\lambda/\partial g_{\alpha\beta} = u_{1\alpha} v_{\beta 1} \tag{4.23}$$

* Here and in what follows we shall write nontransposed vectors as columns and transposed vectors are rows.

and, consequently,

$$w(\Omega^{(\alpha)},\Omega^{(\beta)}) = (g_{\alpha\beta}/\lambda)u_{1\alpha}v_{\beta 1} \tag{4.24}$$

$$w(\Omega^{(\alpha)}) = u_{1\alpha}v_{\alpha 1} \tag{4.25}$$

$$\nu(\Omega^{(\alpha)}) = \lambda/(\lambda - g_{\alpha\alpha}) \tag{4.26}$$

Let us note that if matrix V has a reciprocal, i.e., if its determinant is nonzero (a sufficient condition for this is the absence of multiple eigenvalues of matrix G), then $U = V^{-1}$, and it follows from eq. (4.21) that

$$G = V\Lambda U = V\Lambda V^{-1} \tag{4.27}$$

(Matrix G is reduced to a diagonal form by the similarity transformation of V.)*

Equations (4.24)–(4.26) follow, as well as particular cases from the general equations (4.39), (4.40) (see below). Another method of derivation, based on the determination of the entropy of a chain element as given by information theory, is presented in the paper of Mullins (12).

The terms of partition functions (4.3) or (4.4) are quantities which are proportional to the probabilities of various microstates of the examined one-dimensional cooperative system, and consequently they permit the calculation of the mean value of any function which depends on the states of its elements (in our case, on the conformations of the monomer units). Montroll (6) proposed a simple method for the averaging of the scalar characteristics of the system, expressed through the product of any number of quantities, each of which is defined by the states of one or several separate elements of the system

$$\prod_{k=j+1}^{i} f(\Omega_k,\Omega_{k+1}\ldots\Omega_{k+s})$$

Such scalar characteristics can be, for example, the fraction of monomer units in a given conformation

$$w(\Omega^{(\alpha)}) = \frac{1}{n}\sum_{k=1}^{n} \delta_{\Omega_k\Omega^{(\alpha)}} \tag{4.28}$$

* If matrix G of order f has multiple eigenvalues, then a necessary and sufficient condition for reducing it to a diagnonal form by the similarity transformation is the equality of the rank of matrix $G - I\lambda_k$ to the quantity $f - \mu_k$, where μ_k is the multiplicity of the root λ_k of the characteristic equation (i.e., among the minors of order $f - \mu_k$ of matrix $G - I\lambda_k$, there must be at least one that is nonzero, while all the minors of order $f - \mu_k + 1$ must be equal to zero).

($\delta_{\Omega_k \Omega^{(\alpha}}$ is the Kronecker delta), or the fraction of pairs of neighboring monomer units in given conformations

$$w(\Omega^{(\alpha)},\Omega^{(\beta)}) = \frac{1}{n}\sum_{k=1}^{n} \delta_{\Omega_{k-1}\Omega^{(\alpha)}}\delta_{\Omega_k\Omega^{(\beta)}} \tag{4.29}$$

which we have calculated above.

Let us present the method for averaging the scalar characteristics of the system in the form given by us elsewhere (13). In the simplest case, in which the quantity averaged is the product of quantities each of which is determined by the state of only one element of the system ($s = 0$), we have

$$\overline{\prod_{k=j+1}^{i} f(\Omega_k)} = \frac{1}{Z}\sum_{\Omega_1}\ldots\sum_{\Omega_n}\prod_{k=1}^{j} g(\Omega_{k-1},\Omega_k) \prod_{k=j+1}^{i} g(\Omega_{k-1},\Omega_k)f(\Omega_k) \prod_{k=i+1} g(\Omega_{k-1},\Omega_k) \tag{4.30}$$

Above, in the calculation of the partition function Z of a one-dimensional cooperative system, we represented Z in the form of a linear combination of elements of some matrix of degree n [see eq. (4.8)]. In order to represent in similar manner the numerator of eq. (4.30), let us introduce matrix $Q = GF$, which is the product of matrix G [eq. (4.6)] with the diagonal matrix

$$F = \begin{bmatrix} f(\Omega^{(1)}) & 0 & \ldots & 0 \\ 0 & f(\Omega^{(2)}) & \ldots & 0 \\ \cdot & \cdot & \ldots & \cdot \\ \cdot & \cdot & \ldots & \cdot \\ \cdot & \cdot & \ldots & \cdot \\ 0 & 0 & \ldots & f(\Omega^{(n)}) \end{bmatrix} \tag{4.31}$$

The last matrix is composed of values of functions f which correspond to all possible conformations of the monomer units of the chain. The elements of matrix Q have the form

$$\{Q\}_{\alpha\beta} = \{GF\}_{\alpha\beta} = g(\Omega_{k-1}^{(\alpha)},\Omega_k^{(\beta)})f(\Omega_k^{(\beta)}) \tag{4.32}$$

Setting, as before, $\Omega_0 = \Omega_n$ (cyclic conditions), and taking into account the fact that the trace or spur (Sp) of the product of matrices is invariant relative to their cyclic transposition, we obtain

$$\overline{\prod_{k=j+1}^{i} f(\Omega_k)} = \frac{1}{Z}\,\mathrm{Sp}(G^j Q^{i-j} G^{n-i})$$

$$= \frac{1}{Z}\,\mathrm{Sp}(G^{n-(i-j)} Q^{i-j}) \tag{4.33}$$

If matrix G is reduced by similarity transformation (4.27) to the diagonal form, then

$$G^m = V\Lambda^m V^{-1} \tag{4.34}$$

and eq. (4.33) can be written as

$$\overline{\prod_{k=j+1}^{i} f(\Omega)_k} = \sum_{\nu=1}^{f} \lambda_\nu^{n-(i-j)}\{V^{-1}Q^{i-j}V\}_{\nu\nu} \Big/ \sum_{\nu=1} \lambda_\nu^n \tag{4.35}$$

or, for $n \gg 1$

$$\overline{\prod_{k=j+1}^{i} f(\Omega_k)} \approx \{V^{-1}(Q/\lambda)^{i-j}V\}_{11} \tag{4.36}$$

Introducing matrix

$$W = V^{-1}(Q/\lambda)V = (\Lambda/\lambda)V^{-1}FV \tag{4.37}$$

with elements

$$W_{\alpha\beta} = (\lambda_\alpha/\lambda)\sum_{\nu=1} u_{\alpha\nu}v_{\nu\beta}f(\Omega^{(\nu)}) \tag{4.38}$$

it is convenient to write eq. (4.36) in the form

$$\overline{\prod_{k=j+1}^{i} f(\Omega_k)} = \{W^{i-j}\}_{11} \tag{4.39}$$

Equation (4.36) can be written out also in terms of the right-hand and left-hand eigenvectors of matrix G, which correspond to the largest eigenvalue λ:

$$\overline{\prod_{k=j+1}^{i} f(\Omega_k)} \approx \tilde{\boldsymbol{u}}(\lambda)(Q/\lambda)^{i-j}\boldsymbol{v}(\lambda) \tag{4.40}$$

In this form, it is valid even in those cases in which matrix V has no reciprocal (since the largest eigenvalue of matrix G is always nondegenerate, in accordance with the theorem of Frobenius).

In the case in which matrix V has a reciprocal, it is evident that the calculation of $\overline{\prod_{k=j+1}^{i} f(\Omega_k)}$ can be carried out both with eq. (4.39) and with eq. (4.40). The choice of the most convenient way of calculating must be made in each specific case, with the consideration that the use of eq. (4.40) requires the determination of those eigenvectors of matrix G which correspond only to its largest eigenvalue λ, and also of all the elements of matrix Q^{i-j}, while application of eq. (4.39) requires the determination of all the elements of matrices V and V^{-1} (i.e., all the eigenvectors of matrix G) but only of element 1,1 of matrix W^{i-j}. Let us note as well that substitution of eqs. (4.28) and (4.29) into eq. (4.40) leads to expressions (4.25) and (4.24), respectively, for the first-order and second-order distribution functions $w(\Omega^{(\alpha)})$ and $w(\Omega^{(\alpha)},\Omega^{(\beta)})$.

The method presented can be generalized easily to the case in which the averaged quantity is expressed as the product of quantities, each of which is determined by the state of not one, but several, elements of the system. Thus, in the averaging of $\prod_{k=j+1}^{i} f(\Omega_{k-1}, \Omega_k)$, eqs. (4.39) and (4.40) remain valid; in these equations, matrixes Q and W are expressed now, not by eqs. (4.32), (4.37), and (4.38), but by eqs. (4.41) and (4.42).

$$\{Q\}_{\alpha\beta} = g(\Omega_{k-1}^{(\alpha)},\Omega_k^{(\beta)}(f(\Omega_{k-1}^{(\alpha)},\Omega_k^{(\beta)}) \tag{4.41}$$

$$\{W\}_{\alpha\beta} = \{V^{-1}(Q/\lambda)V\}_{\alpha\beta} \tag{4.42}$$

The results, presented above, can be generalized also for the case in which not only the atoms of neighboring and nearest nonneighboring monomer units participate in the short-range interactions, but also more distant ones [see, for example, (14)]. If the free energy of the chain is expressed in the form

$$U(\Omega_1,\Omega_2, \ldots, \Omega_n) = \sum_{k=1}^{n} U(\Omega_{k-m},\Omega_{k-m+1}, \ldots, \Omega_k) \tag{4.43}$$

($m \ll n$, i.e., we neglect boundary effects), the partition function of the chain will be represented as before by eq. (4.10), where λ is the largest eigenvalue of matrix G of order f^m(f— is the number of conformations of each monomer unit). The elements of matrix G are indexed by the values of two pairs of variables $(\Omega_{k-m}, \Omega_{k-m+1}, \ldots, \Omega_{k-1})$ and $(\Omega_{k-m+1}, \ldots, \Omega_k)$. Furthermore, matrix G will have only f^{m+1} nonzero elements, out of a total number f^{2m}. Let us point out that, in accordance with the theorem of Frobenius (8), a matrix with nonnegative elements has a real, positive eigenvalue $\lambda = \lambda_1$ which is not smaller in modulus than all the other eigenvalues.

In this manner, the system described by eq. (4.43) differs from the system described by eq. (4.2), in which all the elements of matrix G are positive and, consequently, matrix G, in accordance with the theorem of Frobenius, has an eigenvalue which is largest in modulus. In the case of a system described by eq. (4.43), matrix G can have a negative, real eigenvalue λ_2 or two conjugated, complex eigenvalues λ_2 and λ_3, such that $|\lambda_2| = |\lambda_3| = \lambda_1$. In this the partition function of the chain, instead of being expressed by eq. (4.10), will be expressed by the equation

$$Z = \alpha_1\lambda_1^n + \alpha_2\lambda_2^n + \alpha_3\lambda_3^n = \alpha\lambda^n \tag{4.44}$$

where α_1, α_2, α_3, and α are independent of n. Since all the physical properties of a macromolecule are determined by $\ln Z$ or its derivative, they will be the same as for a system with partition function (4.10), with an accuracy up to terms of order n.

All the results obtained are simplified considerably if the statistical system under examination is not cooperative and the conformations of the monomer units are independent of each other, i.e., its energy is defined by eq. (4.1), rather than eq. (4.2). Then, the partition function of the entire system is given by the product of the partition functions of individual elements:

$$Z = \sum_{\Omega_1} \dots \sum_{\Omega_n} e^{-U(\Omega_1 \dots \Omega_n)/kT}$$

$$= \sum_{\Omega_1} e^{-U(\Omega_1)/kT} \dots \sum_{\Omega_n} e^{-U(\Omega_n)/kT} = z_1^n \tag{4.45}$$

where

$$z_1 = \sum_{\nu=1}^{f} e^{-U(\Omega^{(\nu)})/kT} \tag{4.46}$$

Let us note that the calculation of the partition function of such a system, just as the averaging of its properties can be carried out not only in the rotational-isomeric approximation but also for any continuous potential curve. In this case, the summations in eqs. (4.45) and (4.46) must be replaced by integrations. Equations (4.45) and (4.46) can be obtained also as a particular case of eq. (4.10) with condition (4.1). In fact, in the absence of "interlocking" terms in the expression (4.1) of the energy of the system, elements $g_{\alpha\beta}$ of matrix G (4.6) of order f, defined by eqs. (4.5) and (4.7), will be independent of the first index (the conformation of a monomer unit is independent of the conformation of the "preceding" monomer unit), i.e., for any ν

$$g_{\nu\beta} = g_\beta = g(\Omega^{(\beta)}) \qquad (4.47)^*$$

As a result, all the rows of matrix G will be identical in this case. It is easy to show that such a matrix has $f - 1$ zero eigenvalues and only one which is nonzero:

$$\lambda = \sum_{\nu=1}^{f} g(\Omega^{(\nu)}) = z_1 \qquad (4.48)$$

Thus, in this case, eq. (4.9) or (4.10) is transformed to eqs. (4.45) and (4.46).

The basic characteristic of the noncooperative system under examination is now not a second-order, but a first-order distribution function

$$w(\Omega^{(\alpha)}) = g(\Omega^{(\alpha)})/z_1 \qquad (4.49)$$

Higher-order distribution functions can be expressed in a trivial way in terms of first-order distribution functions. Thus,

$$w(\Omega^{(\alpha)}, \Omega^{(\beta)}) = w(\Omega^{(\alpha)})w(\Omega^{(\beta)}) \qquad (4.50)$$

Equations (4.49) and (4.50), which are directly evident for a noncooperative system, can be also obtained as particular cases from eqs. (4.24) and (4.25) taking into consideration eqs. (4.21) and (4.47). With this, it turns out that $v_{\beta 1}$ is independent of β and $u_{1\alpha} \sim g_\alpha/\lambda$. Taking into account normalization (4.22), we have $u_{1\alpha}v_{\beta 1} = g_\alpha/\lambda$, and eqs. (4.24) and (4.25) become eqs. (4.49) and (4.50), respectively.

4.2. Ising Model and Markoff Chains

Above, we have presented the mathematical apparatus (the matrix method of the Ising model) of the statistics of one-dimensional cooperative systems. It is of interest to trace the close relation between this treatment and the more familiar treatment of Markoff chains (15–17). As is known, Markoff chains are sequences of mutually dependent occasional events, i.e., those events whose occurrence is determined by the laws of probability theory, the probability of the occurrence of each event being dependent on the

* Equation (4.47) is valid if $U(\Omega_{k-1}, \Omega_k) = U(\Omega_k) + U_{\text{inter}}(\Omega_{k-1}, \Omega_k)$ [see below, eq. (4.55) with $x = 0$). The more general condition of the absence of cooperativity, $U_{\text{inter}}(\Omega_{k-1}, \Omega_k) = 0$], valid for any method of determination of $U(\Omega_{k-1}, \Omega_k)$ and $g_{\alpha\beta}$, has the form: $g_{\alpha\beta}g_{\beta\alpha} = g_{\alpha\alpha}g_{\beta\beta}$. All the following results are valid for this more general condition as well.

occurrence of one (simple Markoff chain) or several (complex Markoff chain) preceding events. It is obvious that there is a close similarity between the interdependent probabilities of states of the elements of a one-dimensional cooperative system and the interdependent probabilities of the occurrence of events which form a Markoff chain. The difference is that mutually dependent events occur one after another, while in a one-dimensional cooperative system (for example, in a macromolecule) we deal with the states of all its elements which exist simultaneously (in the case of a macromolecule, these states are the conformations of all its monomer units).

In the first case, the principal property of the process is the conditional probability of transition to a given state in the kth step with a fixed state in the $(k - 1)$th step. In the conformational statistics of macromolecules, having introduced arbitrarily the concepts of chain "beginning" and "end," it is possible to examine in the same way the probability of a given conformation of the kth monomer unit with a fixed conformation of the $(k - 1)$th unit. In order to determine this quantity, it is necessary to average over all possible conformations of the chain "end," i.e., over the states of monomer units $k + 1$, $k + 2$, etc. Thus, the conditional transition probability has the form

$$w_{\Omega_{k-1}^{(\alpha)} \rightarrow \Omega_k^{(\beta)}} = \frac{\int e^{-U(\Omega_1 \cdots \Omega_n)/kT} \prod_{i=1}^{n} \frac{d\Omega_i}{d\Omega_{k-1} d\Omega_k}}{\int e^{-U(\Omega_1 \cdots \Omega_n)/kT} \prod_{i=1}^{n} \frac{d\Omega_i}{d\Omega_{k-1}}} = \frac{e^{-U(\Omega_{k-1}^{(\alpha)}, \Omega_k^{(\beta)})/kT} \chi(\Omega_k^{(\beta)})}{\int e^{-U(\Omega_{k-1}^{(\alpha)}, \Omega_k)/kT} \chi(\Omega_k) d\Omega_k} \tag{4.51}$$

where

$$\chi(\Omega_k) = \int \prod_{i=k+1}^{n} e^{-U(\Omega_{i-1}, \Omega_i)/kT} d\Omega_i \tag{4.52}$$

is the partition function of the chain "end," which follows the kth unit that depends on its state. The presence of factor $\chi(\Omega_k^{(\beta)})$ increases the probability of transition into such states Ω_k, for which the partition function of the "tail" of the chain increases (even if the energy $U(\Omega_{k-1}, \Omega_k)$ is sufficiently large for such states). The conditional transition probabilities are independent of the monomer unit number, with an accuracy limited only by the neglect of end effects. In this way, the conformations of monomer units of the macromolecule can be regarded as consecutive and mutually dependent events, the conditional probabilities of transition from one event to another being determined by the partition function of the macromolecule, in accordance with eqs. (4.51) and (4.52). This means that the problem of the conformations of a polymer chain with short-range interactions can be compared to the corresponding problem in the theory of Markoff processes.

By using eqs. (4.18) and (4.19) for the second-order and first-order distribution functions of a one-dimensional cooperative system, it is easy to express the conditional transition probabilities by the characteristics of matrix G, which determines the partition function of the system under examination. In fact, the quantity $w(\Omega_{k-1}{}^{(\alpha)}, \Omega_k{}^{(\beta)})$ determines the probability that two neighboring monomer units are in conformations $\Omega^{(\alpha)}\Omega^{(\beta)}$, while the quantity $w(\Omega_{k-1}{}^{(\alpha)})$ is the *a priori* probability of conformation $\Omega^{(\alpha)}$. From this, the conditional probability of transition from conformation $\Omega^{(\alpha)}$ of the $(k-1)$th monomer unit into conformation $\Omega^{(\beta)}$ of the kth monomer unit, which is the basic property of a Markoff process, is equal to

$$w_{\Omega_{k-1}^{(\alpha)}\to\Omega_k^{(\beta)}} = \frac{w(\Omega_{k-1}^{(\alpha)}, \Omega_k^{(\beta)})}{w(\Omega_{k-1}^{(\alpha)})} = \frac{\dfrac{\partial \ln \lambda}{\partial \ln g_{\alpha\beta}}}{\displaystyle\sum_{\nu=1}^{f} \frac{\partial \ln \lambda}{\partial \ln g_{\alpha\nu}}} \tag{4.53}$$

or, taking eqs. (4.24) and (4.25) into account,

$$w_{\Omega_{k-1}^{(\alpha)}\to\Omega_k^{(\beta)}} = (g_{\alpha\beta}/\lambda)(v_{\beta 1}/v_{\alpha 1}) \tag{4.54}$$

As is seen from eq. (4.54) [see also eq. (4.51)], the quantities

$$g_{\alpha\beta} = \exp\left\{-U(\Omega_{k-1}^{(\alpha)}\Omega_k^{(\beta)})/kT\right\}$$

do not have the meaning of nonnormalized probabilities of transition from conformation $\Omega^{(\alpha)}$ of the $(k-1)$th to conformation $\Omega^{(\beta)}$ of the kth monomer unit. This is related to the effect of the chain end, the partition function of which is a function of the conformation of the kth monomer unit [see eq. (4.52)]. Let us note also that there is a certain uncertainty in the construction of the quantity $g_{\alpha\beta}$. In fact, the quantities $U(\Omega_{k-1}, \Omega_k)$ in eq. (4.2) include both the energy of interaction $U_{\text{inter}}(\Omega_{k-1}, \Omega_k)$ of monomer units, which depends simultaneously on Ω_{k-1} and Ω_k and the energy of monomer units themselves, which can be included in $U(\Omega_{k-1}, \Omega_k)$ in a different way, with an accuracy limited by neglect of end effects:

$$U(\Omega_{k-1}, \Omega_k) = xU(\Omega_{k-1}) + (1-x)U(\Omega_k) + U_{\text{inter}}(\Omega_{k-1}, \Omega_k) \tag{4.55}$$

It is evident that, for any x, the total energy of the molecule will be equal to the sum of the energies of all the monomer units plus the sum of all the energies of interaction, so that the indeterminacy in the choice of $U(\Omega_{k-1}, \Omega_k)$ and $g_{\alpha\beta}$ has no effect on the partition function of the macromolecule and, consequently, on any of its properties. This indeterminacy underlines, however, the fact that in a one-dimensional cooperative system, the quantities $g_{\alpha\beta}$ have no direct physical meaning themselves. On the other hand, if the conformations of monomer units had truly represented a chain of events which took place consecutively in time, the conditional probabilities would have had the form:

$$w_{\Omega_{k-1}^{(\alpha)} \to \Omega_k^{(\beta)}} = g_{\alpha\beta} / \sum_{\nu=1}^{f} g_{\alpha\nu} \tag{4.56}$$

i.e., the quantities $g_{\alpha\beta}$ would have truly represented non-normalized probabilities of transition.

In eqs. (4.30)–(4.40) we have presented the matrix method of averaging arbitrary functions of the conformations of monomer units of a macromolecule, based on the application of the Ising model. The apparatus of Markoff chains also permits the averaging of arbitrary functions of the states of elements of the system, in this case, of the conformations of monomer units of the chain. The mean value of function $f(\Omega_{j+1}, \Omega_{j+2}, \ldots, \Omega_i)$ of the conformations of monomer units number $j+1, j+2, \ldots, i$ is calculated according to eq. (4.57)

$$\begin{aligned}\overline{f(\Omega_{j+1}, \Omega_{j+2}, \ldots, \Omega_i)} &= \sum_{\Omega_{j+1}} \cdots \sum_{\Omega_i} f(\Omega_{j+1}, \ldots, \Omega_i) w(\Omega_{j+1}, \ldots, \Omega_i) \\ &= \sum_{\Omega_j} \sum_{\Omega_{j+1}} \cdots \sum_{\Omega_i} w(\Omega_j) \prod_{k=j+1}^{i} w_{\Omega_{k-1} \to \Omega_k} f(\Omega_{j+1}, \ldots, \Omega_i)\end{aligned} \tag{4.57}$$

where summation is carried out over all sets of possible conformations $\Omega_j, \Omega_{j+1}, \ldots, \Omega_i$. If the averaged quantity, just as in the case examined above [see eq. (4.30)], is the product of $i - j$ quantities, each of which is a function of the conformation of only one monomer unit, then

$$\overline{\prod_{k=j+1}^{i} f(\Omega_k)} = \sum_{\Omega_j} \cdots \sum_{\Omega_i} w(\Omega_j) \prod_{k=j+1}^{i} w_{\Omega_{k-1} \to \Omega_k} f(\Omega_k) \tag{4.58}$$

Equation (4.58) can be written in the form of a matrix. In the case under examination, the probabilities of given conformations of monomer units are independent of their numbers. Let us introduce a diagonal matrix P_a with elements equal to the *a priori* probabilities of the conformations of monomer units:

$$\{P_a\}_{\alpha\beta} = \delta_{\alpha\beta} w(\Omega^{(\alpha)}) \tag{4.59}$$

and matrix P with elements equal to the probabilities of transition to a given conformation of the kth monomer unit, with the condition that the $(k-1)$th unit will have a given fixed conformation:

$$\{P\}_{\alpha\beta} = w_{\Omega_{k-1}^{(\alpha)} \to \Omega_k^{(\beta)}} \tag{4.60}$$

and matrix $\Phi = PF$, which is the product of matrix P with the diagonal matrix F [see eq. (4.31)], the elements of which are the values of the function $f(\Omega_k)$ which correspond to all the possible conformations of the monomer units of the chain. The elements of matrix Φ have the form:

$$\{\Phi\}_{\alpha\beta} = \{PF\}_{\alpha\beta} = w_{\Omega_{k-1}^{(\alpha)} \to \Omega_k^{(\beta)}} f(\Omega_k^{(\beta)}) \tag{4.61}$$

Using the notations of eqs. (4.59)–(4.61), let us transform eq. (4.58) to the form

$$\overline{\prod_{k=j+1}^{i} f(\Omega_k)} = \sum_{\mu\nu=1}^{f} \{P_a \Phi^{i-j}\}_{\mu\nu} \tag{4.62}$$

Let us show that eq. (4.62) leads to the same results as eqs. (4.30)–(4.40) if the conditional transition probabilities are defined by eq. (4.54), while the *a priori* probability is defined by eq. (4.25). In fact, substituting eqs. (4.25) and (4.56) into eq. (4.58), we obtain

$$\begin{aligned}\overline{\prod_{k=j+1}^{i} f(\Omega_k)} &= \sum_{\Omega_j} \cdots \sum_{\Omega_i} u_{1\Omega_j} v_{\Omega_j 1} \prod_{k=j+1}^{i} \frac{g_{\Omega_{k-1},\Omega_k}}{\lambda} \left(\frac{v_{\Omega_k,1}}{v_{\Omega_{k-1},1}}\right) f(\Omega_k) \\ &= \sum_{\Omega_j} \cdots \sum_{\Omega_i} u_{1\Omega_j} \prod_{k=j+1}^{i} \frac{g_{\Omega_{k-1},\Omega_k}}{\lambda} f(\Omega_k) v_{\Omega_i,1} \\ &= \tilde{\boldsymbol{u}}(\lambda)(\Omega/\lambda)^{i-j} \boldsymbol{v}(\lambda)\end{aligned} \tag{4.63}$$

where $\tilde{\boldsymbol{u}}(\lambda)$ and $\boldsymbol{v}(\lambda)$ are the left-hand and right-hand eigenvectors, respectively, which correspond to the largest eigenvalue $\lambda(\equiv\lambda_1)$, and Q is a matrix defined by eq. (4.32). We see that eq. (4.63) is identical with eq. (4.40). It is obvious that, if matrix V has a reciprocal, eq. (4.63) can be transformed into the form of eq. (4.39). Similar results can be obtained as well for a function $f(\Omega_{j+1}, \ldots, \Omega_i)$ of an arbitrary form. In this way, two paths may be used in an equivalent manner in the calculation of the averaged properties of a one-dimensional cooperative system:

either the averaging is carried out with the use of the matrix method of the Ising model, described above [see eqs. (4.30)–(4.40)], or the one-dimensional cooperative system is described by a Markoff chain, in which the conditional transition probabilities are defined by eq. (4.54), and then the averaging is carried out with the apparatus of Markoff chains [see eqs. (4.57)–(4.63)].

If atoms which belong to more distant monomer units participate also in the short-range interactions, and the energy of the chain contains terms which are a function of the conformations of monomer units with numbers $k - m, k - m + 1, \ldots, k$, where $m \ll n$ [see eq. (4.43)], then the equivalent form in the theory of dependent random events will be not the simple, as above, but the complex Markoff chain. Thus, *a polymer chain in which there are only short-range interactions can always be represented by a Markoff chain model with a memory over a finite number of steps.*

It should be pointed out that the relation between the statistics of macromolecules and the apparatus of Markoff chains is treated with insufficient rigor in a number of studies. Thus, Kramers and Wannier (2) assumed that the conditional transition probabilities are defined by eq. (4.56); in this, they eliminated the nonsingularity of the quantities $g_{\alpha\beta}$ for $\alpha \neq \beta$ by setting $x = 0$ in eq. (4.55). Grimley (18), without taking into account the interdependence of the rotations of the elements of one monomer unit, assumed that chains of type $(—CH_2—CRR'—)_n$ require a complex, rather than a simple, Markoff chain to describe them.

From what has been presented above, it can be seen that, in actuality, a Markoff process, with conditional transition probabilities defined by eqs. (4.51)–(4.54), can be compared to any macromolecule with short-range interactions. Furthermore, even if long-range interactions are taken into account, it remains possible to introduce conditional probabilities with the help of the first of eqs. (4.51). In this case, however, the conditional probabilities will certainly not be expressed by the simple eqs. (4.53) and (4.54) and, in particular, they will be a function of the number of the monomer unit.

Let us illustrate now everything that has been said by the simple example of a macromolecule, a monomer unit of which can have only two conformations: $\Omega^{(1)}$ and $\Omega^{(2)}$. Matrix G, in this case, is a second-order matrix

$$G = \begin{pmatrix} g_{11} & g_{12} \\ g_{21} & g_{22} \end{pmatrix} \tag{4.64}$$

with eigenvalues

$$\lambda_{1,2} = \frac{g_{11} + g_{22}}{2} \pm \sqrt{\frac{(g_{11} - g_{22})^2}{4} + g_{12}g_{21}} \tag{4.65}$$

From eqs. (4.24)–(4.26) and (4.54), introducing the notations

$$q = (g_{11} - g_{22})/2g_{11} \tag{4.66}$$

and

$$r = \sqrt{\frac{(g_{11} - g_{22})^2}{4g^2_{11}} + \frac{g_{12}g_{21}}{g^2_{11}}} \tag{4.67}$$

we obtain the second-order distribution functions:

$$w(\Omega^{(1)}, \Omega^{(1)}) = \frac{g_{11}(\lambda_1 - g_{22})}{\lambda_1(\lambda_1 - \lambda_2)} = \frac{r + q}{2r(1 + r - q)}$$

$$w(\Omega^{(2)}, \Omega^{(2)}) = \frac{g_{22}(\lambda_1 - g_{11})}{\lambda_1(\lambda_1 - \lambda_2)} = \frac{(r - q)(1 - 2q)}{2r(1 + r - q)}$$

$$w(\Omega^{(1)}, \Omega^{(2)}) = w(\Omega^{(2)}, \Omega^{(1)}) = \frac{(\lambda_1 - g_{11})(\lambda_1 - g_{22})}{\lambda_1(\lambda_1 - \lambda_2)}$$

$$= \frac{r^2 - q^2}{2r(1 + r - q)} \tag{4.68}$$

first-order distribution functions:

$$w(\Omega^{(1)}) = \frac{\lambda_1 - g_{22}}{\lambda_1 - \lambda_2} = \frac{r + q}{2r},$$

$$w(\Omega^{(2)}) = \frac{\lambda_1 - g_{11}}{\lambda_1 - \lambda_2} = \frac{r - q}{2r}; \tag{4.69}$$

conditional transition probabilities:

$$w_{\Omega^{(1)} \to \Omega^{(1)}} = g_{11}/\lambda_1 = 1/(1 + r - q)$$

$$w_{\Omega^{(1)} \to \Omega^{(2)}} = (\lambda_1 - g_{11})/\lambda_1 = (r - q)/(1 + r - q)$$

$$w_{\Omega^{(2)} \to \Omega^{(1)}} = (\lambda_1 - g_{22})/\lambda_1 = (r + q)/(1 + r - q)$$

$$w_{\Omega^{(2)} \to \Omega^{(2)}} = g_{22}/\lambda_1 = (1 - 2q)/(1 + r - q) \tag{4.70}$$

and mean lengths of regular regions

$$\nu(\Omega^{(1)}) = \lambda_1/(\lambda_1 - g_{11}) = (1 + r - q)/(r - q)$$
$$\nu(\Omega^{(2)}) = \lambda_1/(\lambda_1 - g_{22}) = (1 + r - q)/(r + q) \quad (4.71)$$

Let us note that, just as should have been expected, the condition of the equality of the number of pairs $(\Omega^{(1)}, \Omega^{(2)})$ and $(\Omega^{(2)}, \Omega^{(1)})$ is fulfilled: i.e.,

$$w(\Omega^{(1)}, \Omega^{(2)}) = w(\Omega^{(2)}, \Omega^{(1)})$$

From this, it is easy to obtain that

$$w(\Omega^{(1)})/w(\Omega^{(2)}) = w_{\Omega^{(2)} \to \Omega^{(1)}}/w_{\Omega^{(1)} \to \Omega^{(1)}} \quad (4.72)$$

From eqs. (4.69) and (4.72), it follows that for $g_{11} = g_{22}$, i.e., for $w(\Omega^{(1)}) = w(\Omega^{(2)})$, it is also required that

$$w_{\Omega^{(1)} \to \Omega^{(2)}} = w_{\Omega^{(2)} \to \Omega^{(2)}}$$

although this may be accompanied by $g_{12} \neq g_{21}$, which shows once again that it is impossible to treat the elements of matrix G as non-normalized transition probabilities.

If the conformations of neighboring monomer units are independent, then

$$g_{12}g_{21} = g_{11}g_{22}$$

$$r = (g_{11} + g_{22})/2g_{11}$$

and

$$r + q = 1$$

In this case, the second-order distribution functions are products of first-order functions equal to

$$w(\Omega^{(1)}) = 1/(1 + g)$$
$$w(\Omega^{(2)}) = g/(1 + g) \quad (4.73)$$

where $g = g_{22}/g_{11}$ are the ratios of the statistical weights of conformations $\Omega^{(2)}$ and $\Omega^{(1)}$, and the mean lengths of regular regions are equal to

$$\nu(\Omega^{(1)}) = (1 + g)/g$$
$$\nu(\Omega^{(2)}) = 1 + g \quad (4.74)$$

In the particular case under examination, matrix W, defined by eqs. (4.39) and (4.40), has the form

$$W = \frac{1}{\lambda_1 - \lambda_2} \begin{Vmatrix} (\lambda_1 - g_{22})f(\Omega^{(1)}) + (\lambda_1 - g_{11})f(\Omega^{(2)}) \\ \qquad - g_{12}\frac{v_{22}}{v_{11}}[f(\Omega^{(1)}) - f(\Omega^{(2)})] \\ -\frac{\lambda_2}{\lambda_1} g_{21} \frac{v_{11}}{v_{22}} [f(\Omega^{(1)}) - f(\Omega^{(2)})] \\ \qquad \frac{\lambda_2}{\lambda_1}[(\lambda_1 - g_{11})f(\Omega^{(1)}) + (\lambda_2 - g_{22})f(\Omega^{(2)})] \end{Vmatrix} \quad (4.75)$$

where v_{11} and v_{22} are elements of matrix V with arbitrary values. Setting, for example,

$$v_{22}/v_{11} = -(\lambda_1 - g_{11})/g_{12}$$

and taking into account the notations of eqs. (4.66) and (4.67), we obtain:

$$W = \begin{bmatrix} f + \frac{q}{r}\Delta f & \frac{r-q}{r}\Delta f \\ \frac{1-q-r}{1-q+r}\left(\frac{q+r}{r}\right)\Delta f & \frac{1-q-r}{1-q+r}\left(f - \frac{q}{r}\Delta f\right) \end{bmatrix} \quad (4.76)$$

where

$$f = [f(\Omega^{(1)}) + f(\Omega^{(2)})]/2$$
$$\Delta f = [f(\Omega^{(1)}) - f(\Omega^{(2)})]/2 \quad (4.77)$$

As has been shown in Section 3.3, the monomer units of a number of typical macromolecules have, in fact, two conformations with similar statistical weights. Therefore, the simplest particular case examined above is useful, and eqs. (4.68)–(4.77) will be used by us in what follows (see Chapter 6) in the calculation of the conformational properties of a number of macromolecules.

References

1. Ising, E., *Z. Physik.*, **31,** 253 (1925).
2. Kramers, H. A., and G. H. Wannier *Phys. Rev.*, **60,** 252 (1941).
3. Montroll, E. W., *J. Chem. Phys.*, **9,** 706 (1941).
4. Lassettre, E. N., and J. P. Howe, *J. Chem. Phys.*, **9,** 747 (1941).
5. Montroll, E. W., *J. Chem. Phys.*, **10,** 61 (1942).
6. Montroll, E. W., *Ann. Math. Statistics*, **18,** 18 (1947).

7. Newell, G. F., and E. W. Montroll, *Rev. Mod. Phys.*, **25,** 353 (1953).
8. Gantmakher, F. R., *Teoriya Matrits* (Theory of Matrices), Gostekhizdat, Moscow. 1953.
9. Kirkwood, J. G., *J. Chem. Phys.*, **3,** 300 (1935).
10. Bogolyubov, N. N., *Problemy Dinamicheskoi Teorii v Statisticheskoi Fizike* (Problems of the Dynamic Theory in Statistical Physics), Gostekhizdat, Moscow, 1946.
11. Hill, T., *Statischeskaya Mekhanika* IL, Moscow, 1960 (originally published as *Statistical Mechanics*, McGraw-Hill, New York, 1956).
12. Mullins, W. W., *Phys. Rev.*, **114,** 389 (1959).
13. Birshtein, T. M., and O. B. Ptitsyn, *Zh. Tekhn. Fiz.*, **29,** 1048 (1959); *Soviet Phys.-Tech. Phys.*, **4,** 954 (1959).
14. Nagai, K., *J. Chem. Phys.*, **37,** 490 (1962).
15. Markoff, A. A., *Izbr. Trudy* (Selected Papers), Izdatel'stvo Akad. Nauk SSSR, Moscow, 1951.
16. Chandrasekar, S., *Stokhasticheskie Problemy v Fizike i Astronomii* IL, Moscow, 1947, originally published as "Stochastic Problems in Physics and Astronomy," *Rev. Mod. Phys.*, **15,** 1 (1943).
17. Gnedenko, B. V., *Kurs Teorii Veroyatnostei* (Course in Theory of Probability). Gostekhizdat, Moscow, 1954.
18. Grimley, T. B., *Proc. Phys., Soc.*, **77,** 931 (1961).
19. Lifson, S., and I. Oppenheim, *J. Chem. Phys.*, **33,** 109 (1960).

Chapter 5

THEORY OF THE DIMENSIONS AND DIPOLE MOMENTS OF MACROMOLECULES: GENERAL METHODS

5.1. Methods of Averaging Vector Properties of Macromolecules

In the preceding chapter, we have presented the bases of the so-called matrix method of the Ising model, i.e., of the mathematical method of calculating the partition function and of averaging the scalar properties of a one-dimensional cooperative system. As has been pointed out already, this method was developed (in a somewhat different form), completely independently of the problem of the statistical physics of macromolecules, in connection with the requirements of the theory of ferromagnetism. It is evident that the results obtained with this method cannot explain the properties of ferromagnetic bodies, which are not one-dimensional, but three-dimensional cooperative systems. On the other hand, macromolecules are ideal objects for the application of the statistics of one-dimensional cooperative systems. The only difficulty in this consists in the fact that the principal physical properties of macromolecules, which are determined by the conformations of monomer units and which can be subjected to experimental investigation, are not scalar, but either vector (end-to-end distance of the chain, dipole moment) or tensor (optical anisotropy) quantities. As a result, the application of the statistics of one-dimensional cooperative systems to the calculation of the mean dimensions, dipole moments, and optical anisotropies of polymer chains has required a corresponding generalization of this method.

Gotlib (1) and Birshtein and Ptitsyn (2,3) [see also (4,5,64)] have developed a method for the calculation of the mean-square vector properties of macromolecules; this is reduced to the averaging of linear functions of cosines of the angles between vectors which characterize individual monomer units. Later, Birshtein and Nagai developed as well a method for the calculation of the mean tensor properties (3,6) of macromolecules and the mean values of the fourth powers of their vector properties (68); this is reduced to the averaging of quadratic functions of cosines of the angles between the vectors of monomer units. Below, we shall present the method of averaging the quadratic vector properties of macromolecules over the conformations of the chain (2); this method is the basis of the theory of the dimensions and dipole moments of macromolecules. We shall not present here the more cumbersome method of averaging tensor properties, but we refer the reader to the original literature (3,6,68).

Let **R** be some vector quantity which characterizes the properties of a macromolecule in solution (its end-to-end distance, **h**, or its dipole moments, $\boldsymbol{\mu}$). It is obvious that

$$\mathbf{R} = \sum_{i=1}^{n} \mathbf{r}_i \tag{5.1}$$

where $\mathbf{r}_i$ is the vector of the length or dipole moment of a monomer unit and n is the number of monomer units (degree of polymerization). The mean value of vector **R**, in a spatially immobile system of coordinates, is obviously equal to zero for a molecule which is randomly oriented in space. On the other hand, it is possible to measure experimentally the mean value of the square of this vector, which is expressed by eq. (5.2).

$$\overline{R^2} = \sum_{i=1}^{n} r_i^2 + 2 \sum_{i=2}^{n} \sum_{j=1}^{i-1} \overline{(\mathbf{r}_j, \mathbf{r}_i)} \tag{5.2}$$

It is this quantity that we shall examine in what follows.

Let us set the vector, which characterizes a monomer unit, in the form $\mathbf{r}_i = r_i \mathbf{e}_i$, where $\mathbf{e}_i$ is a unit vector. For the sake of simplicity we shall assume that r_i is a constant quantity, independent of internal rotation. This condition is always fulfilled for the length of a monomer unit in a polyvinyl chain. It is true for the dipole moment of a monomer unit of type $(\text{—CR}_2\text{—CR}'\text{R}''\text{—})_n$ (where R, R′, R″ are polar side groups), if the rotations in the side groups of the monomer unit are independent of the rotations in the chain or if the dipole moments of the side groups are directed along the axis of rotation. This condition is not essential, and it has been introduced here mainly for compactness and ease of calculation. The results obtained can be easily generalized (3) for the case in which the properties of monomer units are functions of the conformation (for example, for the length of a monomer unit which consists of more than two elements, and for the dipole moment of a monomer unit of the polyvinyl chain if rotations in the side group are a function of the location of the monomer units nearest to the given one).

Let us assume also that the quantity $r_i = r$ and the conditions of internal rotation in monomer units are independent of the number i, i.e., let us examine stereoregular homopolymers. The results obtained can be easily generalized to copolymers for the case in which rotation in the chain is independent of the copolymer composition (7). For the case in which rotation in the chain is a function of its composition, averaging of the vector properties of copolymers and nonstereoregular (atactic) homopolymers was carried out only in the approximation that the conformations of monomer units are independent.*

Taking these assumptions into account, we have

$$\overline{R^2} = r^2 \left[n + 2 \sum_{i=2}^{n} \sum_{j=1}^{i-1} \overline{(\mathbf{e}_j, \mathbf{e}_i)} \right] \tag{5.3}$$

Let us introduce n local systems of coordinates, rigidly bound to the monomer units and constructed in accordance with their stereoisomeric structure (see Chapter 6). With the assumptions made, vector $\mathbf{e}_i = \mathbf{e}$, expressed in the ith system of coordinates, is evidently independent of the number i and of the conditions of internal rotation. Vectors $\mathbf{e}_j$ and $\mathbf{e}_i$ must be expressed in a single system of coordinates in order to calculate the mean values of the cosines of the angles between the basis vectors which characterize the monomer units $\overline{(\mathbf{e}_j, \mathbf{e}_i)}$. This can be accomplished, for example, by projecting vector $\mathbf{e}_i$ (equal to $\mathbf{e}$ in its own system of coordinates) on the axis of the jth local system of coordinates; this requires that vector $\mathbf{e}$ be multiplied from the left by the matrix of the cosines of the angles between the axes of the ith and jth local systems. This matrix is, obviously, equal to the product of $(i - j)$ matrices of transition from the ith local system to the $(i - 1)$th, from the $(i - 1)$th to the $(i - 2)$th, etc., up to the matrix of transition from the $(j + 1)$th system to the jth. Then, expressing vector $\mathbf{e}$ as a column, we obtain:

$$\overline{R^2} = r^2 \left[n + 2\tilde{\mathbf{e}} \sum_{i=2}^{n} \sum_{j=1}^{i-1} \overline{\prod_{k=j+1}^{i} S(\Omega_k)}\mathbf{e} \right] \tag{5.4}$$

where $\tilde{\mathbf{e}}$ is the transposed vector $\mathbf{e}$, and $S(\Omega_k)$ is the matrix of the cosines of the angles between the axes of the kth and $(k - 1)$th local systems of

* The attempt of Yoo and Kinsinger (70) to generalize these results for the case of an atactic chain with correlated conformations of chain monomer units gives rise to objection, since they carried out the averaging over the steric structures of the chain in such manner as if these structures could be converted into each other as a result of thermal motion

coordinates; it is a function of the conformation (the totality of the angles of internal rotation) of the kth monomer unit:

$$\{S(\Omega_k)\}_{rs} = (\mathbf{e}_{k-1}^{(r)}, \mathbf{e}_k^{(s)}) \tag{5.5}$$

where $\mathbf{e}_{k-1}^{(r)}$, $\mathbf{e}_k^{(s)}$ are the basis vectors of the $(k - 1)$th and kth systems of coordinates.

If there is no correlation between the conformations of neighboring monomer units, i.e., the potential energy of the chain has the form of eq. (4.1), the partition function of the macromolecule is expressed by eqs. (4.45) and (4.46), and matrices $S(\Omega_k)$ can be averaged independently of each other. Introducing $S = \overline{S(\Omega_k)}$, we have, for this case,

$$\overline{R^2} = r^2 \left[n + 2\tilde{\mathbf{e}} \sum_{i=2}^{n} \sum_{j=1}^{i-1} S^{i-j}\mathbf{e} \right] \tag{5.6}$$

or, after summation of the double geometric progression of the matrix,

$$\overline{R^2} = r^2\{n + 2\tilde{\mathbf{e}}[nS(I - S)^{-1} - S(I - S)^{-2} + S^{n+1}(I - S)^{-2}]\mathbf{e}\} \tag{5.7}$$

where I is a unit matrix.

If the freedom of internal rotation in each monomer unit of the chain tends to zero, i.e., if the conformations of all the monomer units tend to a single fixed conformation, then S tends to a matrix of rotation, the eigenvalues of which are equal to $\lambda_1 = 1$, $\lambda_{2,3} = e^{\pm i}$, where

$$\cos \vartheta = {}^1/_2(\mathrm{Sp}S - 1) \tag{5.8}$$

Since the eigenvalues of the matrix are roots of the equation $D(S - \lambda I) = 0$, then, when matrix S tends toward the rotation matrix, $D(S - 1) \rightarrow 0$, and, consequently, the elements of matrices $(I - S)$ and $(I - S)^{-2}$ tend to infinity. In order to expand the indeterminacy which arises in eq. (5.7) as a result of this, let us use the interpolation polynomial of Lagrange-Silvester [see, for example, (69)] for an arbitrary function of matrix $F(S)$. In the case of a third-order matrix, this polynomial has the form:

$$F(S) = \sum_{(p,q,r)} \frac{(S - \lambda_p I)(S - \lambda_q I)}{(\lambda_r - \lambda_p)(\lambda_r - \lambda_q)} F(\lambda_r) \tag{5.9}$$

where the eigenvalues of matrix S are numbered by indices p, q, r, and summation is carried out over all the cyclic transpositions of these indices (123,231,312). In our case, the function $F(S)$ has the form

$$F(S) = nS(I - S)^{-1} - S(I - S)^{-2} + S^{n+1}(I - S)^{-2} \tag{5.10}$$

Expanding the indeterminacy in $F(\lambda_1)$, where $\lambda_1 = 1$, using the rule of l'Hospital, we obtain:

$$\lim_{\lambda_1 \to 1} F(\lambda_1) = \lim_{\lambda_1 \to 1} [(n\lambda_1 - \lambda_1 + \lambda_1^{n+1})/(1 - \lambda_1)^2]$$

$$= n(n - 1)/2 \quad (5.11)$$

Calculating $F(\lambda_2)$ and $F(\lambda_3)$, where $\lambda_{2,3} = e^{\pm i\vartheta}$, and collecting the terms with $e^{i\vartheta}$ and $e^{-i\vartheta}$, we obtain finally

$$F(S) = \frac{1}{2}\left\{\frac{(S - \lambda_2 I)(S - \lambda_3 I)}{(\lambda_1 - \lambda_2)(\lambda_1 - \lambda_3)} n^2 - nI + \left[I - \frac{(S - \lambda_2 I)(S - \lambda_3 I)}{(\lambda_1 - \lambda_2)(\lambda_1 - \lambda_3)}\right]\left(\frac{1 - \cos n\vartheta}{1 - \cos \vartheta}\right)\right\} \quad (5.12)$$

Substituting eq. (5.12) into eq. (5.7) we have

$$\overline{R^2} = n^2\tilde{r}^2 + (r^2 - \tilde{r}^2)(1 - \cos n\vartheta)/(1 - \cos \vartheta) \quad (5.13)$$

where

$$\tilde{r}^2 = \frac{[r_1(S_{13} + S_{31}) + r_2(S_{23} + S_{32}) + r_3(1 - S_{11} - S_{22} + S_{33})]^2}{2(1 - S_{11} - S_{22} + S_{33})(1 - \cos \vartheta)} \quad (5.14)$$

and r_1, r_2, r_3 are the projections of the vector on the axes of its own local system of coordinates.

We have expressed the square of the vector properties of a macromolecule with identical fixed conformations of monomer units via the parameter $\tilde{r}$, which is a function of the corresponding vector properties of monomer units, and a certain angle ϑ. It is obvious that the macromolecule under examination must have the form of a helix (a particular case of which is a planar, zigzag chain). The geometry of such helices has been examined in section 3.1 in which equations have been derived relating the parameters of the helices with the elements of the matrix of rotation S and thus, with the structure of the monomer units. Comparison of eq. (5.8) with the first of eqs. (3.3) shows that angle ϑ, defined by eq. (5.8), is the angle of rotation about the axis of the helix per single repeating unit of the chain.* Furthermore, if **r** is the vector which links the ends of a monomer unit (**r** = **b**, see Fig. 3.4) and, correspondingly, **R** is the vector which links the ends for (**R** = **h**), then, comparison of eq. (5.14) with the second of eqs.

* In the present case, in which the conformations of all the monomer units are identical, the repeating unit of the chain is, of course, a monomer unit.

(3.3) shows that, in this case, $\bar{r}$ coincides with a step d along the axis of the helix per repeating (monomer) unit of the chain, so that

$$\overline{h^2} = n^2d^2 + (b^2 - d^2)(1 - \cos n\vartheta)/(1 - \cos \vartheta) \quad (5.15)$$

In particular, for a planar *trans* chain, for which the transformation expressed by matrix S is an identity, S is a unit matrix and, consequently, $\cos \vartheta = 1$. As a result, for a planar *trans* chain we have $\overline{h^2} = n^2d^2 = n^2b^2$ (since in this case $d = b$). For a helix of arbitrary form, $\overline{h^2} = n^2d^2$ with the condition that $\cos n\vartheta = 1$ (i.e., n is a multiple of the number of monomer units in a turn of the helix $2\pi/\vartheta$); this result is also directly evident.

All the eigenvalues of matrix S are less than unity in the case of statistically coiled chains. The proof of this statement is given in a separate appendix at the end of the book. In connection with this, in the case of statistically coiled chains, the elements of matrices $(I - S)^{-1}$ and $(I - S)^{-2}$ are finite, and, for $n \gg 1$, the second and third terms in the brackets of the right-hand side of eq. (5.7) are much smaller than the first one. This is obvious for the second term; for the third term this follows from the fact that all elements S^n are linear combinations of the nth powers of the eigenvalues of matrix S (smaller than unity), with coefficients independent of n. Therefore, for a statistically coiled chain, with $n \gg 1$:

$$\overline{R^2} = nr^2[1 + 2\tilde{\mathbf{e}}S(I - S)^{-1}\mathbf{e}] = nr^2[2\tilde{\mathbf{e}}(I - S)^{-1}\mathbf{e} - 1] \quad (5.16)$$

since

$$S(I - S)^{-1} = (S \pm I)(I - S)^{-1} = (I - S)^{-1} - I$$

The quantitative criterion of the validity of eq. (5.16) is the condition

$$n\tilde{\mathbf{e}}S(I - S)^{-1}\mathbf{e} \gg \tilde{\mathbf{e}}S(I - S^n)(I - S)^{-2}\mathbf{e} \quad (5.17)$$

which means that the chain must be sufficiently long ($n \gg 1$) and the averaged matrix S must not be extremely close to the rotation matrix. It is evident that the nearer S is to the rotation matrix (i.e., the stronger the restriction of internal rotation in the chain), the larger must be the value of n, required to satisfy the criterion (5.17) of the validity of eq. (5.16).

In section 1.2 we cited particular cases of eq. (5.16) for the dimensions and dipole moments of polyvinyl chains with independent rotations about neighboring units; these were derived in the studies of Bresler and Frenkel (8), Debye (9), Taylor (10), H. Kuhn (11), Birshtein and Ptitsyn (12–14) and other authors [see eqs. (1.18), (1.19), and (1.21)–(1.27)]. Studies were also cited there in which similar equations were derived for chains of a different structure.

As was shown in the preceding chapter, equations based on the assumption that rotations about neighboring elements of a single monomer unit are independent do not take into account the principal intramolecular interactions, in any case, in chains of type $(\text{—CH}_2\text{—CRR}'\text{—})_n$; therefore, it is senseless to compare them with experiment. Ptitsyn and Sharonov (15) [see also (16–22)] have derived expressions for the dimensions and dipole moments of polyvinyl chains with correlated rotations about the elements of a single monomer unit but independent conformations of monomer units.* These equations (see section 6.1), are of course, also particular cases of the general eq. (5.16), which is valid for $n \gg 1$. Furthermore, particular cases were obtained (24–26) of the more general eq. (5.7), which is valid with any n; these were for $\overline{h^2}$ of chains with symmetric (24) and asymmetric (25) side groups and independent rotations about neighboring elements, and also for isotactic chains with independent conformations of monomer units (26). It should be pointed out that these expressions were derived in the original studies by more complicated methods than is done above. For example, usually the matrices of cosines of the angles were reduced to the diagonal form, which is absolutely unnecessary, as can be seen above. In recent years, a number of papers have appeared (27–29) in which the authors derive anew (as a rule, by more complicated methods) equations for various chains with independent rotations about neighboring elements; such equations have already been derived and investigated in the literature.

Let us pass now to the case of correlated conformations of monomer units, i.e., let us examine a macromolecule having the energy expressed by eq. (4.2). It is evident that, in such case, matrices $S(\Omega_k)$ cannot be averaged independently of each other, and in order to calculate the mean values of products $\overline{\prod_{k=j+1}^{i} S(\Omega_k)}$ it is necessary to use the matrix method of the statistics of one-dimensional cooperative systems, developed in the preceding chapter. In the rotational-isomeric approximation, the quantity $\overline{\prod_{k=j+1}^{i} S(\Omega_k)}$ is expressed by eq. (4.30), where the functions $f(\Omega_k) = S(\Omega_k)$ are now matrices and not scalars, and the partition function of the chain, Z, is expressed, as before by eq. (4.9) or (4.10). By analogy with expression (4.32), let us introduce supermatrix $Q = G \cdot \mathcal{S}$ of order f, which is the product of matrix G [eq. (4.6)] with the so-called direct sum of matrices $S(\Omega)$, i.e., with the diagonal supermatrix $\mathcal{S}$ of order f, the ele-

* Similar equations have been derived (23) for the dimensions of molecules of 1,4-polysaccharides.

ments of which are third-order matrices $S(\Omega)$ that correspond to all possible conformations of the monomer units of the chains:

$$\mathcal{S} = S(\Omega^{(1)}) \dotplus S(\Omega^{(2)}) \dotplus \dots \dotplus S(\Omega^{(f)}) = \begin{bmatrix} S(\Omega^{(1)}) & 0 & \dots & 0 \\ 0 & S(\Omega^{(2)}) & \dots & 0 \\ \dots & \dots & \dots & \dots \\ 0 & 0 & \dots & S(\Omega^{(f)}) \end{bmatrix} \tag{5.18}$$

The elements of matrix G

$$\{Q\}_{\alpha\beta} = \{G\mathcal{S}\}_{\alpha\beta} = g(\Omega_{k-1}^{(\alpha)}, \Omega_k^{(\beta)}) S(\Omega_k^{(\beta)}) \tag{5.19}$$

are, obviously, third-order matrices.

The further calculations do not differ in principle from the method of averaging products of scalar quantities, presented above. As before, we obtain for $\overline{\prod_{k=j+1}^{i} S(\Omega_k)}$ eqs. (4.33),(4.35), and (4.40) with the only difference that, since the elements of matrix Q are now not numbers, but third-order matrices, the trace of matrix Q^{i-j} and the quantity $\tilde{\mathbf{u}}(\lambda_v)Q^{i-j}\mathbf{v}(\lambda_v)$ are also third-order matrices. Thus, in this case also, just as when correlations are absent between the conformations of monomer units, the averaged quantity is presented in the form of the power of some matrix.

Substituting eq. (4.40) into eq. (5.4), we obtain, after summation of a double geometric progression of the matrix [compare eq. (5.7)]:

$$\overline{R^2} = r^2 \left\{ n + 2\tilde{\mathbf{e}}\tilde{\mathbf{u}}(\lambda) \left[n \frac{Q}{\lambda} \left(I - \frac{Q}{\lambda} \right)^{-1} - \frac{Q}{\lambda} \left(I - \frac{Q}{\lambda} \right)^{-2} + \left(\frac{Q}{\lambda} \right)^{n+1} \left(I - \frac{Q}{\lambda} \right)^{-2} \right] \mathbf{v}(\lambda) \mathbf{e} \right\} \tag{5.20}$$

(λ is the largest eigenvalue of matrix G) or, for a statistically coiled chain, with $n \gg 1$

$$\overline{R^2} = nr^2 \left[2\tilde{\mathbf{e}}\tilde{\mathbf{u}}(\lambda) \left(I - \frac{Q}{\lambda} \right)^{-1} \mathbf{v}(\lambda)\mathbf{e} - 1 \right] \tag{5.21}$$

compare eq. (5.16)].

If matrix V, formed of the eigenvectors $\mathbf{v}(\lambda_\nu)$ of matrix G has a reciprocal, then, just as in the case of averaging of a product of scalar quantities, eq. (4.40) is reduced to eq. (4.39), where

$$W = V^{-1} (Q/\lambda) V = (\Lambda/\lambda) V^{-1} \mathcal{S} V \tag{5.22}$$

is now a hypermatrix of order f with elements

$$W_{\alpha\beta} = (\lambda_\alpha/\lambda) \sum_{\nu=1}^{f} u_{\alpha\nu} v_{\nu\beta} S(\Omega^{(\nu)}) \tag{5.23}$$

which are third-order matrices. Substituting eq. (4.39) into eq. (5.4), we obtain, instead of eq. (5.20)

$$\overline{R^2} = r^2 \left| n + 2\tilde{\mathbf{e}}\{ nW(I - W)^{-1} - W(I - W)^{-2} + W^{n+1}(I - W)^{-2}\}_{11}\mathbf{e} \right. \tag{5.24}$$

or, for a statistically coiled chain, with $n \gg k$:

$$\overline{R^2} = nr^2[2\tilde{\mathbf{e}}\{(I - W)^{-1}\}_{11}\mathbf{e} - 1] \tag{5.25}$$

In this manner, in the case of correlated conformations of monomer units as well (just as in the absence of correlations), the calculation of $\overline{R^2}$ is reduced to the construction of a matrix which is the reciprocal of some given matrix $(I - S)^{-1}$, $[I - (Q/\lambda]^{-1}$ or $(I - W)^{-1}$. Matrices S, Q, and W are determined by the geometric properties of the monomer units in various conformations and by the free energies of these conformations.

Equations (5.21) and (5.25) have been derived within the approximation (4.2), which takes into account all the first-, second-, and third-order interactions, and also fourth-order interactions between the nearest non-adjacent bulky groups. This method of averaging, however, can be applied, in principle, also to those cases in which it would be desirable to consider higher-order interactions [see, for example (64)]. In fact, as has been noted in Chapter 4, a higher degree of correlation results only in an increase of the order of matrix G, and consequently also of Q or W. In the papers of Nagai (30,31), a similar method was used to calculate $\overline{h^2}$ and $\overline{\mu^2}$ of a polypeptide chain, the energy of which is determined by terms which are a function of the conformations of four consecutive monomer units. The method presented above was developed within the rotational-isomeric approximation; however, it permits one to take into account torsional oscillations as well, if it is applied to conformations of monomer units for which torsional oscillations have been taken into account in the averaging as described in Section 4.1.

The general equations presented in this section for the mean-square vector properties of macromolecules with correlated conformations of monomer units were derived by Birshtein and Ptitsyn (2). Even earlier, Gotlib (1) derived (in another form) an equation of such type for the mean-square end-to-end distance of a chain of type $(—CH_2—CR_2—)_n$. Later, some particular cases of the matrix equation, eq. (5.25), were also derived by Lifson (32) and Nagai (33). In a recently published paper by Nagai (64), general matrix equations have been derived for $\overline{R^2}$ of a polymer chain of arbitrary structure, with any number of short-range interactions taken into account. In this and other papers (1,2,33–36,43,65–67), equations of the type of eq. (5.25) were used for the calculation of $\overline{h^2}$ and $\overline{\mu^2}$ of polyvinyl chains of different types (see below).

Along with calculations of the mean-square vector properties of macromolecules, it is also of interest to calculate the mean values of the projections of these vectors on the axes of the system of coordinates linked with the macromolecule. For example, for the mean value of the projection of the end-to-end distance of the chain on the direction of the first monomer unit, we have

$$\overline{(\mathbf{h}, \mathbf{e}_1)} = b \sum_{i=1}^{n} \overline{(\mathbf{e}_i, \mathbf{e}_1)} = b \left[1 + \tilde{\mathbf{e}} \sum_{i=2}^{n} \overline{\prod_{k=2}^{i} S(\Omega_k)}\mathbf{e} \right] \qquad (5.26)$$

where b is the length of a monomer unit. Substituting into eq. (5.26) one of the expressions obtained above for the mean value of the product of matrices, for example, the expression $\overline{\prod_{k=2}^{i} S(\Omega_k)} = S^{i-1}$, we obtain:

$$\overline{(\mathbf{h}, \mathbf{e}_1)} = b \left[\tilde{\mathbf{e}} \sum_{i=1}^{n} S^{i-1}\mathbf{e} \right] = b\tilde{\mathbf{e}}(I - S^n)(I - S)^{-1}\mathbf{e} \qquad (5.27)$$

For a macromolecule, in which all the monomer units have identical fixed conformations, we obtain, in a way similar to (5.15):

$$\overline{(\mathbf{h}, \mathbf{e}_1)} = \frac{nd^2}{b} + \frac{b^2 - d^2}{2b} \left(1 - \cos n\vartheta + \frac{\sin n\vartheta \sin \vartheta}{1 - \cos \vartheta} \right) \qquad (5.28)$$

where ϑ and d are expressed by eqs. (3.3). For example, for *trans* conformations of monomer units ($S = I$, $\vartheta = 0$, $d = b$):

$$\overline{(\mathbf{h}, \mathbf{e}_1)} = nb = L \qquad (5.29)$$

where L is the contour length of the chain. For a statistically coiled chain, with $n \gg 1$:

$$\overline{(\mathbf{h}, \mathbf{e}_1)} = b\ [1 + \tilde{\mathbf{e}}(I - S)^{-1}\mathbf{e}] \qquad (5.30)$$

A very useful model for describing the conformational properties of macromolecules with limited flexibility is that of the "wormlike chain" proposed by Kratky and Porod (37,38). In this model, the real molecule, which consists of individual monomer units of finite length, correlationally oriented in space, is replaced by a semirigid string with a continuous curvature. This is done by a limiting transition to $n \to \infty$, $b \to 0$ and a fixed orientation of monomer units relative to each other.* In this the contour length of the chain $L = nb$ must keep its previous value. The projection $\overline{(\mathbf{h}, \mathbf{e}_1)}$ must also remain finite in such a transition; the limiting value of this projection as $L \to \infty$ is called the "*persistence length*" and it characterizes the rigidity of the polymer chain. Using eq. (5.30) we find that the persistence length is

$$a = b\tilde{\mathbf{e}}(I - S)^{-1}\mathbf{e} \tag{5.31}$$

Comparison of eqs. (5.16) and (5.31) shows that, as $n \to \infty$ and $b \to 0$

$$\overline{h^2} = 2La \tag{5.32}$$

i.e., the persistence length $a = \overline{h^2}/2L$. Similar results are easily obtained also in the more general case of correlated conformations of neighboring units.

5.2. Distribution Functions for the Vector Properties of Macromolecules

Fixing the values of vector $\mathbf{R}$ to a given interval defines the macro state of the system (macromolecule), the probability of which is a function of the number and energies of the microstates (conformations of monomer units) that correspond to it. The distribution function for such macro states, i.e. the probability that the value of the vector $\mathbf{R}$ introduced in eq. (5.1), which characterizes the macromolecule, lies between $\mathbf{R} - {}^1/_2 d\mathbf{R}$ and $\mathbf{R} + {}^1/_2 d\mathbf{R}$, is obviously expressed by the equation

$$\begin{aligned} W_n(\mathbf{R})d\mathbf{R} &= \frac{1}{Z}\int \cdots \int e^{-U(\Omega_1, \Omega_2, \ldots, \Omega_n)/kT} \prod_{j=1}^{n} d\Omega_j \\ &= \int \cdots \int W\{\mathbf{r}_j\} d\{\mathbf{r}_j\} \end{aligned} \tag{5.33}$$

where $W\{\mathbf{r}_j\}$ is the distribution function for the orientation of all n vectors $\mathbf{r}_j$, that characterize the monomer units, and the integration over the set of vectors $\{\mathbf{r}_j\}$ is carried out only over the range of micro states of the chain for which the inequality $\mathbf{R} - {}^1/_2 d\mathbf{R} \leqslant \sum_{j=1}^{n} \mathbf{r}_j \leqslant \mathbf{R} + {}^1/_2 d\mathbf{R}$ is valid. For calculating the functions $W_n(\mathbf{R})d\mathbf{R}$ we shall use the method first proposed by Markoff (39) for the particular case in which the orientations of

* Speaking more exactly, the model of Kratky and Porod is based not on molecular units, but on links in a chain, the mutual orientation of which is characterized by the angle γ between them, while transition to a fixed orientation means that $\cos \gamma \to 1$.

neighboring vectors in space are independent of each other [see also (40)]. This method can be generalized easily (41) to the case of interdependent orientations of neighboring vectors $\mathbf{r}_j$.

The integration on the right-hand side of eq. (5.33) can be extended over the entire conformation space, if the following factor is introduced under the integral

$$\Delta\{\mathbf{r}_j\} = \begin{cases} 1 \text{ for } \mathbf{R} - {}^1/_2 d\mathbf{R} \leqslant \sum_{j=1}^{n} \mathbf{r}_j \leq \mathbf{R} + {}^1/_2 d\mathbf{R} \\ 0 \text{ for all other cases} \end{cases} \tag{5.34}$$

It is possible to take as such a factor the product of the discontinuous Dirichlet integrals for all three axes of coordinates ($q = 1, 2, 3$):

$$\delta_q = \frac{1}{\pi} \int_{-\infty}^{\infty} \frac{\sin \alpha_q \rho^{(q)}}{\rho^{(q)}} e^{i\gamma_q \rho^{(q)}} d\rho^{(q)} = \begin{cases} 1 \text{ for } -\alpha_q < \gamma_q < \alpha_q \\ 0 \text{ for all other cases} \end{cases} \tag{5.35}$$

where $\rho^{(q)}$ is the qth component of vector $\boldsymbol{\varrho}$. It is obvious that if we set

$$\alpha_q = {}^1/_2 dR^{(q)}$$

$$\gamma_q = \sum_{j=1}^{n} r_j^{(q)} - R^{(q)} \tag{5.36}$$

then condition (5.34) will be fullfilled with

$$\Delta = \prod_{q=1}^{3} \delta_q \tag{5.37}$$

Consequently

$$W_n(\mathbf{R})d\mathbf{R} = \frac{1}{\pi^3} \int d\boldsymbol{\varrho} \int \cdots \int W\{\mathbf{r}_j\} \prod_{q=1}^{3} \frac{\sin ({}^1/_2\, dR^{(q)}{}_{\rho}{}^{(q)})}{\rho^{(q)}} \times e^{i\left[\left(\vec{\varrho},\, \sum_{j=1}^{n} \mathbf{r}_j\right) - (\vec{\varrho},\, \mathbf{R})\right]} d\{\mathbf{r}_j\} \tag{5.38}$$

or, considering that $dR^{(q)}$ is an infinitely small quantity,

$$W_n(\mathbf{R})d\mathbf{R} = \frac{d\mathbf{R}}{2^3\pi^3} \int e^{-i(\vec{\varrho},\, \mathbf{R})} A_n(\boldsymbol{\varrho}) d\boldsymbol{\varrho} \tag{5.39}$$

where

$$A_n(\boldsymbol{\rho}) = \int e^{i\left(\vec{\rho},\ \sum_{j=\rho}^{n} r_j\right)} W\{\mathbf{r}_j\} d\{\mathbf{r}_j\}$$

$$= \int W_n(\mathbf{R}) e^{i(\vec{\boldsymbol{\rho}},\ \mathbf{R})}\, d\mathbf{R} = \overline{\langle e^{i(\vec{\boldsymbol{\rho}},\ \mathbf{R})} \rangle} \tag{5.40}$$

The bar, as before, indicates averaging over all conformations of the chain, i.e., over all the possible mutual orientations of monomer units, and the angular brackets means averaging over all possible orientations of one of the monomer units of the chain relative to a spatially immobile vector $\boldsymbol{\rho}$. According to eq. (5.39), $A_n(\boldsymbol{\rho})$ is a three-dimensional Fourier transform of function $W_n(\mathbf{R})$. We see that quantity $A_n(\boldsymbol{\rho})$ is more simply related to the physical properties of the chains than the distribution function $W_n(\mathbf{R})d\mathbf{R}$ being sought.

For a hypothetical, freely jointed chain, in which the orientations of neighboring vectors $\mathbf{r}_j$ are independent of each other, we have:

$$W\{\mathbf{r}_j\} = \prod_{j=1}^{n} g(\mathbf{r}_j) \tag{5.41}$$

In the simplest case of a freely-jointed chain with vectors $\mathbf{r}_j$ fixed in length and randomly distributed in space, for which

$$g_j(\mathbf{r}_j) = \frac{1}{4\pi r_j^3} \delta(|\mathbf{r}_j|^2 - \mathbf{r}_j^2) \tag{5.42}$$

where δ is a Dirichlet delta function, $A_n(\boldsymbol{\rho})$ and $W_n(\mathbf{R})$ have been calculated by Rayleigh (42) [see also (40)]. Having shown that, in this case

$$A_n(\boldsymbol{\rho}) = \prod_{j=1}^{n} (\sin \rho r_j / \rho r_j) \tag{5.43}$$

Rayleigh obtained exact relations for $W_n(\mathbf{R})d\mathbf{R}$ for small n ($\leqslant 6$) and equal r_j's, and he showed also that the asymptotic expression for $W(\mathbf{R})d\mathbf{R}$ as $n \rightarrow \infty$ and $r_j = r$ is the Gaussian function

$$W(\mathbf{R})d\mathbf{R} = (3/2\pi n r^2)^{3/2} e^{-3R^2/2nr^2} d\mathbf{R} \tag{5.44}$$

This follows as well from the central limiting theorem of Markoff chains (40). Equation (5.43), which is applicable to macromolecules, was derived first in the well known paper of W. Kuhn (44). The function $W(\mathbf{R})d\mathbf{R}$ was investigated for small n also by others (45–50). Let us note that eq. (5.44) for $n \rightarrow \infty$ is also obtained in the case of a freely-jointed chain with randomly oriented vectors $\mathbf{r}_j$ of various lengths (if the probability distributions for the lengths of all $\mathbf{r}_j$ are equal) (40).

Equation (5.44) can be applied to freely jointed chains with large but finite n only under the condition that $R \ll nr$. With $n \gg 1$ but R comparable to nr, the distribution function has the form (51):

$$W(\mathbf{R})d\mathbf{R} = Be^{-(1/r)\int_0^R \beta\, dR} d\mathbf{R} \tag{5.45}$$

where

$$\beta = \mathfrak{L}^{-1}\left(\frac{R}{nr}\right) = 3\frac{R}{nr} + \frac{9}{5}\left(\frac{R}{nr}\right)^3 + \frac{297}{175}\left(\frac{R}{nr}\right)^5 + \dots \tag{5.46}$$

is the reciprocal of a Langevin function, and B is a normalization constant. For $R \ll nr$, eqs. (5.45) and (5.46) take the form of (5.44), but, unlike eq. (5.44) they give $W(\mathbf{R}) = 0$ for $R = nr$ and, as must be, they lose their meaning at $R > nr$. Comparison of distribution function (5.45) with exact distribution functions for small n (52) shows that it gives good results already for $n > 25$. The problem of the distribution functions for model freely-jointed polymer chains has been presented by Volkenshtein (53).

The valence angles between neighboring units of the chain are fixed in any real macromolecules; this leads to the interdependence of orientations of the vectors which characterize neighboring units (independently of the degree of freedom of internal rotation). Furthermore, since the conformation of the monomer unit Ω_j determines its orientation relative to the preceding monomer unit, i.e., depends on the orientation of vectors $\mathbf{r}_j$ and $\mathbf{r}_{j-1}$, then, for macromolecules with independent conformations of monomer units [see eq. (4.1)], the orientation of each vector is a function of the orientation of one preceding vector:

$$W\{\mathbf{r}_j\} = \frac{1}{Z}\prod_{i=1}^{n} g(\mathbf{r}_{j-1}, \mathbf{r}_j) \tag{5.47}$$

where

$$g(\mathbf{r}_{j-1}, \mathbf{r}_j) = e^{-U(\Omega_j)/kT} = e^{-U(\mathbf{r}_{j-1}, \mathbf{r}_j)/kT} \tag{5.48}$$

For macromolecules with correlated conformations of monomer units, the orientation of each vector $\mathbf{r}_j$ is a function of the orientations of two or more preceding vectors. For example, if the energy of the macromolecule has the form of eqs. (4.2), then

$$W\{\mathbf{r}_j\} = \frac{1}{Z}\prod_{j=1}^{n} g(\mathbf{r}_{j-2}, \mathbf{r}_{j-1}, \mathbf{r}_j) \tag{5.49}$$

where

$$g(\mathbf{r}_{j-2}, \mathbf{r}_{j-1}, \mathbf{r}_j) = e^{-U(\Omega_{j-1}, \Omega_j)/kT} = e^{-U(\mathbf{r}_{j-2}, \mathbf{r}_{j-1}, \mathbf{r}_j)/kT} \tag{5.50}$$

The method of calculating the functions $A_n(\varrho)$ of a chain with interdependent orientations of vectors that characterize neighboring monomer units was developed by Zimm (41) for the particular case of a macromolecule with fixed valence angles $\pi - \alpha$ and free internal rotation, in which*

$$g(\mathbf{r}_{j-1}, \mathbf{r}_j) = \frac{1}{2\pi}\,\delta[(\widehat{\mathbf{r}_{j-1}, \mathbf{r}_j}) - (\pi - \alpha)] \tag{5.51}$$

In this Zimm showed that, in the limit, when $n \to \infty$, the distribution function $W(\mathbf{R})$ is normal (Gaussian) in this case also:

$$W_n(\mathbf{R})d\mathbf{R} = (3/2\pi\overline{R_*^2})^{3/2}\, e^{-3R^2/2\overline{R_*^2}}\, d\mathbf{R} \tag{5.52}$$

($\overline{R_*^2}$ is the mean square length of vector $\mathbf{R}$ at $n \gg 1$). The method of Zimm for calculating $A_n(\varrho)$ and $W_n(\mathbf{R})$ can be generalized also for a chain with fixed valence angles and restricted internal rotation; we shall not present it here, however, but we shall present a simple and more general, although also less rigorous, derivation of function $W_n(\mathbf{R})$, proposed recently by Nagai (68). The advantage of this method is that, with it, it is possible to obtain not only the limiting expression for $W_n(\mathbf{R})$ as $n \to \infty$, but also correction terms which are considerable for rather small n.

Expanding the right-hand side of eq. (5.40) in series in ϱ, we obtain

$$A_n(\varrho) = 1 + i\,\overline{\langle(\varrho, \mathbf{R})\rangle} - {}^1/_2\,\overline{\langle(\varrho, \mathbf{R})^2\rangle} + \ldots + \frac{i^m}{m!}\,\overline{\langle(\varrho, \mathbf{R})^m\rangle} + \ldots \tag{5.53}$$

Since for a free macromolecule, the orientations in space of vector $\mathbf{R}$ are independent of its absolute value, and all the orientations of this vector have equal probabilities, we have

$$\overline{\langle(\varrho, \mathbf{R})^m\rangle} = \rho^m\overline{R^m}\,\langle\cos^m(\varrho, \mathbf{R})\rangle = \begin{cases} 0 & \text{For } m = 2l + 1 \\ \dfrac{1}{m+1}\rho^m\overline{R^m} & \text{For } m = 2l \end{cases} \tag{5.54}$$

* In the paper of Zimm, the vectors $\mathbf{r}_j$ characterized the orientation not of monomer units, but of the links of a polymer chain.

where $\rho = |\boldsymbol{\varrho}|$. Substituting eq. (5.54) into eq. (5.53), we obtain*

$$A_n(\boldsymbol{\varrho}) = 1 - \frac{1}{3!}\rho^2\overline{R^2} + \frac{1}{5!}\rho^4\overline{R^4} + \ldots + \frac{(-1)^l}{(2l+1)!}\rho^{2l}\overline{R^{2l}} + \ldots \tag{5.55}$$

or

$$\ln A_n(\boldsymbol{\varrho}) = -g_2\rho^2 + g_4\rho^4 - g_6\rho^6 + \ldots. \tag{5.56}$$

where

$$g_2 = \frac{1}{3!}\overline{R^2}$$

$$g_4 = \frac{1}{5!}\left[\overline{R^4} - \frac{5}{3}(\overline{R^2})^2\right]$$

$$g_6 = \frac{1}{7!}\left[\overline{R^6} - 7\,\overline{R^4}\,\overline{R^2} + \frac{70}{9}(\overline{R^2})^3\right] \tag{5.57}$$

$$\cdots\cdots\cdots\cdots\cdots\cdots\cdots\cdots\cdots\cdots$$

$$g_{2n} = \frac{1}{(2n+1)!}\overline{R^{2n}} - \sum_{k=1}^{n-1}\frac{n-k}{n}\,g_{2(n-k)}\frac{\overline{R^{2k}}}{(2k+1)!}$$

If $W_n(\mathbf{R})$ is a Gaussian function defined by eq. (5.52), then, substituting it into eq. (5.40) and carrying out the integration, we get

$$A_n^*(\boldsymbol{\varrho}) = e^{-{}^1/_6\,\rho^2\,\overline{R_*^2}} \tag{5.58}$$

Taking the antilogarithm of eq. (5.56) and comparing the result with eq. (5.58) we obtain

$$A_n(\boldsymbol{\varrho}) = e^{-{}^1/_6\,\rho^2\,\overline{R_*^2}}\,(1 - g_2'\rho^2 + g_4'\rho^4 - g_6'\rho^6 + \ldots) \tag{5.59}$$

where

$$g_2' = g_2 - {}^1/_6\,\overline{R_*^2}$$

$$g_4' = g_4 + {}^1/_2\,(g_2')^2$$

$$g_6' = g_6 + {}^2/_3\,g_4 g_2' + {}^1/_3\,g_4' g_2'$$

* Let us note that eq. (5.55) and (5.56) are formally completely analogous to expressions for the partition function and logarithm of the partition function of the chain in a field of external force, first derived by Volkenshtein and Ptitsyn (57) (see section 8.1). They can be obtained from eq. (5.56), if, in these, one sets $\rho = -if/kT$.

and in general (with $k \geqslant 2$)

$$g'_{2k} = \sum_{m=0}^{k-2} [k - (m/k)]\, g_{2(k-m)}\, g'_{2m} + \frac{1}{k} g'_2 g'_{2(k-1)} \qquad (5.60)$$

in which $g'_0 = 1$.

Substituting eq. (5.59) into eq. (5.39) and integrating, we obtain an expression for $W_n(\mathbf{R})$ in the form of the product of the Gaussian function (5.52) with a polynomial in R^2:

$$W_n(\mathbf{R}) = \left(\frac{3}{2\pi \overline{R^2_*}}\right)^{3/2} e^{-3R^2/2\overline{R^2_*}} \left[1 + 9\,\frac{R^2 - \overline{R^2_*}}{(\overline{R^2})^2}\, g'_2 + 9^2\,\frac{R^4 - \frac{10}{3} R^2\overline{R^2_*} + \frac{5}{3}(\overline{R^2_*})^2}{(\overline{R^2_*})^4}\, g'_4 + 9^3\,\frac{R^6 - 7\,R^4\overline{R^2_*} + \frac{35}{3} R^2(\overline{R^2_*})^2 - \frac{35}{9}(\overline{R^2_*})^3}{(\overline{R^2_*})^6}\, g'_6 + \ldots \right] \qquad (5.61)$$

In this way, the problem of calculating the distribution functions $W_n(\mathbf{R})$ is reduced to the problem of the calculation of all the possible even moments of this function. The methods for calculating the second moment $\overline{R^2}$ have been presented in detail above. Nagai (68) has proposed a generalization of these methods which, in principle, makes it possible to calculate any even moment of $W_n(\mathbf{R})$. In actuality, however, the calculations can be carried out completely only for $\overline{R^4}$ and, possibly, for $\overline{R^6}$; for moments of higher order the calculations present enormous difficulties. Fortunately, in the evaluation of the asymptotic behavior of $W_n(\mathbf{R})$ at very large n, it is not necessary to have exact expressions for all $\overline{R^{2m}}$; it is sufficient to examine the dependence on n of the coefficients g'_{2k}, which characterize the deviation from Gaussian behavior of the function $W(\mathbf{R})$.

Let us examine first the dependence on n of the coefficients g_{2k}, related by eq. (5.60) to the factors g'_{2k}. With this goal, let us break up the chain of n monomer units into three sub-chains, the first of which contains n_1 monomers, the second ν monomers, and the third $n_2 = n - n_1 - \nu$ monomers. The quantity ν is chosen in such a way that the mean cosine of the angle between the vectors which characterize the monomer units numbers n_1 and $n_1 + \nu$ be negligibly small. This means, for example, that, with independent conformations of monomer units, the condition must be fulfilled that

$$\tilde{e} S^{\nu} e \ll 1 \tag{5.62}$$

where matrix S is defined by eq. (5.5). When the conformations of the monomer units are correlated, this condition assumes the form

$$\tilde{e} \{ W^{\nu} \}_{1_1} e \ll 1 \tag{5.63}$$

where hypermatrix W is defined by eq. (5.22).

Since in the case of a flexible chain, all the eigenvalues of matrix S are less than unity (see the Appendix), condition (5.62) will obviously be fulfilled starting from some ν (which depends on the stiffness of the chain); furthermore, when the chains are sufficiently long, these values of ν will be much smaller than n. Similar considerations are valid also with respect to condition (5.63). As a result, for chains which are sufficiently long with respect to their stiff region, having set both n_1 and $n_2 \gg \nu$, it is possible to regard the chain as the sum of two subchains of n_1 and n_2 monomers, while the subchain of ν monomers which links them can be approximated by a flexible joint between the first and third subchains. Considering that the orientations in space of these subchains are independent and that $n_2 \approx n - n_1$, we obtain

$$W_n(\mathbf{R}) \approx \int W_{n_1}(\mathbf{R}_0) W_{n-n_1}(\mathbf{R} - \mathbf{R}_0) d\mathbf{R}_0 \tag{5.64}$$

Substituting eq. (5.64) into eq. (5.40), we have

$$A_n(\boldsymbol{\varrho}) \approx A_{n_1}(\boldsymbol{\varrho}) A_{n-n_1}(\boldsymbol{\varrho}) \tag{5.65}$$

which can be understood easily, if the close relation between function $A_n(\boldsymbol{\varrho})$ and the partition function of the chain, noted above, is taken into account.

Expression (5.65) means that

$$\ln A_n(\boldsymbol{\varrho}) \approx \ln A_{n_1}(\boldsymbol{\varrho}) + \ln A_{n-n_1}(\boldsymbol{\varrho}) \tag{5.66}$$

Consequently, the coefficients g_{2k} in eq. (5.56) must satisfy the conditions

$$g_{n,2k} \approx g_{n_1,2k} + g_{n-n_1,2k} \qquad (k = 1,2,\ldots) \tag{5.67}$$

which lead to the linear dependence of $g_{n,2k}$ on n:

$$g_{2k} \approx c_{k,1} n \tag{5.68}$$

(the index n is omitted for g_{2k}). In view of the relation between $A_n(\boldsymbol{\varrho})$ and the partition function, noted above, this result is equivalent to a more or less obvious assertion that the free energy of a macromolecule with short-range interactions must be proportional to the number of monomer units.

Since, in the derivation of eq. (5.68), we neglected the contribution to $\ln A_n(\boldsymbol{\varrho})$ of the second subchain, which must be of order ν, i.e., of the order of unity, a rigorous expression for g_{2k} must have the form

$$g_{2k} = c_{k,1}n + c_{k,0} \tag{5.69}$$

By using eqs. (5.60) and (5.69) it is easy to establish the dependence on n of the coefficients g'_{2k} which interest us. From eq. (5.60) we obtain $g'_2 \sim 1$ (since $g_2 = \overline{R^2}/3!$, while $\overline{R^2}_*$ is the part of the expression for $\overline{R^2}$ which is proportional to n). We find, furthermore, that the terms higher in n in the expressions for g'_4 and g'_6 are of order n, while in the expressions for g'_8 and g'_{10} they are of order n^2, etc. As a result, it is possible to show by the method of mathematical induction that

$$g'_{2k} = \begin{cases} c'_{k,k/2}n^{k/2} + c'_{k,(k-2)/2}n^{(k/2)-1} + \ldots + c'_{k,0} & \text{For even } k \\ c'_{k,(k-1)/2}n^{(k-1)/2} + c'_{k,(k-3)/2}n^{(k-3)/2} + \ldots + c'_{k,0} & \text{For odd } k \end{cases} \tag{5.70}$$

where $c'_{k,l}$ are constants.

Now we can evaluate the order of magnitude of the correction terms in the brackets on the right-hand side of eq. (5.61). For values of R^2 not much different from the maximum of $W_n(\mathbf{R})$, i.e., from $\overline{R^2}$, R^2 is of order n, and, consequently, the coefficient of g'_2 in the brackets is of order $1/n$, the coefficient of g'_4 is of order $1/n^2$, etc. Thus, for $n \to \infty$, all these corrective terms tend to zero, and the distribution function (5.61) goes over into the Gaussian function (5.52).

We see that a Gaussian distribution of the lengths of vectors $\mathbf{R}$ is obtained (as $n \to \infty$) not only for hypothetical, freely jointed chains, but also for macromolecules with fixed valence angles and restricted internal rotation (if long-range interactions are absent). This conclusion (for chains with fixed valence angles) was first made by W. Kuhn (44) on the basis of a formally nonrigorous, but fundamentally valid, examination; this can be reduced to the statement that the correlation between the orientations of chain elements decreases rapidly with an increase in the difference of their numbers, as a result of which a chain with fixed valence angles can be broken up into independently oriented segments ("statistical segments") which contain several links of the chain. Later, Zimm

(41), as has been pointed out above, gave a rigorous foundation to this conclusion for chains with fixed valence angles and free internal rotation. The evidence, proposed by Nagai (68) for the validity of Kuhn's considerations for any macromolecules with short-range interactions has been presented above.

As has already been pointed out, eq. (5.52), strictly speaking, is valid only in the limit, as $n \to \infty$, while each monomer unit may interact directly only with a finite number of neighbors along the chain. Equation (5.52) can be applied to real macromolecules, which consist of a large but finite number of monomer units, only in the case that n is considerably greater than the number of monomer units in a stiff region of the chain, which is defined, for example, as $\overline{(\mathbf{h}, \mathbf{e}_1)}/b$ [see eq. (5.27)]. Consequently, a Gaussian distribution function is valid if $n \gg \overline{(\mathbf{h}, \mathbf{e}_1)}/b)$, i.e., if

$$n \gg \mathsf{e}(I - S^n)(I - S)^{-1}\mathbf{e} \tag{5.71}$$

This is practically identical with criterion (5.17) of the validity of eq. (5.16), according to which $\overline{R^2} \sim n$.* We see that, as the degree of restriction of internal rotation in the chain increases, both the proportionality between $\overline{R^2}$ and n and the Gaussian distribution for $\mathbf{R}$ require larger n for validity. It is possible to state that *a polymeric chain can be described by a Gaussian distribution function if it is sufficiently long relative to any of its stiff regions.* The criterion of the validity of an equation of the type of eq. (5.16) has been examined in detail in the studies of Volkenshtein and Ptitsyn (54,55) for the particular case of chains with symmetric side groups and independent rotations about all the units. The correction terms of eq. (5.61), which are important for chains that are not too long relative to their stiff region, are expressed through the quantities $\overline{R^{2k}}$ which, in principle, can be calculated by the method proposed by Nagai (68).

It is obvious that, in the case of real macromolecules as well (just as for freely-jointed chains), a Gaussian distribution function is valid for finite n only under the condition that $R \ll nr$. This can be seen, for example, from the fact that the correction terms in the general equation, eq. (5.61), will not be small at all if $R \sim nr$. It can also be seen easily that, in this case, the coefficients of all g_{2k}' in the brackets on the right-hand side of eq. (5.61) will be of the order of unity and, consequently, the correction terms will be of the order of g_{2k}', i.e., of the order of $n^{k/2}$ or $n^{(k-1)/2}$ [see eq. (5.70)].

* A rigorous criterion of the validity of eq. (5.52) must include the evaluations not only of the linear, but also of the quadratic functions of the cosines of the angles between vectors, which characterize monomer units. We shall not dwell on this point, since this criterion does not differ essentially from inequalities (5.17) and (5.71).

Up to now no distribution function in closed form, valid for $R \sim nr$, such as the Langevin distribution for freely jointed chains, has been obtained for chains with correlated orientations of the vectors that characterize the monomer units. However, Volkenshtein and Ptitsyn (56,57), Scott and Tobolsky (58), Birshtein (59), and Krigbaum and Kaneko (60) have obtained, in their studies, partition functions for a number of model chains, the elements of which occupy positions correlated with each other on a one-dimensional (56–58) lattice, square (57,59) and hexagonal (59) two-dimensional lattices, and cubic three-dimensional (60) lattices.* The partition functions examined in the studies of Scott and Tobolsky (58) and Krigbaum and Kaneko (60) were for chains with a fixed vector of the end-to-end distance **h**, which corresponds to an ensemble of the isothermal-isochoric type, while the partition functions examined in the studies of Volkenshtein and Ptitsyn (56,57) and Birshtein (59) were for chains with a random vector **h**, but a fixed external force, which corresponds to an ensemble of the isothermal-isobaric type. These two types of investigation are, of course, essentially equivalent at sufficiently large n.

In two studies (57,59), it was shown that the distribution functions of model one-dimensional and two-dimensional chains for any **h** are close to the distribution functions of freely-jointed chains, if the number and length of segments in these chains is set in such manner that the mean-square and maximal lengths of freely jointed chains would coincide with the corresponding quantities of the model chains examined. Therefore, it is probable that, in the case of three-dimensional chains, the distribution function in **h**, for any **h**, will be close to a Langevin distribution function, eqs. (5.45), (5.46), for a freely jointed chain in which the number of segments n and the length of the segment r are determined by the conditions

$$nr^2 = \overline{h^2}$$

$$nr = h_{\max} \tag{5.72}$$

where $\overline{h^2}$ and $h_{\max}$ are calculated for a real macromolecule. The conditions of eq. (5.72) which determine the *most favorable values* of n and r were introduced first by W. Kuhn (44). They mean, essentially, that the statistical segments of the chain are assigned a conformation which corresponds to the conformation of a chain stretched to the limit.

The investigation of a distribution function for short and/or stiff macro-

*The type of correlation of orientations of units in a cubic three-dimensional lattice examined by Krigbaum and Kaneko (60) reduces the study to the investigation of three one-dimensional lattices.

molecules, with a length comparable to the length of the stiff region of the chain, meets with very serious mathematical difficulties. It has been possible to overcome them to a certain degree only for the model of a wormlike chain, which effectively takes into account the stiffness of short segments of the macromolecules (see above, p. 138). Hermans and Ullman (61) have obtained an equation which describes the function $W(\mathbf{h})$ for a wormlike chain. This equation does not permit direct calculation of $W(\mathbf{h})$ in an analytical form, but it does present the possibility of obtaining in principle any even moment of this function. Using this method, Hermans and Ullman (61) have calculated $\overline{h^4}$, while Heine, Kratky, and Porod (63) have calculated $\overline{h^6}$ for a wormlike chain. $\overline{h^2}$ had been calculated for such a chain by Kratky and Porod (37) even earlier.

Daniels (62) has obtained an expression for $W(\mathbf{h})$ for chains which are sufficiently long relative to their stiff region, i.e., for sufficiently large L/a, where L is the contour length of the wormlike chain, and a is its persistence length [see eqs. (5.31) and (5.32)]. In a spherical system of coordinates, the origin of which coincides with one of the ends of the chain and the polar axis with the direction of the tangent to the chain in the origin of the coordinates, the distribution function of Daniels has the form:

$$W(\mathbf{h})d\mathbf{h} = \left(\frac{3}{4\pi La}\right)^{3/2} e^{-3h^2/4La}\left[1 - \frac{5a}{4L} + \frac{2h^2}{L^2} - \frac{33h^4}{80L^3a} + \left(\frac{3h}{2L} - \frac{25ha}{8L^2} + \frac{153h^3}{40L^3} - \frac{99h^5}{160L^4}\right) P_1(\cos\vartheta) + \frac{h^2}{2L^2} P_2(\cos\vartheta) + \ldots\right] h^2 \sin\vartheta \, dh \, d\vartheta \, d\varphi \quad (5.73)$$

Integration of expression (5.73) over the angles ϑ and φ gives

$$W(h)h^2dh = \left(\frac{3}{4\pi La}\right)^{3/2} 4\pi e^{-3h^2/4La}\left[1 - \frac{5a}{4L} + \frac{2h^2}{L^2} - \frac{33h^4}{80L^3} + \ldots\right] h^2dh \quad (5.74)$$

This expression, just as the distribution function (5.61) for a real chain, contains the first-order correction terms to the Gaussian distribution which could have been calculated in an explicit form for the simplified model (wormlike chain) under examination.

An idea of the precision of the results obtained with the function of Daniels is given by a comparison of the value of $\overline{h^2}$ and $\overline{h^4}$ calculated with it with their exact values calculated by Kratky and Porod (37) and Hermans and Ullman (61), respectively:

$$\overline{h^2} = \begin{cases} 2La - 2a^2 & \text{Daniels (62)} \\ 2La - 2a^2(1 - e^{-L/a}) & \text{exact value (37)} \end{cases}$$

$$\overline{h^4} = \begin{cases} \frac{20}{3} L^2a^2 - \frac{208}{9} La^3 & \text{Daniels (62)} \\ \frac{20}{3} L^2a^2 - \frac{208}{9} La^3 + \frac{8}{27} a^4(e^{-3L/a} - 1) & \\ + 32a^4 (1 - e^{-L/a}) - 8La^3e^{-L/a} & \text{exact value (61)} \end{cases} \quad (5.75)$$

We see that, with large L/a, the function of Daniels gives a very good approximation.

References

1. Gotlib, Yu. Ya., *Zh. Tekhn. Fiz.*, **29**, 523 (1959); *Soviet Phys.-Tech. Phys.*, **4**, 465 (1959).
2. Birshtein, T. M., and O. B. Ptitsyn, *Zh. Tekhn. Fiz.*, **29**, 1048 (1959); *Soviet Phys.-Tech. Phys.*, **4**, 954 (1959).
3. Birshtein, T. M., Candidate Dissertation, Institut Vysokomolekulyamykh Soedinenii Akad. Nauk SSSR, 1960.
4. Lifson, S., *J. Chem. Phys.*, **30**, 964 (1959).
5. Nagai, K., *J. Chem. Phys.*, **31**, 1169 (1959).
6. Birshtein, T. M., *Vysokomol. Soedin.*, **1**, 798 (1959); *Polymer Sci. USSR*, **1**, 276 (1960).
7. Birshtein, T. M., L. L. Burshtein, and O. B. Ptitsyn, *Zh. Tekhn. Fiz.*, **29**, 896 (1959); *Soviet Phys.-Tech. Phys.*, **4**, 810 (1959).
8. Bresler, S. E., and Ya. I. Frenkel, *Zh. Eksp. Teor. Fiz.*, **9**, 1094 (1939); Ya. I. Frenkel, *Sobranie Trudov* (Collected Works), Vol. 2, Izdatel'stvo Acad. Nauk SSSR, Moscow, 1958.
9. Debye, P. J. W., Report No. 637 to Rubber Reserve Company, 9.04, 1945, published in *The Collected Papers of Peter J. W. Debye*, Interscience, New York–London, 1954.
10. Taylor, W. J., *J. Chem. Phys.*, **15**, 412 (1947).
11. Kuhn, H., *J. Chem. Phys.*, **15**, 843 (1947).
12. Birshtein, T. M., and O. B. Ptitsyn, *Zh. Fiz. Khim.*, **26**, 1215 (1952).
13. Birshtein, T. M., and O. B. Ptitsyn, *Zh. Fiz. Khim.*, **28**, 213 (1954).
14. Birshtein, T. M., and O. B. Ptitsyn, *Zh. Tekhn. Fiz.*, **24**, 1998 (1954).
15. Ptitsyn, O. B., and Yu. A. Sharonov, *Zh. Tekhn. Fig.*, **27**, 2744 (1957); *Soviet Phys.-Tech. Phys.*, **2**, 2544 (1957).
16. Lifson, S., *J. Chem. Phys.*, **29**, 80 (1958).
17. Birshtein, T. M., O. B. Ptitsyn, and E. A. Sokolova, *Vysokmol. Soedin.*, **1**, 852 (1959).
18. Nagai, K., *Busseiron Kenkyu*, **4**, 65 (1958); *J. Chem. Phys.*, **30**, 660 (1959).

19. Magnasco, V., and C. Rossi, *J. Chem. Phys.*, **32,** 1881 (1960).
20. Rossi, C., and V. Magnasco, *Makromol. Chem.*, **41,** 45 (1960).
21. Mori, T., *Busseiron Kenkyu,* **8,** 175 (1960); *J. Phys. Soc. Japan,* **15,** 1482, 1638 (1960).
22. Mori, T., *Busseiron Kenkyu,* **9,** 473 (1961); *ibid.*, **10,** 36 (1961).
23. Eliezer, J., and H. G. Hayman, *J. Polymer Sci.*, **23,** 387 (1957).
24. Benoit, H., *J. Chim. Phys.*, **44,** 18 (1947).
25. Borsellino, A., *J. Chem. Phys.*, **30,** 857 (1959).
26. Magnasco, V., *Ric. Sci.*, **30,** 405 (1960).
27. Tobolsky, A. V., *J. Chem. Phys.*, **31,** 387 (1959).
28. Smith, R. P., *J. Chem. Phys.*, **33,** 876 (1960).
29. Meyer, V. E., J. B. Kinsinger, and P. H. Parker, *J. Chem. Phys.*, **34,** 1429 (1961).
30. Nagai, K., *J. Phys. Soc. Japan,* **15,** 407 (1960); *Busseriron Kenkyu,* **2–5,** 677 (1959).
31. Nagai, K., *J. Chem. Phys.*, **34,** 887 (1961).
32. Lifson, S., *J. Chem. Phys.*, **30,** 964 (1959).
33. Nagai, K., *J. Chem. Phys.*, **31,** 1169 (1959).
34. Hoeve, C. A. J., *J. Chem. Phys.*, **32,** 888 (1960).
35. Hoeve, C. A. J., *J. Chem. Phys.*, **35,** 1266 (1961).
36. Corradini, P., and G. Allegra, *Atti Accad. Nazl. Lincei Rend. Classe Sci. Fis. Mat Nat.*, [8] **30,** 516 (1961).
37. Kratky, O., and G. Porod, *Rec. Trav. Chim.*, **68,** 1106 (1949).
38. Porod, G., *Makromol. Chem.*, **9,** 244 (1949).
39. Markoff, A. A., *Izbr. Trudy* (Selected Papers), Izdatel'stvo Akad. Nauk SSSR, Moscow, 1951.
40. Chandrasekar, S., *Stokhasticheskie Problemy v Fizike i Astromomii* IL, Moscow, 1947 originally published as "Stochastic Problems in Physics and Astronomy," *Rev. Mod. Phys.*, **15,** 1 (1943).
41. Zimm, B. H., *J. Polymer Sci.*, **16,** 245 (1955).
42. Rayleigh, J. W. S., *Scientific Papers,* **6,** 604 (1919).
43. Allegra, G., P. Ganis, and P. Corradini, *Makromol. Chem.*, **61,** 225 (1963).
44. Kuhn, W., *Kolloid-Z.*, **68,** 2 (1934).
45. Irwin, J., *Biometrica,* **19,** 225 (1927).
46. Hall, P., *Biometrica,* **19,** 240 (1927).
47. Treloar, L. R. G., *Trans. Faraday Soc.*, **42,** 77 (1946).
48. Nagai, K., *J. Phys. Soc. Japan,* **13,** 928 (1958).
49. O'Connor, D., *Acta Phys. Polon.*, **17,** 273 (1958).
50. Hsing, C.-H., H.-C. Hsiung, and A. A. Gordus, *J. Chem. Phys.*, **34,** 535 (1961).
51. Kuhn, W., and F. Grün, *Kolloid-Z.*, **101,** 248 (1942).
52. Treloar, L. R. G., *Fizika Uprugosti Kauchuka,* IL, Moscow, 1953 (originally published as *Physics of Rubber Elasticity,* Clarendon Press, Oxford, 1949).
53. Volkenshtein, M. V., *Konfigurationnaya Statistika Polimernykh Tsepei,* Izdatel'stvo Akad. Nauk SSSR, Moscow, 1959 (published in translation as *Configurational Statistics of Polymeric Chains,* Interscience, New York, 1963).
54. Volkenshtein, M. V., and O. B. Ptitsyn, *Dok . Akad. Nauk SSSR,* **78,** 657 (1951).
55. Volkenshtein, M. V., and O. B. Ptitsyn, *Zh. Fiz. Khim.*, **26,** 1061 (1952).
56. Volkenshtein, M. V., and O. B. Ptitsyn, *Dokl. Akad. Nauk SSSR,* **91,** 1313 (1953).
57. Volkenshtein, M. V., and O. B. Ptitsyn, *Zh. Tekhn. Fiz.*, **25,** 649 (1955).
58. Scott, K. W., and A. V. Tobolsky, *J. Colloid Sci.*, **8,** 465 (1953).

59. Birshtein, T. M., *Zh. Tekhn. Fiz.*, **28**, 2493 (1958).
60. Krigbaum, W. R., and M. Kaneko, *J. Chem. Phys.*, **36**, 99 (1962).
61. Hermans, J. J., and R. Ullman, *Physica*, **18**, 951 (1952).
62. Daniels, H. E., *Proc. Roy. Soc. (Edinburgh)*, **63**, 290 (1952).
63. Heine, S., O. Kratky, and G. Porod, *Makromol. Chem.*, **44–46**, 682 (1961).
64. Nagai, K., *J. Chem. Phys.*, **37**, 490 (1962).
65. Birshtein, T. M., and O. B. Ptitsyn, *Vysokomol. Soedin.*, **2**, 628 (1960).
66. Nagai, K., and T. Ishikawa, *J. Chem. Phys.*, **37**, 496 (1962).
67. Birshtein, T. M., *Vysokomol. Soedin.*, **5**, 1675 (1963).
68. Nagai, K., *J. Chem. Phys.*, **38**, 924 (1963).
69. Gantmakher, F. R., *Teoriya Matrits* (Matrix Theory), Gostekhteorizdat, Moscow, 1954.
70. Yoo, S. J., and J. B. Kinsinger, *J. Chem. Phys.*, **36**, 1371 (1962).
71. Faddeeva, V. N., *Vychislitelnye Metody Lineinoi Algebry* (Computational Methods of Linear Algebra), Gostekhteorizdat, Moscow, 1950.

Chapter 6

THEORY OF THE DIMENSIONS AND DIPOLE MOMENTS OF MACROMOLECULES: EQUATIONS FOR REAL CHAINS

6.1. Dimensions and Dipole Moments of Macromolecules with Independent Conformations of Neighboring Monomer Units

In Chapters 4 and 5 we have presented the foundations of the mathematical method for the averaging of the different properties of macromolecules over their micro states, i.e., over the conformations of monomer units. Below, we shall apply the results of Chapter 5 to the calculation of the mean dimensions and mean dipole moments of macromolecules of various structures. Comparison of the results of these calculations with experiment will enable us to obtain information on the conformations of macromolecules in solution (see Chapter 7). As is known, there are at present no direct experimental methods for studying the conformations of macromolecules in solution, so that the conformational structure of polymer chains can be investigated only indirectly, by comparing with experimental data the theories of dimensions and dipole moments, based on definite hypotheses on this structure.

Modern concepts of the conformational structure of macromolecules are presented in Chapter 3. As was shown, the crystalline conformations of polymer chains, which can be determined by the method of x-ray analysis, can be explained in most cases on the basis of intramolecular interactions. As a result, it was concluded that the one-dimensional short-range order in free macromolecules (in solution or in the highly elastic bulk state) must be similar to the one-dimensional long-range order in crystalline chains. The short-range order in free flexible macromolecules can be disturbed as a result of both rotational isomerization and torsional oscillations of units about a single equilibrium position. The relative role of these mechanisms can be established in the simplest cases by calculations based on potentials of internal rotation. (The results of such calculations for a number of macromolecules are given in Chapter 3.) In most cases, however, the rela-

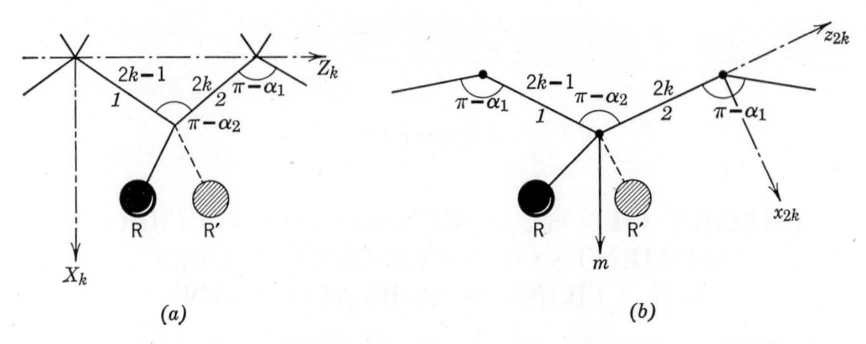

Fig. 6.1. Monomer unit of a polymer chain of type $(—CH_2—CRR'—)_n$ and local coordinate systems related to it. (a) system X, Y, Z; (b) system x, y, z.

tive role of these mechanisms can be investigated only by determining the dimensions and dipole moments of the macromolecules in solution and comparing the values obtained with theoretical equations based on various ideas about the mechanism of chain flexibility.

Below, we shall present expressions for the mean dimensions and dipole moments of a number of typical macromolecules, derived by us and other authors by methods described in the preceding chapter. We did not set ourselves the goal of presenting a list of all expressions of such type found in the literature, since most of them contain assumptions which are too crude to permit comparison of theory with experiment, as has been repeatedly pointed out above. The equations given below in this chapter are for macromolecules made up of monomer units consisting of two elements of the main chain. Just as in Chapter 3, for the sake of precision, we shall talk of macromolecules of type $(—CH_2—CRR'—)_n$; the results obtained, however, are valid also for molecules of polymers such as polyaldehydes or polysiloxanes. In this chapter we shall limit ourselves to the investigation of chains which are regular both from the chemical and stereochemical points of view, i.e., we shall examine only stereoregular homopolymers. The results obtained can be easily generalized to nonstereoregular homopolymers and to copolymers for the case in which the conformations of monomer units are independent; in the general case, however, this method permits the examination only of those irregular chains in which the conditions of internal rotation in the chain are independent of their composition.

The general equations derived in the previous chapter for the averaged vector properties of macromolecules, [eqs. (5.16), (5.21), or (5.25)], require the determination of matrices $S(\Omega_k)$ of the cosines of the angles between the unit vectors of the local systems of coordinates linked to neighboring monomer units. Let us introduce n local systems of coordinates (where n is the degree of polymerization), linked to the monomer units of the chain in such manner as shown in Figure 6.1*a*. The Z_k axes of these systems are directed along the vectors of the lengths of the monomer units; the X_k axes lie in the planes of the bonds of the monomer units and are directed in the direction of the bulky side groups. The directions of the Y_k axes are arbitrary and identical for all monomer units in the case of polymers of type $(\text{—CH}_2\text{—CR}_2\text{—})_n$, while for polymers of type $(\text{—CH}_2\text{—CRR}'\text{—})_n$ they are selected in such a way that the projections on them of some given bonds (CR or CR′) are positive.* (This means that, in the case of an isotactic chain, all the local systems of coordinates would be either left-handed or right-handed, while for a syndiotactic chain, right-handed and left-handed systems of coordinates would alternate). In order to determine the matrices $S(\Omega_k)$ of the cosines of the angles between the axes of the kth and $(k-1)$th systems of coordinates, let us introduce N auxiliary systems of coordinates (N is the number of links), x_{2k-1}, y_{2k-1}, z_{2k-1} and x_{2k}, y_{2k}, z_{2k}, linked with all the links of the chain as shown in Figure 6.1*b*. Axes z_p ($p = 2k-1, 2k$) are directed along the pth bonds, the x_p axes lie in the plane of the p and $p-1$ bonds and are directed in the direction of the *trans* position of the $p+1$ bond, while the y_p axes are directed in such a manner that these systems of coordinates are the same (left- or right-handed) as the corresponding system of coordinates X_k, Y_k, Z_k.

The matrices of the cosines of the angles between the axes of the auxiliary systems of coordinates have the form given in eqs. (6.1) and (6.2). (Angles φ_p of the rotation of pth bonds are measured in the direction from x_{p-1} to y_{p-1}.)

$$A(\varphi_{2k-1}) = \left|\begin{array}{c|ccc} & x_{2k-1} & y_{2k-1} & z_{2k-1} \\ \hline x_{2k-2} & -\cos\varphi_{2k-1}\cos\alpha_1 & \pm\sin\varphi_{2k-1} & \cos\varphi_{2k-1}\sin\alpha_1 \\ y_{2k-2} & -\sin\varphi_{2k-1}\cos\alpha_1 & \mp\cos\varphi_{2k-1} & \sin\varphi_{2k-1}\sin\alpha_1 \\ z_{2k-2} & \sin\alpha_1 & 0 & \cos\alpha_1 \end{array}\right| \tag{6.1}$$

$$A(\varphi_{2k}) = \left|\begin{array}{c|ccc} & x_{2k} & y_{2k} & z_{2k} \\ \hline x_{2k-1} & -\cos\varphi_{2k}\cos\alpha_2 & \pm\sin\varphi_{2k} & \cos\varphi_{2k}\sin\alpha_2 \\ y_{2k-1} & \mp\sin\varphi_{2k}\cos\alpha_2 & -\cos\varphi_{2k} & \pm\sin\varphi_{2k}\sin\alpha_2 \\ z_{2k-1} & \sin\alpha_2 & 0 & \cos\alpha_2 \end{array}\right| \tag{6.2}$$

* In the case of chains of type $(\text{—CH}_2\text{—CHR—})_n$, the directions of the Y_k axes are selected in such a way that the projections on them of the CR bonds are positive.

[In matrices (6.1) and (6.2) the upper signs are for polymers with symmetric side groups and for isotactic polymers, while the lower signs are for syndiotactic polymer.]

Then, matrix $S(\Omega_k)$ will have the form:

$$S(\Omega_k) = TA(\varphi_{2k-1})\,A(\varphi_{2k})T^{-1} \tag{6.3}$$

where

$$T = \begin{Vmatrix} \cos\alpha_2/2 & 0 & -\sin\alpha_2/2 \\ 0 & 1 & 0 \\ \sin\alpha_2/2 & 0 & \cos\alpha_2/2 \end{Vmatrix} \tag{6.4}$$

is the matrix of the cosines of angles between the systems of coordinates X_k, Y_k, Z_k and x_{2k}, y_{2k}, z_{2k}; it represents a matrix of rotation by an angle $\alpha_2/2$ relative to the y_k axis. From eqs. (6.1)–(6.4) we find that the elements of the matrix $S(\Omega_k) = S(\varphi_{2k-1}, \varphi_{2k})$ have the form

$$\begin{aligned}
S_{11} &= 1/2(\cos\varphi_{2k-1}\cos\varphi_{2k}\cos\alpha_1 - \sin\varphi_{2k-1}\sin\varphi_{2k})(1+\cos\alpha_2) \\
&\quad + 1/2\,(\cos\varphi_{2k-1} + \cos\varphi_{2k})\sin\alpha_1\sin\alpha_2 \\
&\quad - 1/2\cos\alpha_1\,(1-\cos\alpha_2) \\
S_{12} &= \mp\cos\alpha_2/2\,(\cos\varphi_{2k-1}\sin\varphi_{2k}\cos\alpha_1 + \sin\varphi_{2k-1}\cos\varphi_{2k}) \\
&\quad \mp \sin\varphi_{2k}\sin\alpha_1\sin\alpha_2/2 \\
S_{13} &= -1/2\,(\cos\varphi_{2k-1}\cos\varphi_{2k}\cos\alpha_1 - \sin\varphi_{2k-1}\sin\varphi_{2k})\sin\alpha_2 \\
&\quad + 1/2\,[\cos\varphi_{2k-1}(1+\cos\alpha_2) - \cos\varphi_{2k}(1-\cos\alpha_2)]\sin\alpha_1 \\
&\quad - 1/2\sin\alpha_2\cos\alpha_1 \\
S_{21} &= \cos\alpha_2/2\,(\sin\varphi_{2k-1}\cos\varphi_{2k}\cos\alpha_1 + \cos\varphi_{2k-1}\sin\varphi_{2k}) \\
&\quad + \sin\varphi_{2k-1}\sin\alpha_1\sin\alpha_2/2 \\
S_{22} &= \pm\cos\varphi_{2k-1}\cos\varphi_{2k} \mp \sin\varphi_{2k-1}\sin\varphi_{2k}\cos\alpha_1 \\
S_{23} &= -(\sin\varphi_{2k-1}\cos\varphi_{2k}\cos\alpha_1 + \cos\varphi_{2k-1}\sin\varphi_{2k})\sin\alpha_2/2 \\
&\quad + \sin\varphi_{2k-1}\sin\alpha_1\cos\alpha_2/2 \\
S_{31} &= 1/2\,(\cos\varphi_{2k-1}\cos\varphi_{2k}\cos\alpha_1 - \sin\varphi_{2k-1}\sin\varphi_{2k})\sin\alpha_2 \\
&\quad + 1/2\,[\cos\varphi_{2k-1}(1-\cos\alpha_2) - \cos\varphi_{2k}(1+\cos\alpha_2)]\sin\alpha_1 \\
&\quad + 1/2\sin\alpha_2\cos\alpha_1 \\
S_{32} &= \mp(\cos\varphi_{2k-1}\sin\varphi_{2k}\cos\alpha_1 + \sin\varphi_{2k-1}\cos\varphi_{2k})\sin\alpha_2/2 \\
&\quad \pm \sin\varphi_{2k}\sin\alpha_1\cos\alpha_2/2 \\
S_{33} &= -\,(1/2\,(\cos\varphi_{2k-1}\cos\varphi_{2k}\cos\alpha_1 - \sin\varphi_{2k-1}\sin\varphi_{2k})(1-\cos\alpha_2) \\
&\quad + 1/2\,(\cos\varphi_{2k-1} + \cos\varphi_{2k})\sin\alpha_1\sin\alpha_2 \\
&\quad + 1/2\cos\alpha_1\,(1+\cos\alpha_2)
\end{aligned} \tag{6.5}$$

[Just as in eqs. (6.1) and (6.2), here the upper signs are for polymers with symmetric side groups and for isotactic polymers, while the lower signs are for syndiotactic polymers.]

The vectors of the length and dipole moment of a monomer unit are expressed in its own system of coordinates by eqs. (6.6) and (6.7), respectively:

$$\mathbf{r}_h = 2l \cos \alpha_2/2 \begin{pmatrix} 0 \\ 0 \\ 1 \end{pmatrix} \tag{6.6}$$

and

$$\mathbf{r}_\mu = m \begin{pmatrix} \sin \beta/2 \\ \cos \beta/2 \\ 0 \end{pmatrix} \tag{6.7}$$

where m is the absolute value of vector $\mathbf{m}$ of the *summation* dipole moment of a monomer unit, which lies in the plane X_k, Y_k at an angle of $(\pi - \beta)/2$ with respect to axis X_k.* It is evident that, for polymers of type $(—CH_2—CR_2—)_n$, where R is a polar side group, $\beta = \pi$, while for polymers $(—CH_2—CHR—)_n$ the angle $(\pi - \beta)/2$ is equal to the angle between the X_k axis and the CR bond.

Below, we shall examine primarily polymers which have bulky side groups attached to every alternate atom of the chain, for example polymers of type $(—CH_2—CR_2—)_n$ or $(—CH_2—CRR'—)_n$. In such chains, the conformations of monomer units are determined mainly by the interactions between neighboring bulky groups (see Chapter 3), so that, for such chains, the case of independent conformations of neighboring monomer units should be examined as a first approximation. In this case, by using the general equation, eq. (5.16), and introducing into it the matrix $S = \overline{S(\Omega_k)}$, the elements of which are defined by eqs. (6.5), and the vectors $\mathbf{r}$, calculated according to eqs. (6.6) or (6.7), we obtain the expressions for $\overline{h^2}$ and $\overline{\mu^2}$ for various types of macromolecules compiled in Table 6.1. (It is to be noted that we are examining only those molecules of which the monomer units contain two bonds of the main chain.)

Equations (6.8), (6.9), (6.19), and (6.20) are the most general ones for the dimensions and dipole moment of macromolecules of type $(—CH_2—CR_2—)_n$ and isotactic molecules of type $(—CH_2—CRR'—)_n$ with indepen-

* It is easy to ascertain that in all the cases examined in the present investigation, vector $\mathbf{m}$ can be expressed in this form.

TABLE 6.1

Dimensions and Dipole Moments of Macromolecules with Independent Conformations of Neighboring Monomer Units,[a]

$$U\ (\Omega_1,\ \Omega_2,\ \ldots\ \Omega_n) = \sum^{n} U\ (\Omega_i)$$

Conditions of internal rotation	$\overline{h^2}$, $\overline{\mu^2}$	References
	Molecules of type $(\text{—}CH_2\text{—}CR_2\text{—})_n$	
Interdependent rotations about neighboring links of a monomer unit, general case	$\overline{h^2} = Nl^2 \dfrac{(1+\cos\alpha_1)(1+\cos\alpha_2)[1-\eta^{(1)}\eta^{(2)}+\cos\alpha_1(\eta^{(1)}\eta^{(2)}-\zeta)+\xi]}{(1-\cos\alpha_1\cos\alpha_2)(1+\zeta)+\sin^2\alpha_1(\eta^{(1)}\eta^{(2)}-\zeta)-(\eta^{(1)}+\eta^{(2)})\sin\alpha_1\sin\alpha_2+\xi(\cos\alpha_2-\cos\alpha_1)}$ (6.8)	1
	$\overline{\mu^2} = nm^2 \dfrac{(1-\cos\alpha_1)[1-\eta^{(1)}\eta^{(2)}-\cos\alpha_1(\eta^{(1)}\eta^{(2)}-\zeta)-\xi]}{(1-\cos\alpha_1\cos\alpha_2)(1+\zeta)+\sin^2\alpha_1(\eta^{(1)}\eta^{(2)}-\zeta)-(\eta^{(1)}+\eta^{(2)})\sin\alpha_1\sin\alpha_2+\xi(\cos\alpha_2-\cos\alpha_1)}$ (6.9)	
Interdependent rotations taking symmetry conditions into account $U(\varphi_1,\varphi_2) = U(-\varphi_1,-\varphi_2) = U(\varphi_2,\varphi_1) = U(-\varphi_2,-\varphi_1)$; $\eta^{(1)}=\eta^{(2)}=\eta$	$\overline{h^2} = Nl^2 \dfrac{(1+\cos\alpha_1)(1+\cos\alpha_2)[1-\eta^2+\cos\alpha_1(\eta^2-\zeta)+\xi]}{(1-\cos\alpha_1\cos\alpha_2)(1+\zeta)+\sin^2\alpha_1(\eta^2-\zeta)-2\eta\sin\alpha_1\sin\alpha_2+\xi(\cos\alpha_2-\cos\alpha_1)}$ (6.10)	2
	$\overline{\mu^2} = nm^2 \dfrac{(1-\cos\alpha_1)[1-\eta^2-\cos\alpha_1(\eta^2-\zeta)-\xi]}{(1-\cos\alpha_1\cos\alpha_2)(1+\zeta)+\sin^2\alpha_1(\eta^2-\zeta)-2\eta\sin\alpha_1\sin\alpha_2+\xi(\cos\alpha_2-\cos\alpha_1)}$ (6.11)	
Interdependent rotations taking symmetry conditions into account and with all valence angles in the chain equal $U(\varphi_1,\varphi_2) = U(-\varphi_1,-\varphi_2) = U(\varphi_2,\varphi_1) = U(-\varphi_2,-\varphi_1)$; $\eta^{(1)}=\eta^{(2)}=\eta$; $\alpha_1=\alpha_2=\alpha$	$\overline{h^2} = Nl^2 \dfrac{1+\cos\alpha}{1-\cos\alpha}\cdot\dfrac{1+\eta}{1-\eta}(1+\Delta)$ (6.12); $\overline{\mu^2} = nm^2 \dfrac{1}{1+\cos\alpha}\cdot\dfrac{1+\eta}{1-\eta}(1-\Delta)$ (6.13); $\Delta = \dfrac{\cos\alpha(\eta^2-\zeta)+\xi}{1-\eta^2}$ (6.14)	3,4
Independent rotations about neighboring links of a monomer unit $U(\Omega) = U(\varphi_1)+U(\varphi_2)$; $\zeta = \eta^{(1)}\eta^{(2)}$; $\xi = 0$	$\overline{h^2} = Nl^2 \dfrac{(1+\cos\alpha_1)(1+\cos\alpha_2)(1-\eta^{(1)}\eta^{(2)})}{(1-\cos\alpha_1\cos\alpha_2)(1+\eta^{(1)}\eta^{(2)})-(\eta^{(1)}+\eta^{(2)})\sin\alpha_1\sin\alpha_2}$ (6.15)	5
	$\overline{\mu^2} = nm^2 \dfrac{(1-\cos\alpha_1)(1-\eta^{(1)}\eta^{(2)})}{(1-\cos\alpha_1\cos\alpha_2)(1+\eta^{(1)}\eta^{(2)})-(\eta^{(1)}+\eta^{(2)})\sin\alpha_1\sin\alpha_2}$ (6.16)	1

Independent rotations taking symmetry conditions into account and with all valence angles in the chain equal
$U(\Omega) = U(\varphi_1) + U(\varphi_2)$
$\zeta = \eta^{(1)}\eta^{(2)}$
$\xi = 0$
$U(\varphi_1) = U(\varphi_2)$
$\eta^{(1)} = \eta^{(2)} = \eta$
$\alpha_1 = \alpha_2 = \alpha$

$$\overline{h^2} = Nl^2 \frac{1 + \cos\alpha}{1 - \cos\alpha}\frac{1 + \eta}{1 - \eta} \quad (6.17)$$
6–8

$$\overline{\mu_2} = nm^2 \frac{1}{1 + \cos\alpha}\frac{1 + \eta}{1 - \eta} \quad (6.18)$$
9

Isotactic molecules of type (—CH_2—CRR′—$)_n$

Interdependent rotations about neighboring links of a monomer unit, general case

$$\overline{h_i^2} = Nl^2(1 + a)(1 + b) \times \frac{(1 + \nu_1)(1 + \nu_2) + \tau_1\tau_2 + (1 - a)[\epsilon^{(1)}\eta^{(2)}\tau_2 + \epsilon^{(2)}\eta^{(1)}\tau_1 + \epsilon^{(1)}\epsilon^{(2)}(1 + \nu_2) - \eta^{(1)}\eta^{(2)}(1 + \nu_1)]}{(1 + \nu_1)(d - c\eta^{(1)})(d - c\eta^{(2)}) - \epsilon^{(1)}\epsilon^{(2)}c^2(b - \nu_2) + \epsilon^{(1)}c\tau_2(d - \eta^{(2)}c) + \epsilon^{(2)}c\tau_1(d - \eta^{(1)}c) - (a - b)\tau_1\tau_2} \quad (6.19)$$
1,10–13

$$\overline{\mu_i^2} = nm^2 \times \left[-1 + \frac{A\sin^2\frac{\beta}{2} + B\cos^2\frac{\beta}{2} + C\sin\beta\cos\frac{\alpha_2}{2} + D\sin\beta\sin\frac{\alpha_2}{2}}{(1 + \nu_1)(d - c\eta^{(1)})(d - c\eta^{(2)}) - \epsilon^{(1)}\epsilon^{(2)}c^2(b - \nu_2) + \epsilon^{(1)}c\tau_2(d - \eta^{(2)}c) + \epsilon^{(2)}c\tau_1(d - \eta^{(1)}c) - (a - b)\tau_1\tau_2}\right]$$

$$A = (1 + \nu_1)[2 - a(1 + b) + \nu_2(1 - b) - (\eta^{(1)} + \eta^{(2)})cd] - (1 - b)\tau_1\tau_2 + (\epsilon^{(1)}\tau_2 + \epsilon^{(2)}\tau_1)cd - \epsilon^{(1)}\epsilon^{(2)}c^2(1 + b) \quad (6.20)$$
1,13

$$B = 2[(d - \eta^{(1)}c)(d - \eta^{(2)}c) - (a - b)(\nu_2 + b)]$$

$$C = (b - a)\tau_1 + (ab + \eta^{(2)}cd - 1)\tau_2 + \epsilon^{(1)}cd - \eta^{(2)}\epsilon^{(1)}c^2 + \eta^{(1)}\epsilon^{(2)}bc^2 - \epsilon^{(2)}\nu_2cd$$

$$D = \tau_1(d - \eta^{(1)}c) + \tau_2(ad - \eta^{(2)}bc) + \nu_2c(\epsilon^{(1)} + \epsilon^{(2)}c) + \eta^{(1)}\epsilon^{(2)}c^2d - c(\epsilon^{(1)}b + \epsilon^{(2)})$$

Interdependent rotations taking symmetry conditions into account and with all valence angles in the chain equal
$U(\varphi_1, \varphi_2) = U(-\varphi_2, -\varphi_1)$
$\eta^{(1)} = \eta^{(2)} = \eta$
$\epsilon^{(1)} = -\epsilon^{(2)} = \epsilon$
$\chi^{(1)} = -\chi^{(2)} = \chi$
$\alpha_1 = \alpha_2 = \alpha$

$$\overline{h_i^2} = Nl^2 \frac{1 + \cos\alpha}{1 - \cos\alpha} \times \frac{(1 - \zeta + \xi\cos\alpha)[1 - \eta^2 + \cos\alpha(\eta^2 - \zeta) + \xi] - (1 - \cos\alpha)\epsilon^2(1 - \zeta\cos\alpha + \xi) + (1 - \cos\alpha)^2\chi(2\eta\epsilon - \chi)}{(1 - \zeta + \xi\cos\alpha)(1 - \eta)^2 + \epsilon^2\cos\alpha\left(1 - \zeta + \frac{\xi}{\cos\alpha}\right) + 2(1 - \cos\alpha)\epsilon\chi(1 - \eta)} \quad (6.21)$$

$$\overline{\mu_i^2} = nm^2\left\{-1 + \frac{A\sin^2\frac{\beta}{2} + B\cos^2\frac{\beta}{2} + C\sin\beta\cos\frac{\alpha}{2}}{(1 + \cos\alpha)\{(1 - \eta)^2(1 - \zeta + \xi\cos\alpha) + 2\epsilon\chi(1 - \eta)(1 - \cos\alpha) + \epsilon^2[\xi + (1 - \zeta)\cos\alpha]\}}\right\}$$
3,4

$$A = (1 - \zeta + \xi\cos\alpha)(2 - 2\eta - \xi + \cos\alpha(1 - 2\eta + \zeta)) + [\epsilon(1 + \cos\alpha) + \chi(1 - \cos\alpha)]^2 \quad (6.22)$$

$$B = 2(1 + \cos\alpha)(1 - \eta)^2$$

$$C = 2[\epsilon(1 - \eta - \xi) - \epsilon(\eta - \zeta)\cos\alpha - \chi(1 - \eta)(1 - \cos\alpha)]$$

(continued)

TABLE 6.1 (*continued*)

Conditions of internal rotation	$\overline{h^2}$, $\overline{\mu^2}$	References
Independent rotations about neighboring links of a monomer unit with all valence angles in the chain equal $U(\Omega) = U(\varphi_1) + U(\varphi_2)$ $\zeta = \eta^{(1)}\eta^{(2)}$ $\xi = \epsilon^{(1)}\epsilon^{(2)}$ $\chi^{(1)} = \epsilon^{(1)}\eta^{(2)}$ $\chi^{(2)} = \eta^{(1)}\epsilon^{(2)}$ $\alpha_1 = \alpha_2 = \alpha$	$\overline{h_i^2} = Nl^2 \frac{1+\cos\alpha}{1-\cos\alpha} \cdot \frac{1 + 2(\epsilon^{(1)}\epsilon^{(2)} - \eta^{(1)}\eta^{(2)}) + (\epsilon^{(1)2} + \eta^{(1)2})(\epsilon^{(2)2} + \eta^{(2)2})}{(1-\eta^{(1)})(1-\eta^{(2)}) - [\epsilon^{(1)2} - \eta^{(1)}(1-\eta^{(1)})][\epsilon^{(2)2} - \eta^{(2)}(1-\eta^{(2)})]}$ (6.23) $\overline{\mu_i^2} = nm^2 \left\{ -1 + \frac{\cos\alpha \sin^2 \frac{\beta}{2}}{1+\cos\alpha} + \frac{A \sin^2 \frac{\beta}{2} + B\cos^2 \frac{\beta}{2} + C \sin\beta \cos\frac{\alpha}{2}}{(1+\cos\alpha)\{(1-\eta^{(1)})(1-\eta^{(2)}) - [\epsilon^{(1)2} - \eta^{(1)}(1-\eta^{(1)})][\epsilon^{(2)2} - \eta^{(2)}(1-\eta^{(2)})]\}} \right\}$ $A = 2(1 - \eta^{(1)}\eta^{(2)} - \epsilon^{(1)}\epsilon^{(2)}) - \eta^{(1)}(1 - \eta^{(2)2} - \epsilon^{(2)2}) - \eta^{(2)}(1 - \eta^{(1)2} - \epsilon^{(1)2})$ (6.24) $B = 2(1+\cos\alpha)(1-\eta^{(1)})(1-\eta^{(2)})$ $C = \epsilon^{(1)}(1-\eta^{(2)})^2 - \epsilon^{(2)}(1-\eta^{(1)})^2 + \epsilon^{(1)}\epsilon^{(2)}(\epsilon^{(2)} - \epsilon^{(1)})$	14,15
Independent rotations taking symmetry conditions into account and with valence angles of the chain equal ($\overline{\mu_i^2}$ for tetrahedral valence angles, $\pi - \alpha = 109°30'$) $U(\Omega) = U(\varphi_1) + U(\varphi_2)$ $\zeta = \eta^{(1)}\eta^{(2)}$ $\xi = \epsilon^{(1)}\epsilon^{(2)}$ $\chi^{(1)} = \epsilon^{(1)}\eta^{(2)}$ $\chi^{(2)} = \eta^{(1)}\epsilon^{(2)}$ $\alpha_1 = \alpha_2 = \alpha$ $U(\varphi_1) = U(-\varphi_2)$ $\eta^{(1)} = \eta^{(2)} = \eta$ $\epsilon^{(1)} = -\epsilon^{(2)} = \epsilon$	$\overline{h_i^2} = Nl^2 \frac{1+\cos\alpha}{1-\cos\alpha} \frac{1-\eta^2-\epsilon^2}{(1-\eta)^2+\epsilon^2}$ (6.25) $\overline{\mu_i^2} = nm^2 \frac{1}{1-\eta^2-\epsilon^2} \left[\frac{11}{12}(1+\eta^2+\epsilon^2) + \frac{\eta}{2} - \frac{4}{3} \frac{\epsilon^2}{(1-\eta)^2+\epsilon^2} + \frac{2\sqrt{3}}{3}\epsilon \right]$ (6.26)	16,17 9
	Syndiotactic molecules of type $(\text{—}CH_2\text{—}CRR'\text{—})_n$	
Interdependent rotations about neighboring links of a monomer unit taking symmetry conditions into account and with valence angles in the chain equal	$\overline{h_s^2} = Nl^2 \frac{1+\cos\alpha}{1-\cos\alpha} \times \frac{(1+\zeta-\xi\cos\alpha)[1-\zeta\cos\alpha - \eta^2(1-\cos\alpha)+\xi] - \epsilon^2(1-\cos\alpha)(1-\zeta\cos\alpha+\xi) - \chi(1+\cos\alpha)[2\eta\epsilon(1-\cos\alpha) + \chi(1+\cos\alpha)]}{(1+\zeta-\xi\cos\alpha)(1-\eta)^2 + \epsilon^2\cos\alpha\left(1-\zeta+\frac{\xi}{\cos\alpha}\right) - 2(1+\cos\alpha)\chi\epsilon(1-\eta)}$ (6.27)	3,5,18

Conditions	Formula	Ref.
$U(\varphi_1, \varphi_2) = U(\varphi_2, \varphi_1)$ $\eta^{(1)} = \eta^{(2)} = \eta$ $\epsilon^{(1)} = \epsilon^{(2)} = \epsilon$ $\chi^{(1)} = \chi^{(2)} = \chi$ $\alpha_1 = \alpha_2 = \alpha$	$\overline{\mu_s^2} = nm^2 \left\{ -1 + \dfrac{A \sin^2 \frac{\beta}{2} + B \cos^2 \frac{\beta}{2} + C \sin \beta \cos \frac{\alpha}{2}}{(1 + \cos \alpha)\{(1-\eta)^2(1 + \zeta - \xi \cos \alpha) - 2\epsilon\chi(1-\eta)(1+\cos\alpha) + \epsilon^2[(1-\zeta)\cos\alpha + \xi]\}} \right\}$ (6.28) $A = (1 + \zeta - \xi \cos \alpha)[2 + \cos \alpha - 2\eta(1 + \cos \alpha) + \zeta \cos \alpha - \xi] + (1 + \cos \alpha)^2(\epsilon - \chi)^2$ $B = 2(1 + \cos \alpha)(1 - \eta)^2$ $C = 2[\epsilon(1 - \eta - \xi) - \epsilon(\eta - \zeta) \cos \alpha + \chi(1 - \eta)(1 + \cos \alpha)]$	
Independent rotations about neighboring links of a monomer unit taking symmetry conditions into account and with all valence angles in the chain equal ($\overline{\mu_s^2}$ for tetrahedral valence angles, $\pi - \alpha =$ 109°30′) $U(\Omega) = U(\varphi_1) + U(\varphi_2)$ $U(\varphi_1) = U(\varphi_2)$ $\zeta = \eta^2$ $\xi = \epsilon^2$ $\chi = \eta\epsilon$ $\alpha_1 = \alpha_2 = \alpha$	$\overline{h_s^2} = Nl^2 \dfrac{1 + \cos \alpha}{1 - \cos \alpha} \dfrac{1 - (\eta^2 + \epsilon^2)^2}{(1 - \eta)^2 + (\eta - \eta^2 - \epsilon^2)^2}$ (6.29) $\overline{\mu_s^2} = nm^2 \dfrac{1 - \eta^2 - \epsilon^2}{(1 - \eta)^2 + (\eta - \eta^2 - \epsilon^2)^2} \left[\dfrac{11}{12}(1 + \eta^2 + \epsilon^2) - \dfrac{4}{3}\eta + \dfrac{2\sqrt{3}}{3} \right]$ (6.30)	17 9

[a] Definitions: N = number of elements in chain; n = degree of polymerization; l = length of a bond; m = dipole moment of a monomer unit; $\pi - \alpha_1$ = valence angle in the main chain at the —CH_2— group; $\pi - \alpha_2$ = valence angle in the main chain at the —CRR′— group; $a = \cos \alpha_1$; $b = \cos \alpha_2$; $(\pi - \beta)/2$ = angle between the direction of the total dipole moment of a monomer unit and the bisectrix of the angle RCR′ in the side group (see Fig. 6.1*b*) [for polymers of type (—CH_2—CR_2—)$_n$, $(\pi - \beta)/2 = 0$]; φ_1 = angle of rotation of bond number $2k - 1$, i.e., of bond CH_2—CRR′ (Fig. 6.1); φ_2 = angle of rotation of bond number $2k$, i.e., at bond —CRR′—CH_2; $\eta^{(1)} = \cos \varphi_1$; $\eta^{(2)} = \cos \varphi_2$; $\epsilon^{(1)} = \sin \varphi_1$; $\epsilon^{(2)} = \sin \varphi_2$; $\zeta = \cos \varphi_1 \cos \varphi_2$; $\xi = \sin \varphi_1 \sin \varphi_2$; $\chi^{(1)} = \sin \varphi_1 \cos \varphi_2$; $\chi^{(2)} = \cos \varphi_1 \sin \varphi_2$; $\nu_1 = \xi \cos \alpha_1 - \zeta$; $\nu_2 = \zeta \cos \alpha_1 - \xi$; $\tau_1 = \chi^{(1)} \cos \alpha_1 + \chi^{(2)}$; $\tau_2 = \chi^{(1)} + \chi^{(2)} \cos \alpha^{(1)}$.

dent conformations of monomer units. They take into account both the differences in the valence angles at the —CH_2— and —CRR′— groups, and the possible different conditions of rotations of —CH_2—CRR′— and —CRR′—CH_2— bonds. As we have seen above (see Table 3.5), definite symmetry conditions, presented in Table 6.1, are fulfilled in the polymeric chains under examination with independent conformations of monomer units. This symmetry determines completely the definite interdependence of the conditions of internal rotation about two bonds of a monomer unit. For example, for a macromolecule of type $(—CH_2—CR_2—)_n$, for which

$$U(\varphi_1, \varphi_2) = U(-\varphi_1, -\varphi_2) = U(\varphi_2, \varphi_1) = U(-\varphi_2, \varphi_1) \tag{6.31}$$

the conditions of internal rotation about both bonds of a monomer unit must be identical, i.e., $\eta^{(1)} = \eta^{(2)} = \eta$. For isotactic molecules of type $(—CH_2—CRR'—)_n$ we have

$$U(\varphi_1, \varphi_2) = U(-\varphi_2, -\varphi_1) \tag{6.32}$$

and, consequently, $\eta^{(1)} = \eta^{(2)} = \eta$, $\epsilon^{(1)} = -\epsilon^{(2)} = \epsilon$, and $\chi^{(1)} = -\chi^{(2)} = \chi$.

This does not mean, however, that general equations with arbitrary $\eta^{(1)}$, $\eta^{(2)}$, etc. are devoid of sense, since they can be used successfully for macromolecules in which rotational isomerization does not take place because of strong correlation between the conformations of monomer units, as a result of which some sequences of conformations are impossible, or because of high potential barriers. In what follows we shall call the conformations of monomer units of such macromolecules "*quasi-independent*." The flexibility of chains with quasi-independent conformations of monomer units is determined by vibrations of links about the single conformation that can actually exist $(\varphi_1, \varphi_2)_n$. Since in this case the vibrations of even and odd elements take place near different positions of equilibrium, it is evident that, for such chains, $\eta^{(1)} \neq \eta^{(2)}$, etc.

Equations which take into account the different conditions of internal rotation about even and odd bonds have not been derived for syndiotactic chains, since the overwhelming majority of known crystal structures of such chains are characterized by identical angles of rotation about even and odd bonds (see Table 3.1). Symmetry conditions for syndiotactic macromolecules with independent conformations of monomer units have the form:

$$U(\varphi_1, \varphi_2) = U(\varphi_2, \varphi_1) \tag{6.33}$$

with

$$\eta^{(1)} = \eta^{(2)} = \eta$$
$$\epsilon^{(1)} = \epsilon^{(2)} = \epsilon$$
$$\chi^{(1)} = \chi^{(2)} = \chi$$

Equations for $\overline{h^2}$ and $\overline{\mu^2}$ for macromolecules of the type $(\text{—}CH_2\text{—}CR_2\text{—})_n$, and also isotactic and syndiotactic molecules of the type $(\text{—}CH_2\text{—}CRR'\text{—})_n$ in which symmetry conditions of eqs. (6.31), (6.32), and (6.33) are fulfilled are also presented in Table 6.1 [see eqs. (6.10)–(6.14), (6.21), (6.22), (6.27), and (6.28)]. In Table 6.1, particular cases of general equations, valid for chains in which not only the rotations of links of different monomer units, but also the rotations of two elements of the same monomer unit are independent of each other, are also presented [see eqs. (6.15)–(6.18), (6.23)–(6.26), (6.29), and (6.30)]. Let us examine, for example for chains of the type $(\text{—}CH_2\text{—}CR_2\text{—})_n$, the way in which the correlation between the rotations of two elements of a single monomer unit influences the mean dimensions and mean dipole moments of the macromolecules. As can be seen from eqs. (6.12) and (6.13), this correlation increases $\overline{h^2}$ and decrease $\overline{\mu^2}$. It follows from this that correlation between neighboring rotations cannot be described by introducing the effective values of η into eqs. (6.17) and (6.18) which do not take such a correlation into account. Evaluation of the quantities Δ in eqs. (6.12) and (6.14) by means of the rotational-isomeric approximation, when four energetically equal rotational isomers of each monomer unit are present (φ_1, φ_2), $(-\varphi_1, -\varphi_2)$, (φ_2, φ_1) and $(-\varphi_2, -\varphi_1)$ (see Table 3.5), gives:

$$\Delta = \frac{\cos\alpha(\cos\varphi_1 - \cos\varphi_2) + 4\sin\varphi_1\sin\varphi_2}{4 - (\cos\varphi_1 + \cos\varphi_2)^2} \tag{6.34}$$

From this, $-1 \leqslant \Delta \leqslant +1$, with $\Delta = +1$ or -1, respectively for $\varphi_1 = \varphi_2$ and $\varphi_1 = -\varphi_2$ (3). Therefore, correlation between neighboring rotations is reflected to a great extent on the dimensions and dipole moments of macromolecules. The values of $\overline{h^2}$ and $\overline{\mu^2}$, calculated with eqs. (6.17) and (6.18), should coincide for two chains, the monomer units of which are characterized by rotational isomers $\pm(\varphi, \varphi)$ and $\pm(\varphi, -\varphi)$, respectively. For rotational isomers $\pm(\varphi, \varphi)$, however, $\Delta = +1$, while for rotational isomers $\pm(\varphi, -\varphi)$, $\Delta = -1$, so that consideration of correlations in the first case doubles $\overline{h^2}$ and leads to $\overline{\mu^2} = 0$, while in the second case, to the contrary, it leads to $\overline{h^2} = 0$ and doubles $\overline{\mu^2}$.*

* The example cited is strictly illustrative, since the monomer unit conformations $(\varphi, -\varphi)$ cannot actually exist in real molecules. In this case, the identity period of the helix in a crystalline macromolecule would be equal to zero, as follows from eq. (3.4).

6.2. Dimensions and Dipole Moments of Macromolecules with Correlated Conformations of Neighboring Monomer Units

The equations presented in Table 6.1 are completely general in character, in the sense that they do not contain any assumptions on the mechanism of flexibility of polymer chains. They are based, however, on the assumption that the conformations of the chain monomer units are independent (or quasi-independent), i.e. on the fact that considerable contributions to the potential energy of the chain are made only by first-order* interactions and second-order interactions between neighboring bulky groups of the chain.† As was pointed out in Chapter 3, these interactions, in fact, play the determining role in typical macromolecules; in a number of cases, however, the properties of chains are a strong function also of interactions of higher order, for example of fourth-order interactions between the closest nonadjacent bulky groups. This leads to the necessity of taking into account the correlation between the conformations of neighboring monomer units; this can be done as well by the method presented in the preceding chapter [see eq. (5.21) or (5.25)]. As was stressed before, these equations have been derived within the rotational-isomeric approximation; they can be used, however, also for macromolecules with a continuous curve of internal rotation, since it can be divided to a finite number of regions in which the energy may be considered constant with a given degree of accuracy (see Chapter 4, p. 109). In the real case, these equations can be used for averaging the physical properties of those macromolecules in which torsional oscillations are possible within the limits of several more or less narrow potential wells, that correspond to the most favorable conformations of monomer units. In this, the elements of matrix S are averaged in two stages: first, over the torsional oscillations within the limits of each potential well (by using the fact that torsional oscillations of neighboring monomer units can be considered as independent with a good degree of accuracy), and then over all possible potential wells (conformations) of each monomer unit, by taking the cooperative nature of the system into account. In other words, matrices $S(\Omega_k)$, which enter into eqs. (5.19) and (5.23), and, thus, into eqs. (5.21) and (5.25), are, in the general case, the result of

* Let us recall that by interactions of the mth order we mean interactions between atoms or groups of atoms which are separated by m bonds of the main chain. These interactions are a function, therefore, of m consective angles of internal rotation.

† In the case of macromolecules with quasi-independent conformations (see above), a very large contribution to the potential energy of the chain is also made, of course, by interactions of higher orders; the averaging is carried out, however, over only those conformations of the chain for which these last interactions are unimportant.

averaging over the torsional oscillations within the limits of the potential well near the equilibrium position under examination.

In what follows, we shall limit ourselves to the simplest case in which each monomer unit of the chain can be present in two discrete conformations. The introduction of a large number of rotational isomers for each monomer unit would have made it impossible to obtain the final results in a simple algebraic form. It should be stressed that for molecules of type $(—CH_2—CHR—)_n$ all rotational isomers except two may be neglected, as has been shown above on the basis of a detailed analysis of their conformations (see Chapter 3).

Let us examine first isotactic molecules of type $(—CH_2—CRR'—)_n$ and, of these, the particular case of molecules with symmetric side groups $(—CH_2—CR_2—)_n$. In such chains, the $—CH_2—$ group may be replaced by any other symmetric groups, for example, by —O—.

As has been shown in Chapter 3, it follows from the equivalence postulate of Natta and Corradini (19,20) that the crystalline conformations of such chains are described by the expression, $(\varphi_1, \varphi_2)_n$, where n is the degree of polymerization, while φ_1 and φ_2 are the angles of internal rotation of the $—CH_2—CRR'—$ and $—CRR'—CH_2—$ bonds of the monomer unit (see Fig. 6.1). It follows from Table 3.3 that in a free macromolecule each monomer unit of such a chain must have conformations (φ_1, φ_2), $(-\varphi_1, -\varphi_2)$, (φ_2, φ_1), and $(-\varphi_2, -\varphi_1)$ if the side groups are symmetric, and conformations (φ_1, φ_2), $(-\varphi_2, -\varphi_1)$ if they are a symmetric. If we limit ourselves to the case of two rotational isomers for each monomer unit, we must consider that, for chains with symmetric side groups, $\varphi_1 = \varphi_2 = \varphi$, so that the monomer units of such chains have conformations (φ, φ) and $(-\varphi, -\varphi)$. Furthermore, macromolecules with symmetric side groups can be regarded as a particular case of macromolecules of type $(—CH_2—CRR'—)_n$ with conformations (φ_1, φ_2) and $(-\varphi_2, -\varphi_1)$, which corresponds to $\varphi_1 = \varphi_2 = \varphi$. In what follows, we shall indicate by numbers 1 and 2, the conformations (φ_1, φ_2) and $(-\varphi_2, -\varphi_1)$.

Regular sequences of 11...1 and 22...2 conformations are segments of enantiomorphous helices (see section 3.1) and, therefore have identical energies.* Consequently, the condition $g_{11} = g_{22}$ is fulfilled in the second-order matrix G with elements

$$g_{\alpha\beta} = e^{-U(\Omega^{(\alpha)},\Omega^{(\beta)})/kT}$$

* Isotactic polymers with asymmetric carbon atoms in the side groups are exceptions. The conformational structure of such chains is examined in section 7.1.

which characterizes the energetics of internal rotation in the chain [see eq. (4.6)].

The conformational structure of a polymer chain each monomer unit of which can exist in only two states, may be described by eqs. (4.68)–(4.71), which determine the second-order and first-order distribution functions, the conditional probabilities of the transitions, and the mean lengths of the regular regions of the chain. With the condition $g_{11} = g_{22}$, we obtain from eq. (4.68) the second-order distribution functions:

$$\begin{aligned} w(\Omega^{(1)}, \Omega^{(1)}) &= w(\Omega^{(2)}, \Omega^{(2)} = 1/[2(1 + p)] \\ w(\Omega^{(1)}, \Omega^{(2)}) &= w(\Omega^{(2)}, \Omega^{(1)}) = p/[2(1 + p)] \end{aligned} \tag{6.35}$$

where

$$\Omega^{(1)} = (\varphi_1, \varphi_2)$$

$$\Omega^{(2)} = (-\varphi_2, -\varphi_1)$$

$$p = \frac{\sqrt{g_{12}g_{21}}}{g_{11}} = e^{-\Delta U/kT} \tag{6.36}$$

while

$$\Delta U = 1/2[U(\Omega^{(1)}, \Omega^{(2)}) + U(\Omega^{(2)}, \Omega^{(1)})] - U(\Omega^{(1)}, \Omega^{(1)}) \tag{6.37}$$

is the mean value the of free energy of transition from a regular to an irregular sequence of monomer unit conformations (the *energy of breaking helical structure of the chain*).

The quantity p is clearly a measure of correlation between the conformations of neighboring monomer units. It is equal to the ratio of the number of pairs of neighboring monomer units in different conformations to the number of pairs in identical conformations. If the conformations of neighboring monomer units are completely independent, then $\Delta U = 0$, $p = 1$, and any sequence of neighboring monomer unit conformations has an identical probability, equal to ¼. For first-order distribution functions, in the case that $g_{11} = g_{22}$, eq. (4.69) leads to the trivial result (independent of the value of p):

$$w(\Omega^{(1)}) = w(\Omega^{(2)}) = 1/2 \tag{6.38}$$

As should have been expected, in the absence of correlation, the second-order distribution function is equal to the product of the corresponding first-order functions. If the correlation is very strong and only identical conformations of neighboring monomer units are possible, then $\Delta U \to \infty$, $p \to 0$, $w(\Omega^{(\beta)}, \Omega^{(\alpha)}) \to 1/2$ and $w(\Omega^{(\alpha)}, \Omega^{(\alpha)}) \to 0$ $(\alpha, \beta = 1, 2;\ \alpha \neq \beta)$.

For conditional transition probabilities, in accordance with eq. (4.70), we obtain, for $g_{11} = g_{22}$:

$$\begin{aligned} w_{\Omega^{(1)} \to \Omega^{(1)}} &= w_{\Omega^{(2)} \to \Omega^{(2)}} = 1/(1 + p) \\ w_{\Omega^{(1)} \to \Omega^{(2)}} &= w_{\Omega^{(2)} \to \Omega^{(1)}} = p/(1 + p) \end{aligned} \tag{6.39}$$

The average number of successive monomer units present in a regular region of the chain, i.e., having identical conformations, turns out to be [see eq. (4.71)]:

$$\nu(\Omega^{(1)}) = \nu(\Omega^{(2)}) = (1 + p)/p \tag{6.40}$$

It is evident that, when correlations between monomer unit conformations are absent ($p = 1$), $\nu(\Omega^{(\alpha)}) = 2$, while if correlations prohibit completely a sequence of different conformations ($p \to 0$), $\nu(\Omega^{(\alpha)}) \to \infty$.* The analysis of the conformational structure of isotactic macromolecules in which segments of right-handed and left-handed helices have identical energies, i.e., $g_{11} = g_{22}$, can be carried out also without using the Ising model. Let us examine as a chain element not one, but two, consecutive monomer units. Then, four states of each pair of units are essentially possible: 11, 22, 12, and 21. Furthermore, states 11 and 22, in which the monomer units belong to regular chain segments, have identical energies, so that the number of 11 states is equal to the number of 22 states, while states 12 and 21 at the junctions between helical regions have different energies; however, the number of 12 junctions is equal to the number of 21 junctions. Therefore, two states of monomer units may be examined, i.e., they may either belong to a regular region of the helix, or lie at a junction between regular helical regions. Furthermore, the states of a pair of monomer units with numbers k and $k + 1$ are not dependent on the states of the pair $k - 1$ and k. The energy of a pair in a regular region of the chain is equal to U_{11} $(= U_{22})$; the energy at a junction is equal to $(U_{12} + U_{21})/2$. Then the statistical weight of a junction is equal to $p/(1 + p)$, where, as before, $p = \sqrt{g_{12} \cdot g_{21}}/g_{11}$, and the length of a regular helical region of the chain is $(1 + p)/p$.

The mean-square value of a vector property of a statistically coiled chain can be expressed by eq. (5.25), as long as G is a second-order matrix with nonzero elements and different eigenvalues, so that it can be diagonalized by a similarity transformation. The second-order supermatrix W which enters into this equation is expressed by eq. (5.22), where $\mathcal{S}$ is a diagonal second-order supermatrix, which is the direct sum of matrices $S^{(1)} =$

* We obtain here $\nu(\Omega^{(\alpha)}) \to \infty$, and not $\nu(\Omega^{(\alpha)}) \to n$, since boundary effects were not taken into account in the derivation of eq. (4.71); strictly speaking, this is valid only for $n \to \infty$.

$S(\varphi_1, \varphi_2)$ and $S^{(2)} = S(-\varphi_2, -\varphi_1)$. Such a supermatrix has been written out explicitly in Chapter 5 [see eq. (5.18)]. Substituting into this equation $S^{(1)}$ and $S^{(2)}$ instead of $f^{(1)}$ and $f^{(2)}$ and using the condition $g_{11} = g_{22}$, we obtain:

$$W = \begin{vmatrix} \dfrac{S^{(1)} + S^{(2)}}{2} & \dfrac{S^{(1)} - S^{(2)}}{2} \\ \dfrac{1-p}{1+p}\cdot\dfrac{S^{(1)} - S^{(2)}}{2} & \dfrac{1-p}{1+p}\cdot\dfrac{S^{(1)} + S^{(2)}}{2} \end{vmatrix} \tag{6.41}$$

In order to calculate the elements of the sixth-order matrix $(I - W)^{-1}$ which enter into eq. (5.25), let us use the symmetry conditions which relate the elements of matrices $S^{(1)}$ and $S^{(2)}$. Substituting for these elements into eq. (6.5) the quantities $\varphi_{2k-1} = \varphi_1$, and $\varphi_{2k} = \varphi_2$ (for $S^{(1)}$) and $\varphi_{2k-1} = -\varphi_2$ and $\varphi_{2k} = -\varphi_1$, (for $S^{(2)}$), we find that, in our case,

$$\begin{aligned} S_{11}^{(1)} &= S_{11}^{(2)} \\ S_{12}^{(1)} &= S_{21}^{(2)} \\ S_{13}^{(1)} &= -S_{31}^{(2)} \\ S_{21}^{(1)} &= S_{12}^{(2)} \\ S_{22}^{(1)} &= S_{22}^{(2)} \\ S_{23}^{(1)} &= -S_{32}^{(2)} \\ S_{31}^{(1)} &= -S_{13}^{(2)} \\ S_{32}^{(1)} &= -S_{23}^{(2)} \\ S_{33}^{(1)} &= S_{33}^{(2)} \end{aligned} \tag{6.42}$$

Similarly, using the fact that, if torsional oscillations are neglected, matrices $S^{(\alpha)}$ ($\alpha = 1, 2$) are matrices of rotation, i.e., they are orthonormalized by rows and columns, and their determinants are equal to unity, we find that in this case the sums and differences of the nondiagonal elements of matrix $S^{(\alpha)}$ ($\alpha = 1, 2$)

$$\begin{aligned} s_{pq}^{(\alpha)} &= S_{pq}^{(\alpha)} + S_{qp}^{(\alpha)} \\ \sigma_{pq}^{(\alpha)} &= S_{pq}^{(\alpha)} - S_{qp}^{(\alpha)} \end{aligned} \tag{6.43}$$

($p, q = 1, 2;\ 2, 3;\ 3, 1$) are linked to the trace of this matrix $\mathrm{Sp}S^{(\alpha)}$ and its diagonal elements $S_{pp}^{(\alpha)}$ ($p = 1, 2, 3$) by the equations:

$$\begin{aligned} s_{pq}^2 &= \gamma_p\gamma_q \\ \sigma_{pq}^2 &= \delta\cdot\gamma_r \\ s_{pq}s_{qr} &= \gamma_q s_{rp} \\ \sigma_{pq}\sigma_{qr} &= \delta\cdot s_{rp} \\ \sigma_{pq}s_{qr} &= \gamma_r s_{rp} \\ s_{pq}\sigma_{qr} &= \gamma_p\sigma_{rp} \end{aligned} \tag{6.44}$$

where

$$\begin{aligned} \gamma_p &= 1 - \mathrm{Sp}S + 2S_{pp} \\ \delta &= 1 + \mathrm{Sp}S = 4 - \gamma_1 - \gamma_2 - \gamma_3 \end{aligned} \tag{6.45}$$

Furthermore, it follows from eqs. (6.42) that γ_p and δ are identical for matrices $S^{(1)}$ and $S^{(2)}$. Using relations (6.42) and (6.45) for calculating the elements of matrix $(I - W)^{-1}$ and taking into account eqs. (6.6) and (6.7) for $\mathbf{r}_h$ and $\mathbf{r}_\mu$, we obtain:

$$\overline{h^2} = 4nl^2 \frac{\gamma_3}{p(\gamma_1 + \gamma_2)} \cos^2 \frac{\alpha_2}{2} \tag{6.46}$$

and

$$\overline{\mu^2} = nm^2 \frac{\gamma_1 + \gamma_2 + p^2\delta}{p\gamma_3} \sin^2 \frac{\beta + \psi}{2} \tag{6.47}$$

where

$$\begin{aligned} \cos\psi &= (\gamma_1 - \gamma_2)/(\gamma_1 + \gamma_2) \\ \sin\psi &= 2s_{12}/(\gamma_1 + \gamma_2) \end{aligned} \tag{6.48}$$

We omit the superscript in s_{12} since, according to eqs. (6.42) and (6.43) $s_{12}^{(1)} = s_{12}^{(2)}$. Here, as previously, n is the number of monomer units in the chain, l is the length of each link of the main chain, $\pi - \alpha_2$ is the valence angle in the main chain at the —CRR′— group, m is the absolute value of vector $\mathbf{m}$ of the summation dipole moment of a monomer unit, and $(\pi - \beta)/2$ is the angle between $\mathbf{m}$ and the bisectrix of the angle $\angle$RCR′ in the side group (for chains $(\text{—CH}_2\text{—CHR—})_n$, $\pi - \beta$ is equal to the valence angle $\angle$HCR, while for chains of the type $(\text{—CH}_2\text{—CR}_2\text{—})_n$, $\pi - \beta = 0$).

The calculation of the mean vector properties of macromolecules, taking into account torsional oscillations about the equilibrium conformations 1 and 2, cannot be carried out in a simple analytical form because, in this case, eq. (6.44) is not followed; it requires the use of electronic computers. Nevertheless, eqs. (6.35)–(6.40) which characterize the conformational structure of the chain are valid also in this case (if it is considered that conformations 1 and 2 are not rigidly fixed states of the monomer units, but include also torsional oscillations).

In Chapter 3 we examined the crystal structures of macromolecules and established the relation between the parameters of crystal structures, namely, of the steps along the axis of the helix d and angle of turn ϑ per monomer unit, on the one hand, and the matrices of the cosines of the angles between the axes of the local systems of coordinates linked with neighboring monomer units, on the other hand. For isotactic macromolecules, this relationship is given by eqs. (3.3) in which vector **b** (b_1, b_2, b_3) determines the position of the origin of coordinates (X_k, Y_k, Z_k) in the system (X_{k-1}, Y_{k-1}, Z_{k-1}), i.e., it is the vector of the length of a monomer unit. Considering that, in the local systems of coordinates which we have selected, the Z axes of which are directed along the vector of the length of a monomer unit (see Fig. 6.1), $b_1 = b_2 = 0$, and $b_3 = 2l \cos \alpha_2/2$, and, using the notation of eq. (6.45), we can rewrite eq. (3.3) in the form

$$\begin{aligned} 2(1 + \cos \vartheta) &= \delta \\ 2d^2(1 - \cos \vartheta) &= 4l^2\gamma_3 \cos^2 (\alpha_2/2) \end{aligned} \tag{6.49}$$

Comparison of eqs. (6.46) and (6.47) with eq. (6.49) permits one to express the dimnesions and dipole moments of free isotactic chains in terms of the parameters d and ϑ which characterize the crystal helical structures of these chains.

We have, then,

$$\overline{h^2} = n[d_t^2 d^2/(d_t^2 - d^2)](1/p) \tag{6.50}$$

$$\overline{\mu^2} = nm^2 \left[\frac{d_t^2}{d^2}\left(\frac{1}{p} + p \cot^2 \frac{\vartheta}{2}\right) - \frac{1}{p}\right] \sin^2 \frac{\beta + \psi}{2} \tag{6.51}$$

where

$$d_t = 2l \cos (\alpha_2/2) \tag{6.52}$$

is a step along the axis of the helix per single monomer unit in a planar *trans* chain, and angle ψ is related to the valence angles $\pi - \alpha_1$ and $\pi - \alpha_2$ and the angles of internal rotation φ_1 and φ_2 by the equation

$$\sin \psi = \frac{-2\sin(\Delta\varphi)\sin\frac{\alpha_1}{2}\left[\cos(\Delta\varphi)\sin\frac{\alpha_1}{2}\cos\frac{\alpha_2}{2} - \cos\varphi\cos\frac{\alpha_1}{2}\sin\frac{\alpha_2}{2}\right]}{\left(\cos(\Delta\varphi)\sin\frac{\alpha_1}{2}\cos\frac{\alpha_2}{2} - \cos\varphi\cos\frac{\alpha_1}{2}\sin\frac{\alpha_2}{2}\right)^2 + \sin^2(\Delta\varphi)\sin^2\frac{\alpha_1}{2}} \tag{6.53}$$

where

$$\begin{aligned} \varphi &= (\varphi_1 + \varphi_2)/2 \\ \Delta\varphi &= (\varphi_1 - \varphi_2)/2 \end{aligned} \tag{6.54}$$

which follows from eqs. (6.48), (6.43), (6.45) and (6.5). Equations (6.50) and (6.51), as should have been expected, lead to an unlimited increase of $\overline{h^2}$ and $\overline{\mu^2}$ as $\varphi_1, \varphi_2 \to 0°$ (when $d \to d_t$ and $\vartheta \to 0°$).

Introducing into eqs. (6.50) and (6.51) eqs. (3.4), which express d and ϑ in terms of the valence angles $\pi - \alpha_1$ and $\pi - \alpha_2$ and the angles of internal rotation φ_1 and φ_2, and also by use of eq. (6.52), we obtain finally (21):

$$\overline{h^2} = \frac{2Nl^2}{p}\cdot\frac{\sin^2\varphi\cos^2\frac{\alpha_1}{2}\cos^2\frac{\alpha_2}{2}}{\left(\cos(\Delta\varphi)\sin\frac{\alpha_1}{2}\cos\frac{\alpha_2}{2} - \cos\varphi\cos\frac{\alpha_1}{2}\sin\frac{\alpha_2}{2}\right)^2 + \sin^2(\Delta\varphi)\sin^2\frac{\alpha_1}{2}} \tag{6.55}$$

and

$$\overline{\mu^2} = nm^2\,\frac{\left(\cos\Delta\varphi\sin\frac{\alpha_1}{2}\cos\frac{\alpha_2}{2} - \cos\varphi\cos\frac{\alpha_1}{2}\sin\frac{\alpha_2}{2}\right)^2 + \sin^2(\Delta\varphi)\sin^2\frac{\alpha_1}{2}}{\sin^2\varphi\cos^2\frac{\alpha_1}{2}}$$

$$\times\left[\frac{1}{p} + p\,\frac{\left(\cos\varphi\cos\frac{\alpha_1}{2}\cos\frac{\alpha_2}{2} + \cos(\Delta\varphi)\sin\frac{\alpha_1}{2}\sin\frac{\alpha_2}{2}\right)^2}{\left(\cos(\Delta\varphi)\sin\frac{\alpha_1}{2}\cos\frac{\alpha_2}{2} - \cos\varphi \times \cos\frac{\alpha_1}{2}\sin\frac{\alpha_2}{2}\right)^2 + \sin^2(\Delta\varphi)\sin^2\frac{\alpha_1}{2}}\right] \times \sin^2\frac{\beta+\psi}{2} \tag{6.56}$$

where $N = 2n$ is the number of bonds in the main chain and ψ is expressed by eq. (6.53). Analysis shows that, for the crystal structures of isotactic chains given in Table 3.1, $|\psi| < \pi/2$, and $\psi \lessgtr 0$, if the dipolar side groups repel each other more strongly than the nonpolar ones. Let us note that eq. (6.55) may be written in the simple form

$$\overline{h^2} = (\overline{h^2})'/p \tag{6.57}$$

where

$$(\overline{h^2})' = \frac{4nl^2}{p} \cdot \frac{\sin^2 \varphi \cos^2 \frac{\alpha_1}{2} \cos^2 \frac{\alpha_2}{2}}{\left(\cos (\Delta\varphi) \sin \frac{\alpha_1}{2} \cos \frac{\alpha_2}{2} - \cos \varphi \cos \frac{\alpha_1}{2} \sin \frac{\alpha_2}{2}\right)^2 + \sin^2 (\Delta\varphi) \sin^2 \frac{\alpha_1}{2}} \tag{6.58}$$

is the value of $\overline{h^2}$ calculated without taking into account correlations between the conformations of neighboring monomer units (i.e., for $p = 1$). Equation (6.57) for chains with symmetric side groups was first derived by Gotlib (22). It is evident that quantity $(\overline{h^2})'$, defined by eq. (6.58), is identical with the quantities calculated from eq. (6.10) for chains with symmetric side groups and from eq. (6.23) (for $\alpha_1 = \alpha_2$) for isotactic chains, when the proper internal rotation parameters calculated by the rotational-isomeric approximation are introduced into them. As the energy of breaking helical structure of the chain increases, i.e., as the degree of correlation between the conformations of neighboring units increases, $p \to 0$ and $\overline{h^2}$, as expected, increases without limit.* For isotactic chains with tetrahedral valence angles, which crystallize in the form of 3_1 helices for which $\varphi_1 = 0°$ and $\varphi_2 = 120°$,

$$\overline{\mu^2} = (\overline{\mu^2})' \, {}^1\!/_2[p + (1/p)] \tag{6.59}$$

where $(\overline{\mu^2})'$ is the value of $\overline{\mu^2}$ at $p = 1$.

Equations (6.55) and (6.56) are valid (in the rotational-isomeric approximation under investigation) for isotactic chains which crystallize in the form of helices $(\varphi_1, \varphi_2)_n$, and chains with symmetric side groups, which

* Actually, when $p \to 0$, one should, of course, use not eq. (5.25), which is the basis of eq. (6.57), but rather the more general equation, eq. (5.24), which, in this case, becomes eq. (5.15), according to which $\overline{h^2} \sim n^2$.

crystallize in the form of helices $(\varphi, \varphi)_n$. These equations have been derived by Birshtein (21). In the case of chains with symmetric side groups we have $\beta = 0°$, $\varphi_1 = \varphi_2 = \varphi$, $\Delta\varphi = 0°$; $\psi = 0°$, so that eqs. (6.55) and (6.56) assume the form

$$\overline{h^2} = \frac{Nl^2(1 + \cos\alpha_1)(1 + \cos\alpha_2)(1 - \cos^2\varphi)}{2p\left(\sin\frac{\alpha_1}{2}\cos\frac{\alpha_2}{2} - \cos\varphi\cos\frac{\alpha_1}{2}\sin\frac{\alpha_2}{2}\right)^2} \tag{6.60}$$

and (for $\varphi \neq 0°$)

$$\overline{\mu^2} = 0 \tag{6.61}$$

Consequently, in the case of macromolecules with symmetric side groups and monomer unit conformations (φ, φ) and $(-\varphi, -\varphi)$, the mean-square value of the dipole moment is equal to zero in the rotational-isomeric approximation, independent of the values of the angle of internal rotation φ (if $\varphi \neq 0°$) and the correlation parameter $p(1)$. In the case of real macromolecules of such structure, $\overline{\mu^2}$ may differ from zero because of the torsional oscillations of the elements; it is possible to expect, however, that the quantity $\overline{\mu^2}$ in such molecules will be much smaller than nm^2. For $\alpha_1 = \alpha_2$:

$$\overline{h^2} = 2Nl^2\left(\frac{1 + \cos\alpha}{1 - \cos\alpha}\right)\left(\frac{1 + \cos\varphi}{1 - \cos\varphi}\right)\frac{1}{p} \tag{6.62}$$

In the particular case of isotactic chains, which crystallize in the form of $(0, \varphi)_n$ helices, e.g., for macromolecules of type $(\text{—}CH_2\text{—}CHR\text{—})_n$ which crystallize in the form of 3_1 helices, for which $\varphi = 120°$, we have $\varphi_1 = 0°$, $\varphi_2 = \varphi$, so that, for $\alpha_1 = \alpha_2$, $\psi = 0°$, and eqs. (6.55) and (6.56) become, respectively, (for $\alpha_1 = \alpha_2 = \alpha$):

$$\overline{h^2} = Nl^2\left[\frac{(1 + \cos\alpha)^2}{1 - \cos\alpha}\right]\frac{1}{p} \tag{6.63}$$

$$\overline{\mu^2} = nm^2\left(\frac{1 - \cos\alpha}{1 + \cos\alpha}\right)\left(\frac{1 - \cos\beta}{2}\right)\frac{1}{p}\left[1 + \left(\frac{2p^2}{1 - \cos\alpha}\right)\left(\frac{1 + \cos\varphi}{1 - \cos\varphi}\right)\right] \tag{6.64}$$

which were obtained by Birshtein and Ptitsyn (23). It is interesting that, for such chains, $\overline{h^2}$ is independent of the value of the angle of internal rotation, φ. The dependences of $(\overline{h^2}/\overline{h^2}_{\text{fr. rot.}})^{1/2}$ and $(\overline{\mu^2}/nm^2)^{1/2}$ on p, calculated with eqs. (6.55) and (6.56), are shown in Figure 6.2. It can be seen from this figure that $\overline{h^2}$ of isotactic macromolecules is a much stronger function of

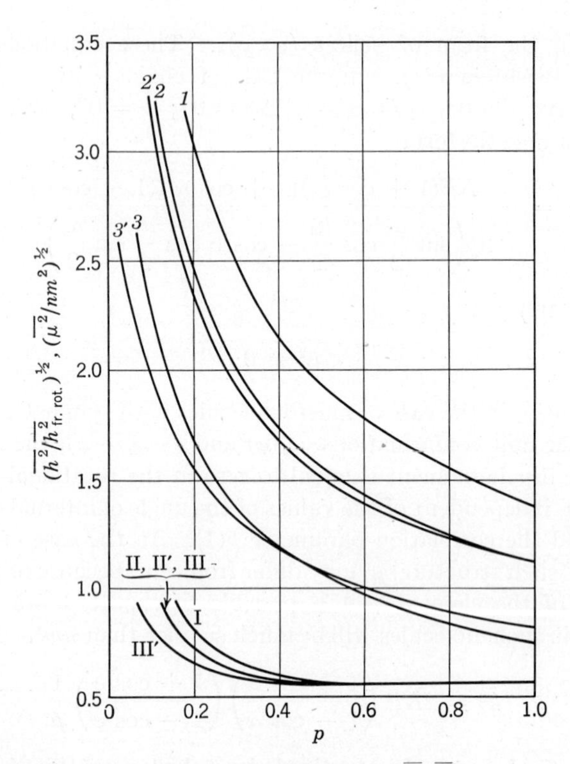

Fig. 6.2. Dependence on p of (*1–3*) mean dimensions $(\overline{h^2}/\overline{h^2}_{\text{fr. rot.}})^{1/2}$ and (*I–III*) mean dipole moments $(\mu^2/nm^2)^{1/2}$ of isotactic polymers; $\pi - \alpha = 116°30'$; $\pi - \beta = 109°30'$: (*1*), (*I*) $\varphi_1 = 0°$, $\varphi_2 = 120°$; (*2*), (*II*) $\varphi_1 = -15°$, $\varphi_2 = 105°$; (*2′*), (*II*)′ same, with torsional oscillations in a flat well with a 15° half-width; (*3*), (*III*) $\varphi_1 = -30°$, $\varphi_2 = 90°$; (*3′*), (*III′*) same, with torsional oscillations in a flat well with a 30° half-width.

p than $\overline{\mu^2}$. The same functions, calculated with torsional oscillations taken into account (see section 7.1), are also shown in Figure 6.2.

Corradini and co-workers (24,29) have obtained results similar to eq. (6.63); they carried out the calculations in the same approximation for isotactic molecules which crystallize in the form of 3_1 helices with internal rotation angles (0°, 120°). Unlike Birshtein and Ptitsyn (23), these authors assumed that conformation (0°, 120°; −120°, 0°) does not exist in neighboring monomer units, because of its high conformational energy, but it is replaced by one of the isoenergetic conformations (0°, 120°; −60°, 0°) or (0°, 60°; −120°, 0°) (see section 3.3). Let us note that, in the studies of Corradini (24,29), calculation of the averaged products of matrices was not carried out with an equation of the type (4.39), based directly on the

Ising model as was done above; instead the conditional probability of transition between conformations was calculated first, i.e., the Ising model was compared to the corresponding Markoff chain (see Chapter 4), after which the averaging was carried out by the method of Markoff chains [see eq. (4.62)]. Therefore, the calculation parameter was not the quantity p, but the conditional probability of transition from a given conformation of the $(k - 1)$th monomer unit to the nonidentical conformation of the kth monomer unit, equal to $p/(1 + p)$ [see eq. (6.39)]. This quantity is also equal to the reciprocal value of the average number of monomer units ν in a regular helical region of the chain [eq. (6.40)]. The final result of Corradini et al. (24,29) has the form (with the assumption that the valence angles are tetrahedral):

$$\overline{h^2} = \frac{8}{3} Nl^2\nu \left(1 - \frac{1}{2\nu} - \frac{35}{288\nu^2} - \dots\right) \tag{6.65}$$

which is identical with eq. (6.63) with a precision up to linear terms in $1/\nu$ or in p (for tetrahedral valence angles).

Let us examine now the averaged vector properties of syndiotactic macromolecules of the type $(—CH_2—CRR'—)_n$, taking into account correlation between the conformations of neighboring monomer units. According to the equivalence postulate of Natta and Corradini (19,20) (see section 3.1), the helical crystalline conformations of such chains are characterized by the sequence of angles of internal rotation in the chain $(\varphi_1, \varphi_1, \varphi_2, \varphi_2)^{n/2}$, where n is the degree of polymerization and (φ_1, φ_1) and (φ_2, φ_2) are the angles of internal rotation of the $—CH_2—CRR'—$ and $—CRR'—CH_2—$ bonds of the monomer unit (see Fig. 6.1). It follows from Table 3.3 that each monomer unit of a free macromolecule can be present in one of two conformations, $\Omega^{(1)} = (\varphi_1, \varphi_1)$ or $\Omega^{(2)} = (\varphi_2, \varphi_2)$. Furthermore, $\varphi_1 \neq \varphi_2$ (with the exception of the case $\varphi_1 = \varphi_2 = 0°$),* so that conformations $\Omega^{(1)}$ and $\Omega^{(2)}$ are different.

In contrast to isotactic molecules, in which the two possible conformations of monomer units are related by symmetry conditions, such a relation does not exist in syndiotactic molecules. Therefore, conformation sequences (φ_1, φ_1), (φ_1, φ_1) and (φ_2, φ_2), (φ_2, φ_2) have, in general, different energies, so that elements g_{11} and g_{22} of the second-order matrix G [see eq.

* In the particular case in which $\varphi_1 = \varphi_2 = 0°$, the polymer chain crystallizes as a planar zigzag with identical conformations of all monomer units. Investigation of the flexibility of such a chain requires that energetically less favorable conformations be taken into account; such conformations are not found in the crystalline chain; they can, however, exist in a statistically coiled chain.

(4.6)] are different. On the other hand, conformation sequences (φ_1, φ_1), (φ_2, φ_2) and (φ_2, φ_2), (φ_1, φ_1) are segments of enantiomorphous helices (see Section 3.1), and, therefore, have identical energies; this determines the relation between elements g_{12} and g_{21} of matrix G.* The conformational structure of a syndiotactic chain, in which each monomer unit may have two different conformations, is described by eqs. (4.64)–(4.72).

In calculating the mean squares of the vector properties of macromolecules, it is possible to use eq. (5.25), in which supermatrix W is given by eq. (5.22) or, in explicit form, by eq. (4.76) for $f(\Omega^{(1)}) = S(\Omega^{(1)}) = S(\varphi_1, \varphi_1)$ and $f(\Omega^{(2)}) = S(\Omega^{(2)}) = S(\varphi_2, \varphi_2)$. Because of the difficulty of these calculations, they were carried out only for the case in which conformations $\Omega^{(1)}$ and $\Omega^{(2)}$ correspond to internal rotation angles (0°, 0°) and (−120°, −120°); this corresponds to the experimentally observed helical structure of the molecules of crystalline syndiotactic polypropylene and also to the results of the theoretical calculation (1,25,28) of the energetically most favorable conformations of the monomer units of syndiotactic polypropylene (see section 3.2). Defining the elements of matrices $S(\Omega^{(1)})$ and $S(\Omega^{(2)})$ by eqs. (6.5), using the fact that, in this case, all the elements of these matrices are equal to 0 or 1, and assuming that the valence angles are tetrahedral, we find that, as a result of calculation according to eq. (5.25),

$$\overline{h^2} = \frac{4}{3} Nl^2 \frac{r+q}{r-q}\left[\left(\frac{r}{1-q}\right) + \left(\frac{1-q}{r}\right)\right] \tag{6.66}$$

and

$$\overline{\mu^2} = \frac{1}{3} nm^2 \frac{1-q}{r}\left(\frac{r+q}{r-q}\right) \tag{6.67}$$

where

$$q = (g_{11} - g_{22})/2g_{11}$$

$$r = \left[\frac{(g_{11} - g_{22})^2}{4g_{11}^2} + \frac{g_{12}g_{21}}{g_{11}^2}\right]^{1/2} \tag{6.68}$$

By using eqs. (4.68) and (4.69), the equations, eqs. (6.66) and (6.67) derived by Birshtein and Ptitsyn (26) [see also Allegra et al. (29)], can be

* For example, if the terms $U(\Omega_{k-1}, \Omega_k)$, into which the energy of the chain is broken down, are defined in such a way that the energies of the conformations of the $(k-1)$th and kth monomer units enter symmetrically [in eq. (4.55), $x = 1/2$], then $g_{12} = g_{21}$.

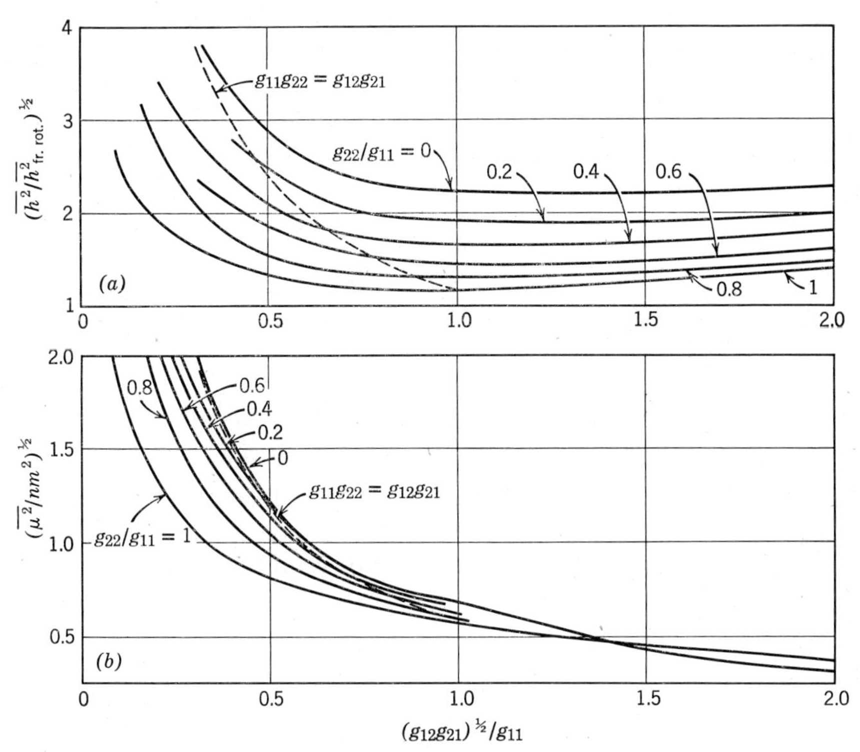

Fig. 6.3. Dependence on $(g_{12}g_{21})^{1/2}/g_{11}$ and g_{22}/g_{11} of (*a*) mean dimensions and (*b*) mean dipole moments of syndiotactic macromolecules. The dashed lines correspond to the absence of correlations between the conformations of adjacent monomer units.

represented by the first-order and second-order distribution functions of the monomer unit conformations:

$$\overline{h^2} = \frac{4}{3} Nl^2 \frac{w(\Omega^{(1)})}{w(\Omega^{(2)})} \left[\frac{2w(\Omega^{(1)})w(\Omega^{(2)}) - w(\Omega^{(1)}, \Omega^{(2)})}{w(\Omega^{(1)}, \Omega^{(2)})} + \frac{w(\Omega^{(1)}\Omega^{(2)})}{2w(\Omega^{(1)})w(\Omega^{(2)}) - w(\Omega^{(1)}, \Omega^{(2)})} \right] \tag{6.69}$$

$$\overline{\mu^2} = \frac{1}{3} nm^2 \frac{w(\Omega^{(1)})}{w(\Omega^{(2)})} \left[\frac{2w(\Omega^{(1)})w(\Omega^{(2)}) - w(\Omega^{(1)}, \Omega^{(2)})}{w(\Omega^{(1)}, \Omega^{(2)})} \right] \tag{6.70}$$

If there is no correlation between the conformations of neighboring monomer units ($g_{12}g_{21} = g_{11}g_{22}$ and $r + q = 1$), then

$$(\overline{h^2})' = (8/3g)Nl^2 \tag{6.71}$$

and

$$(\overline{\mu^2})' = (1/3g)nm^2 \tag{6.72}$$

where $g = g_{22}/g_{11}$.

Consequently, in the absence of correlations between the conformations of neighboring monomer units

$$\frac{(\overline{h^2}/\overline{h^2}_{\text{fr. rot.}})^{1/2}}{(\overline{\mu^2}/nm^2)^{1/2}} = 2 \tag{6.73}$$

(where $\overline{h^2}_{\text{fr. rot.}}$ is the value of $\overline{h^2}$ for free rotation). On the other hand, if correlations are present,

$$\frac{(\overline{h^2}/\overline{h^2}_{\text{fr. rot.}})^{1/2}}{(\overline{\mu^2}/nm^2)^{1/2}} = 2\sqrt{1 + \frac{2(g_{12}g_{21} - g_{11}g_{22})}{(g_{11} + g_{22})^2}} \tag{6.74}$$

i.e., this is greater than two if $g_{12}g_{21}/g_{11}g_{22} > 1$, and less than two if $g_{12}g_{21}/g_{11}g_{22} < 1$. The dependences of $(\overline{h^2}/\overline{h^2}_{\text{fr. rot.}})^{1/2}$ and $(\overline{\mu^2}/nm^2)^{1/2}$ on $\sqrt{g_{12}g_{21}/g_{11}}$ and g_{22}/g_{11} are shown in Figure 6.3. In this figure, the dotted lines are for eqs. (6.71) and (6.72), i.e., for the absence of correlations, when $g_{22} = g_{12}g_{21}/g_{11}$. As is evident for Figure 6.3, correlation has a stronger effect on $\overline{h^2}$ than on $\overline{\mu^2}$, just as in the case of isotactic polymers.

References

1. Birshtein, T. M., Candidate Dissertation, Institut Vysokomolekulyarnykh Soedinenii, Leningrad, Akad. Nauk SSSR, 1960.
2. Birshtein, T. M., O. B. Ptitsyn, and E. A. Sokolova, *Vysokomol. Soedin.*, **1**, 852 (1959).
3. Ptitsyn, O. B., and Yu. A. Sharonov, *Zh. Tekhn. Fiz.*, **27**, 2744 (1957); *Soviet Phys.-Tech. Phys.*, **2**, 2544 (1957).
4. Lifson, S., *J. Chem. Phys.*, 29, 80 (1958).
5. Chistorazum, A. A., *Dokl. Akad. Nauk SSSR*, **89**, 999 (1953).
6. Debye, P. J. W., Report No. 637 to Rubber Reserve Company 9.04. 1945, published in *The Collected Papers of Peter J. W. Debye*, Interscience, New York–London, 1954.
7. Taylor, W. J., *J. Chem. Phys.*, **15**, 412 (1947).
8. Kuhn, H., *J. Chem. Phys.*, **15**, 843 (1947).
9. Birshtein, T. M., and O. B. Ptitsyn, *Zh. Tekhn. Fiz.*, **24**, 1998 (1954).
10. Magnasco, V., *Ric. Sci.*, **30**, 405 (1960).
11. Magnasco, V., and C. Rossi, *J. Chem. Phys.*, **32**, 1881 (1960).
12. Rossi, C., and V. Magnasco, *Makromol. Chem.*, **41**, 45 (1960).
13. Mori, T., *J. Phys. Soc. Japan*, **15**, 1482, 1638, 2118 (1960).
14. Nagai, K., *Busseiron Kenkyu*, **4**, 65 (1958).
15. Nagai, K., *J. Chem. Phys.*, **30**, 660 (1959).
16. Birshtein, T. M., and O. B. Ptitsyn, *Zh. Fiz. Khim.*, **26**, 1215 (1952).

17. Birshtein, T. M., and O. B. Ptitsyn, *Zh. Fiz. Khim.*, **28,** 213 (1954).
18. Mori, T., *Busseiron Kenkyu*, **9,** 473 (1961); *ibid.*, **10,** 36 (1961).
19. Natta, G., and P. Corradini, *J. Polymer Sci.*, **39,** 29 (1959).
20. Natta, G., and P. Corradini, *Nuovo Cimento* (*Suppl. 1*), **15,** 9 (1960).
21. Birshtein, T. M., *Vysokomol. Soedin.*, in press.
22. Gotlib, Yu. Ya., *Zh. Tekhn. Fiz.*, **29,** 523 (1959); *Soviet Phys.-Tech. Phys.*, **4,** 465 (1959).
23. Birshtein, T. M., and O. B. Ptitsyn, *Zh. Tekhn. Fiz.*, **29,** 1048 (1959); *Soviet Phys.-Tech. Phys.*, **4,** 954 (1959).
24. Corradini, P., and G. Allegra, *Atti Accad. Nazl. Lincei Rend. Classe Sci. Fis. Mat. Nat.*, [8] **30,** 516 (1961).
25. Natta, G., P. Corradini, and P. Ganis, *Makromol. Chem.*, **39,** 238 (1960).
26. Birshtein, T. M., and O. B. Ptitsyn, *Vysokomol. Soedin.*, **2,** 628 (1960).
27. Natta, G., P. Corradini, and P. Ganis, *J. Polymer Sci.*, **58,** 1191 (1962).
28. Borisova, N. P., and T. M. Birshtein, *Vysokomol. Soedin.*, **6** 1234 (1964).
29. Allegra, G., P. Ganis, and P. Corradini, *Makromol. Chem.*, **61,** 225 (1963).

Chapter 7

COMPARISON OF THE THEORY WITH EXPERIMENT AND CONFORMATIONS OF TYPICAL MACROMOLECULES IN SOLUTION

7.1. Conformations of Isotactic and Syndiotactic Macromolecules

As was pointed out in section 6.1, comparison of the theory of the dimensions and dipole moments of macromolecules with experiment can yield valuable information on the conformational structure of macromolecules. We shall start with an examination of the conformational structure of stereoregular macromolecules of type $(—CH_2—CHR—)_n$, which have been subjected to the most extensive studies in the theoretical literature (1–13,86). First, let us note that the results obtained in Chapter 6 point to the fact that the dimensions and dipole moments of isotactic and syndiotactic molecules must, in general, be different from each other. This conclusion, which was first reached by Birshtein and Ptitsyn in 1954 (14,15) on the basis of a theory which assumed independent rotations about all the bonds of a chain, obviously remains valid also in the cases in which correlations between rotations within monomer units (1) and between them (5,7) are taken into account. At the present time, however, the theory cannot predict the magnitudes of these differences, since the derived equations contain parameters which can be evaluated quantitatively only in an approximate manner (see section 3.3). In recent years, a large number of attempts have been made to compare the dimensions of molecules of isotactic and atactic (nonstereoregular) polystyrene (16–21), polypropylene (22–27) and poly(methyl methacrylate) (28,87), determined from the intrinsic viscosity and by light scattering. In all cases, except for poly(methyl methacrylate) in acetone (87), the dimensions of the molecules of isotactic and atactic polymers were found to be identical. All these measurements were carried out in nonideal solvents in which the dimensions of the macromolecules are determined not only by the flexibility of the chain, but also by long-range interactions (see Introduction). As is shown by the theory of long-range interactions (29,30), such interactions increase the dimensions of macromolecules, and the increase is the greater, the smaller their dimensions in a Θ-solvent. When the long-range interactions are sufficiently large, the dimensions of polymer chains are completely independent of chain flexibility and of other factors which have an effect on their dimensions in ideal solvents (31) (including microtacticity, i.e., the fraction of isotactic and syndiotactic combinations of monomer units in the chains). Therefore, the identity of the dimensions of isotactic and atactic chains in solvents which are far from ideal can be explained by the compensating role of long-range interactions. In fact, the second virial coefficients of solutions of polystyrene, polypropylene and poly-1-butene, which are functions not only of the dimensions of molecules in a given solvent, but also of their dimensions in an ideal solvent (and also of the molecular weight) (29,30), differ for isotactic and atactic chains of a given molecular weight (18,20,26,32,82). This means that, in ideal solvents, the dimensions of the molecules of these polymers are a function of the microtacticity, although these differences, apparently, are rather small.

When the effect of long-range interactions was eliminated with the help of an approximate theory which takes these interactions into account, it was found that the dimensions of isotactic molecules are somewhat larger than those of atactic molecules in the case of polystyrene (20) and especially of poly-1-butene (82). It was possible to detect directly by experiment the difference in the dimensions of isotactic and atactic molecules of poly(methyl methacrylate) (87). While the intrinsic viscosity of poly(methyl methacrylate) in benzene is practically identical for isotactic and atactic samples (28,87) of identical molecular weight, in acetone the intrinsic viscosity of isotactic samples is considerably larger than that of the atactic polymers. This difference is quite understandable, since deviations from ideality of the solvent are much smaller for acetone than for benzene, so that differences in the unperturbed dimensions are less compensated in the first case by the different effects of long-range interactions. Having calculated the unperturbed dimensions of poly(methyl methacrylate) chains from the dependence of the intrinsic viscosity on the molecular weight, Krause and Cohn-Ginsburg (87) obtained for isotactic samples $(\overline{h^2}/\overline{h^2}_{\text{fr. rot.}})^{1/2} = 2.3$, while for the atactic samples investigated they found $(\overline{h^2}/\overline{h^2}_{\text{fr. rot.}})^{1/2} = 2.0$ (compare Table 1.1).

Finally, most recently, it has been possible to find Θ-solvents for isotactic poly(methyl methacrylate) (acetone at 27.6°C.) (101) and polypropylene (diphenyl ether at 145°C.) (102) and to measure directly the dimensions of isotactic macromolecules in Θ-solvents. In both cases, it was found that the dimensions of isotactic macromolecules are 10–15% greater than those of atactic chains: in poly(methyl methacrylate), $(\overline{h^2}/\overline{h^2}_{fr.\ rot.})^{1/2}$ is 2.3_5 for an isotactic sample and 2.0 for an atactic sample (101), in polypropylene $(\overline{h^2}/\overline{h^2}_{fr.\ rot.})^{1/2}$ is 1.9_5 for an isotactic sample and 1.7_5 for an atactic sample (102). (The data for the atactic sample also refer to diphenyl ether at a Θ-temperature of 153°C.)

At present, the difference predicted by theory between the dipole moments of isotactic molecules and atactic polymers has been established in a number of investigations; in all the cases studied, i.e., polystyrene (33), poly(methyl methacrylate) (34–36), poly(*n*-butyl methacrylate) (89), poly(*tert*-butyl methacrylate) (90), and poly(vinyl isobutyl ether) (36), the dipole moments of isotactic polymers were found to be larger than those of atactic polymers. In the case of syndiotactic poly(methyl methacrylate) and poly(*n*-butyl methacrylate) the dipole moment was found to be identical within experimental error with that of atactic samples; such measurements have not yet been carried out for other syndiotactic polymers. Thus, the dipole moments and dimensions of macromolecules are, evidently, a function of their microtacticity; however, since the differences between their values in molecules of isotactic and atactic polymers are relatively small (~10–15%), for the sake of simplicity, in what follows, we shall consider the dipole moments and even more so the dimensions of the molecules of isotactic and syndiotactic polymers as equal to the corresponding quantities of atactic chains in comparing theory with experiment.

As is evident from the data of Tables 1.1 and 1.2, in the case of polymers of type $(—CH_2—CHR—)_n$, the root mean-square dimensions of macromolecules $(\overline{h^2})^{1/2}$ are 1.8–2.5 as large as the root mean-square dimensions of chains with free rotation $(\overline{h^2}_{fr.\ rot.})^{1/2}$, while the root mean-square dipole moment, $(\overline{\mu^2})^{1/2}$, (for polymers with rigidly bonded polar groups) is approximately 1.5 times smaller than the root mean-square dipole moment of a freely jointed chain $n^{1/2}m$ (close to the root mean-square dipole moment of a chain with free rotation). For example, the most reliable value of $(\overline{h^2}/\overline{h^2}_{fr.\ rot.})^{1/2}$ for polystyrene is 2.3 (38), while $(\overline{\mu^2}/nm^2)^{1/2}$ for poly-*p*-chlorostyrene is 0.65 (39). Is it possible to account for these results in terms of the concepts of short-range order in macromolecules developed above and of the two possible mechanisms of chain flexibility (rotational isomerization and torsional oscillations)?

We shall examine first the model of torsional oscillations, i.e., we shall consider that rotational isomerization is not possible in the macromolecule and that the winding of the chain can occur only as a result of torsional oscillations about a single equilibrium position (a right-handed or left-handed 3_1 helix for isotactic molecules and a planar *trans* chain for syndiotactic molecules). Examination of molecular models has shown that torsional oscillations in neighboring monomer units are practically independent, so that in calculating $\overline{h^2}$ and $\overline{\mu^2}$, it is possible to use equations which do not take into account the correlation between oscillations in neighboring quasi-independent monomer units, i.e., eqs. (6.19) and (6.20) for isotactic chains and eqs. (6.27) and (6.28) for syndiotactic chains. Furthermore, in this case it is possible to regard as independent even the rotations about two bonds of a single monomer unit, i.e., to use the simpler equations, eqs. (6.23) and (6.24) for isotactic chains and eqs. (6.29) and (6.30) for syndiotactic chains.

Investigation of the conditions of internal rotation in isotactic chains of type $(\text{—CH}_2\text{—CHR—})_n$ (37) (see section 3.3) shows that the potential well close to the position that corresponds to the crystalline conformation of the chain has quite steep walls, so that it can be approximated best by a right angle potential well, and not by the usually employed cosinusoidal potential. Therefore, we shall consider that torsional oscillations in isotactic (and also syndiotactic) chains of type $(\text{—CH}_2\text{—CHR—})_n$ take place in a right angle potential well with a half width $\delta\varphi$ and the center at φ_0. Then

$$\overline{\cos\,\varphi} = \frac{\sin\,(\delta\varphi)}{\delta\varphi}\cos\,\varphi_0$$
$$\overline{\sin\,\varphi} = \frac{\sin\,(\delta\varphi)}{\delta\varphi}\sin\,\varphi_0 \qquad (7.1)$$

In studies in which the influence of torsional oscillations on the mean dimensions and dipole moments of the chains was examined in detail (4,6, 8–10), the following was demonstrated. For the model of quasi-independent monomer units, the statistical coiling of an isotactic chain, described by the ratio $(\overline{h^2}/\overline{h^2}_{\text{fr. rot.}})^{1/2}$, is determined principally by the amplitude of oscillations about the equilibrium position $\varphi_1 = 0°$ and is practically independent of the amplitude of oscillations about the equilibrium position $\varphi_2 = 120°$. The quantity $(\overline{\mu^2}/nm^2)^{1/2}$ for isotactic chains depends in general on the amplitudes of oscillations about the equilibrium position of both bonds of the monomer unit; in this case also, however, the main role is played by the amplitude of oscillations about $\varphi_1 = 0°$ (4,8,9). The dependence of $(\overline{h^2}/\overline{h^2}_{\text{fr. rot.}})^{1/2}$ on $\delta\varphi$ for independent torsional oscillations of neighboring bonds (curve *1*), calculated by eq. (6.23), is shown in Figure 7.1, as well as the same dependence calculated with eq. (6.19) with the assumption that the two bonds of a monomer unit deviate simultaneously from the equilibrium position by identical angles in the same direction (curve *2*) or in opposite directions (curve *3*). As can be

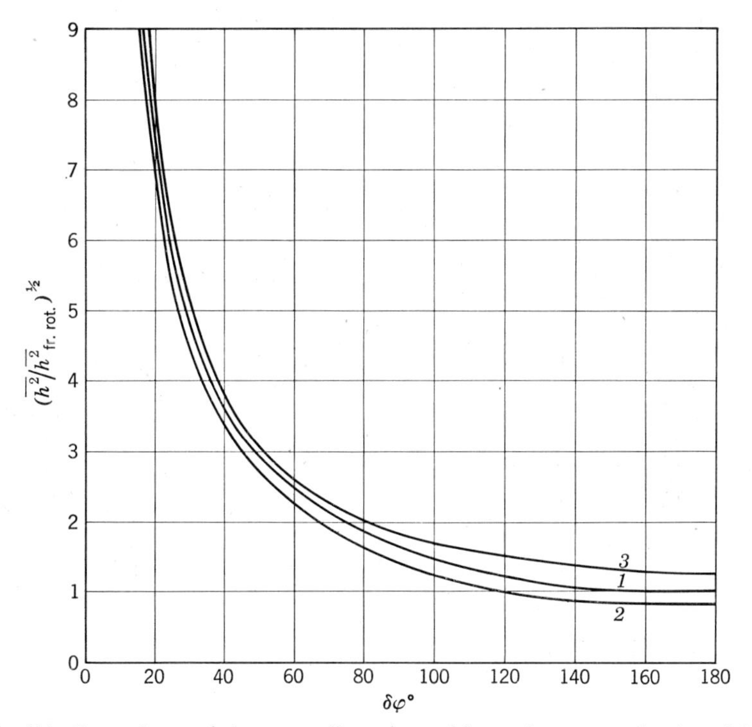

Fig. 7.1. Dependence of the mean dimensions of isotactic macromolecules with torsional oscillations of the bonds on the half-width, $\delta\varphi$, of a symmetrical potential well: (*1*) independent oscillations of adjacent bonds, $\delta\varphi_1 = \delta\varphi_2$; (*2*) $\varphi_2 = \varphi_1 + 120°$; (*3*) $\varphi_2 = -\varphi_1 + 120°$.

seen from the figure, it is necessary to assume that $\delta\varphi \approx 60°$ in order to interpret the experimental value of $(\overline{h^2}/\overline{h^2}_{\text{fr. rot.}})^{1/2}$ of 2.2–2.5 (for typical macromolecules). This value changes little even when the interdependence of oscillations of bonds inside monomer units is taken into account. However, such a value of $\delta\varphi$ is found to be too small to explain the observed value of the dipole moment, since in this case $(\overline{\mu^2}/nm^2)^{1/2} \approx 1.2$, instead of the experimental value ≈ 0.65. Values of $(\overline{\mu^2}/nm^2)^{1/2} < 1$, obtained in experiments, cannot be obtained at all on the basis of the model of symmetric torsional oscillations with any values of $\delta\varphi$.*

* Mori (9) explains such disagreements within general equations of the type of eq. (5.7) by the effect of long-range interactions. Equation (5.7), however, does not take these interactions into account, and, moreover, the experimental data discussed with regard to the dimensions of macromolecules are for θ-solvents, while the dipole moments of macromolecules are practically completely independent of long-range interactions.

As is shown by an analysis of models of the molecules and also by calculations of potentials of intramolecular interactions (37,40,88) (see section 3.3), the potential wells of real chains are not symmetrical relative to the equilibrium position, but are displaced toward angles $\varphi_1 < 0°$ and $\varphi_2 < 120°$. Even when the asymmetry of torsional oscillations is taken into account, however, it is still not possible to bring into agreement the values of $(\overline{h^2}/\overline{h^2}_{\text{fr. rot.}})^{1/2}$ and $(\overline{\mu^2}/nm^2)^{1/2}$ of isotactic chains (6). In fact, in the limiting case in which the oscillations of the elements occur only in one direction from positions that correspond to the crystal structure, it is necessary to have an asymmetric well with a half-width $\delta\varphi \approx 35°$ in order to account for the experimental value of $(\overline{h^2}/\overline{h^2}_{\text{fr. rot.}})^{1/2}$, i.e., the deviation from staggered conformations ($\varphi_1 = 0°$, $\varphi_2 = 120°$) must be by 70° in one direction. This is accompanied by a value of $(\overline{\mu^2}/nm^2)^{1/2} \approx 1.0$, i.e., 1.5 times greater than the experimental value. On the other hand, the experimental value of $(\overline{\mu^2}/nm^2)^{1/2} \approx 0.65$ requires torsional oscillations within an interval of φ_1 of $-90°$ to $0°$ and of φ_2 of $30°$ to $120°$, which gives $(\overline{h^2}/\overline{h^2}_{\text{fr. rot.}})^{1/2} = 1.2$.

Thus, the experimental values of the dimensions and dipole moments of isotactic chains cannot be explained simultaneously in terms of the model of torsional oscillations with any assumptions concerning the potential wells. In order to illustrate this fact, Figure 20 gives values of $(\overline{\mu^2}/nm^2)^{1/2}$ as a function of $(\overline{h^2}/\overline{h^2}_{\text{fr. rot.}})^{1/2}$ calculated with eqs. (6.23) and (6.24) or (6.19) and (6.20), with the parameter $\delta\varphi$ left out. As can be seen from the figure, the experimental data deviate considerably from the theoretical relations, both within the assumption of independent rotations of bonds of the monomer units (curves *1* and *2*), and within the assumption of correlated rotations of two bonds of a single monomer unit (curves *3* and *4*). In the last case a value of $(\overline{\mu^2}/nm^2)^{1/2} < 1$ is never obtained for any values of $\delta\varphi$.

Let us add to this that the range of torsional oscillations necessary to explain the real flexibility of isotactic macromolecules is too large and is not consistent with the conditions of internal rotation in the molecules under investigation. It is known (see section 2.1) that, even in the case of ethane molecules, deviations from staggered positions of elements by 60° are accompanied by an increase of the energy by 3000 cal/mole. Calculation of the intramolecular potential energy in isotactic polypropylene (37) has shown that free torsional oscillations can take place only within an interval of angles φ_1 of $-30°$ to $0°$ and φ_2 of $90°$ to $120°$. Calculations on the basis of eqs. (6.23) and (6.24) for this case give $(\overline{h^2}/\overline{h^2}_{\text{fr. rot.}})^{1/2} = 8.2$ and $(\overline{\mu^2}/nm^2)^{1/2} = 3.7$; this is in sharp disagreement with the experimental values.

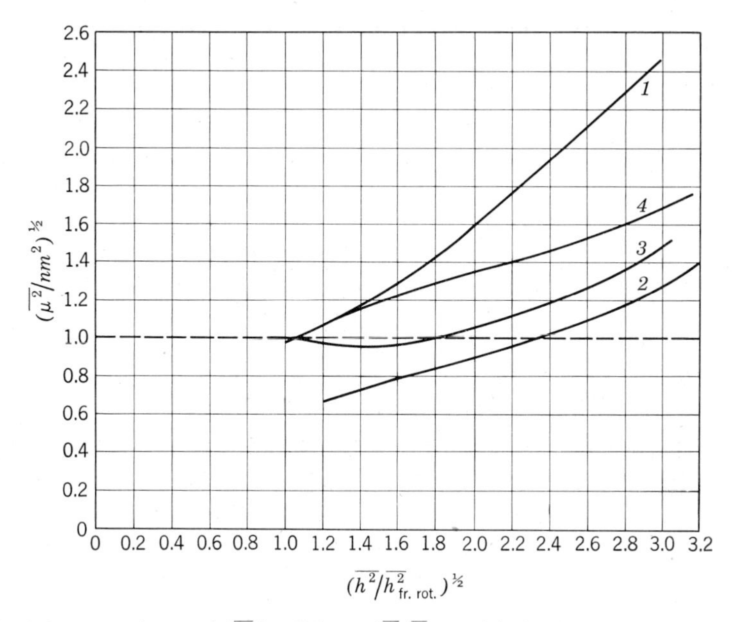

Fig. 7.2. Dependence of $(\overline{\mu^2}/nm^2)^{1/2}$ on $(\overline{h^2}/\overline{h^2}_{\text{fr. rot.}})^{1/2}$ for isotactic molecules with torsional oscillations of the bonds: (*1*) independent oscillations of adjacent bonds in symmetric potential wells; (*2*) independent oscillations of adjacent bonds in potential wells with limiting symmetry; (*3*) $\varphi_2 = \varphi_1 + 120°$; (*4*) $\varphi_2 = -\varphi_1 + 120°$ (--) $(\overline{\mu^2}/nm^2)^{1/2} = 1$.

Similar results may be obtained also for syndiotactic molecules. While in this case the experimental values of $(\overline{h^2}/\overline{h^2}_{\text{fr. rot.}})^{1/2}$ and $(\overline{\mu^2}/nm^2)^{1/2}$ can be explained simultaneously by assuming the presence of free torsional oscillations of all elements within an interval of rotation angles from $-50°$ to $0°$, this interval is obviously too large and, in particular, is in complete disagreement with calculations of the intramolecular potential energy of syndiotactic polypropylene (40,83,88). These calculations indicate that torsional oscillations are possible within a much narrower range of angles, approximately from $-30°$ to $0°$. On the other hand, even oscillations within an interval of $-40°$ to $0°$ give $(\overline{h^2}/\overline{h^2}_{\text{fr. rot.}})^{1/2} = 3.4$ and $(\overline{\mu^2}/nm^2)^{1/2} = 1.0$, which is in complete disagreement with experiment. We may assert, therefore, that the *torsional oscillation model cannot give a quantitative explanation of the experimentally observed values of the dimensions and dipole moments of typical macromoleculs.*

Let us pass now to the rotational isomeric model. In the case of isotactic macromolecules, eqs. (6.50) and 6.51) for $\overline{h^2}$ and $\overline{\mu^2}$, which do not take torsional oscillations into account, contain the parameter $p = e^{-\Delta U/kT}$, where

ΔU is the energy of breaking of the helical structure of the chain. For molecules which crystallize in a 3_1 helix (for example, for polystyrene), d = 6.5 Å. Using this value, we find that eq. (6.50) reproduces the experimental value of $(\overline{h^2}/\overline{h^2}_{\text{fr. rot.}})^{1/2} \approx 2.3$ for $p = 0.35$, which corresponds to $\Delta U = 600$ cal/mole (5). Introducing this value of p into eq. (6.51), and remembering that, according to (6.53), $\psi = 0$ for chains that crystallize in the form of 3_1 helices, we obtain $(\overline{\mu^2}/nm^2)^{1/2} = 0.60$ (5), which is close to the experimental value. Thus, in the case of isotactic chains, the rotational-isomeric approximation, contrary to the approximation based on torsional oscillations of the elements, is found to be self-consistent in the sense that it leads to agreement between the two experimentally observed quantities, $(\overline{h^2}/\overline{h^2}_{\text{fr. rot.}})^{1/2}$ and $(\overline{\mu^2}/nm^2)^{1/2}$, with the use of a single parameter of chain flexibility.

The existence of rotational isomerism in statistically coiled isotactic macromolecules is confirmed by direct calculation of the potential energies of different conformations of monomer units of isotactic polypropylene (11,37,86) (see Section 3.3). However, the calculated mean energy of breaking of the chain helix $\Delta U \approx 1500$ cal/mole ($p \sim 0.1$), i.e., it is considerably larger than the value $\Delta U \approx 600$ cal/mole determined above from experimental data on the basis of a purely rotational-isomeric mechanism of flexibility of the macromolecules. Consequently, the quantity $\Delta U \approx 600$ cal/mole is the effective value of the chain flexibility parameter, which takes into account both helix breaking (rotational isomerization) of the macromolecules and torsional oscillations in monomer units. In fact, detailed calculation of the potential energy of isotactic polypropylene (37) indicates the presence of almost free oscillations of the chain elements which enter into the regular regions of the helix in one direction from the equilibrium position (3_1 helix), with a width $2\delta\varphi \approx 20$–$30°$.

Birshtein (13) has carried out recently a calculation of the dimensions and dipole moments of isotactic macromolecules taking into account both rotational isomerization and torsional oscillations of the bonds. In this, in accordance with section 6.2, the averaging of the vector properties of macromolecules was carried out in two stages: first, averaging over the torsional oscillations with a given conformation of a monomer unit, (φ_1, φ_2) or $(-\varphi_2, -\varphi_1)$, where φ_1 and φ_2 lie within the limits

$$\begin{aligned} \varphi_1 - \delta\varphi_1 \leq \varphi_1 \leq \varphi_1 + \delta\varphi_1 \\ \varphi_2 - \delta\varphi_2 \leq \varphi_2 \leq \varphi_2 + \delta\varphi_2 \end{aligned} \tag{7.2}$$

and then averaging over the conformations of monomer units, taking into account correlations between conformations. In other words, the vector properties of macromolecules were calculated with eq. (5.25), in which supermatrix W [see eq. (5.23)] is composed of matrices S [see eq. (6.5)], averaged over the torsional oscillations of the elements [see eq. (7.1)]. Calculations carried out with the use of an electronic computer have shown that, if the interval of free rotations of elements does not exceed 30° and the energy of helix breaking of the chain is not very large (so that $(\overline{h^2}/\overline{h^2}_{\text{fr. rot.}})^{1/2} \leq 3$ and $(\overline{\mu^2}/nm^2)^{1/2} \leq 1$), the dimensions and dipole moments of the macromolecules are determined not by the width of the intervals of torsional oscillations but only by the values of the angles of internal rotation which correspond to the centers of these intervals. The values of $\overline{h^2}$ and $\overline{\mu^2}$ of isotactic macromolecules can be calculated in this case as well with eqs. (6.55) and 6.56), which neglect torsional oscillations, if φ_1 and φ_2 are referred not to the crystal structure of the chain, but to the centers of the intervals of torsional oscillations. Thus, if the macromolecule crystallizes in the form of a 3_1 helix, i.e., if its monomer units have conformations (0°, 120°) and (−120°, 0°) and oscillations of the elements take place in solution within the angular intervals of φ_1 from −30° to 0° and of φ_2 from 90° to 120°, then the values of $\overline{h^2}$ and $\overline{\mu^2}$ can be calculated from eqs. (6.55) and (6.56) for $\varphi_1 = -15°$, $\varphi_2 = 105°$. Using this, we find that (with the assumption that free rotation can take place within an interval of angles $\approx 30°$) the experimental values of $(\overline{h^2}/\overline{h^2}_{\text{fr. rot.}})^{1/2}$ and $(\overline{\mu^2}/nm^2)^{1/2}$ for polystyrene correspond to $p \approx 0.2$, i.e., $\Delta U \approx 1000$ cal/mole. This value of ΔU can be regarded as consistent with the calculated value, $\Delta U \approx 1500$ cal/mole (11,37,86), since the accuracy of the calculation of the energy of steric interaction is not very large. In this way, direct calculation of the potential energy of different conformations of isotactic macromolecules makes it possible to calculate values consistent with experiment of $\overline{h^2}$ and $\overline{\mu^2}$ that characterize the flexibility of macromolecules.

The value found, $\Delta U \approx 1000$–1500 cal/mole ($p = 0.1$–0.2), corresponds to an average number of monomer units in a regular helical region of the chain $\nu = (1 + p)/p = 6$–10 [see eq. (6.40)]. Consequently, *isotactic macromolecules which crystallize in the form of a 3_1 helix, consist in solution of segments of right-handed and left-handed helices which contain on the average 6–10 monomer units* and are slightly deformed by oscillations of bonds near the equilibrium positions.* Let us note that, in calculations of $\overline{h^2}$, we do not take into account differences between the conformations of monomer units at junctions between helical regions and conformations in

* The effective value, $\Delta U \approx 600$ cal/mole, obtained from experimental data in the purely rotational-isomeric approximation, corresponds to $\nu = 3$.

the regular helical region of the chain; this does not introduce, however, considerable changes into the calculated values of $\overline{h^2}$, as was noted in section 6.2 in which (6.61) and (6.65) were compared.

In the paper of Allegra, Ganis, and Corradini (86), agreement between the rotational isomeric model and experiment was reached, not by taking torsional oscillations in all monomer units into account [as is done by Birshtein (13)], but by assuming that the entropy of a monomer unit at a junction is greater than that in a helical region of the chain. Allegra et al. rely in this on the results of their calculations, according to which the energy minimum in a regular region of the helix of a given sign corresponds to a single monomer unit conformation, while at junctions between helical regions there are two or more conformations (see section 3.3). As a result, the free energy of breaking of the helix can decrease from the value $\Delta U = 1500$ cal/mole, which is obtained if the entropic terms are neglected, to values which follow from experimental data on $\overline{h^2}$. It is possible that, in actuality, both factors noted above (torsional oscillations of monomer units and the fact that junctions are entropically favorable) make contributions to the decrease in chain dimensions with an average energy of junctions of the order of 1500 cal/mole; this results in a further improvement of the agreement between the theoretical and experimental data.

Let us pass now to a comparison of the theory with experiment for syndiotactic macromolecules (7). Equations (6.66) and (6.67) for $\overline{h^2}$ and $\overline{\mu^2}$ of such molecules, derived without taking into account torsional oscillations of the elements, contain two parameters, r and q, which are functions of the energy differences $\Delta U_{ik} = U_{ik} - U_{11}$ between different sequences of monomer unit conformations. An approximate examination of conditions of internal rotation in syndiotactic chains (6) shows that the energies of the (0°, 0°; 0°, 0°), (0°, 0°; −120°, −120°) and (−120°, −120°; 0°, 0°) sequences are more or less similar, while the energy of the sequence (−120°, −120°; −120°, −120°) is considerably greater. Consequently, in this case, it is possible to set as a first approximation $\Delta U_{12} = \Delta U_{21} \ll kT$, and $\Delta U_{22} \gg kT$, i.e., $g_{12} = g_{21} \approx g_{11}$ and $g_{22} \ll g_{11}$ ($g_{ik} = e^{-U_{ik}/kT}$; $i, k = 1, 2$). Introducing these values of g_{ik} into eqs. (4.66) and (4.67), we obtain $r = \sqrt{5}/2$ and $q = 1/2$. Introduction of these theoretical values of the internal rotation parameters into eqs. (6.66) and (6.67) gives $(\overline{h^2}/\overline{h^2}_{\text{fr. rot.}})^{1/2} = 2.2$ and $(\overline{\mu^2}/nm^2)^{1/2} = 0.65$ (7); this is very close to the experimental results. Introduction of the values of r and q into eq. (4.71) gives for the average number of monomer units in regular regions of a syndiotactic chain $\nu(\Omega^{(1)}) = \nu_{\text{planar}} \approx 2.6$ and $\nu(\Omega^{(2)}) = \nu_{\text{coiled}} = 1$. Consequently, in this approximation, we find that *a syndiotactic chain consists of segments of a planar trans chain which contain on the average 2.6 monomer units and are separated by monomer units in coiled conformations.* In this way, although the energies of the flat and coiled conformations are identical, the existence of correlation between conformations, which can be reduced to the fact that two consecutive coiled conformations are forbidden, results in an inequality in the *a priori* probabilities of realization of flat and coiled conformations. Using eqs. (4.68) and (4.69), taking the values of r and q found above, we have $w(\Omega^{(1)}) = w_{\text{planar}} = 0.72$, $w(\Omega^{(2)}) = w_{\text{coiled}} = 0.28$, $w(\Omega^{(1)}, \Omega^{(1)}) = 0.45$, $w(\Omega^{(1)}, \Omega^{(2)}) = w(\Omega^{(2)}, \Omega^{(1)}) = 0.28$, and $w(\Omega^{(2)}, \Omega^{(2)}) = 0$.

A more detailed investigation of the conditions of internal rotation in real syndiotactic polymers, e.g., polypropylene (40,83,86), poly-1,2-butadiene (83), polystyrene (83), and poly(vinyl chloride) (86), has shown that in polystyrene ΔU_{12} and ΔU_{21} are actually close to zero, while in the other polymers investigated they may be considerably different from zero. Thus, according to these estimates, in polypropylene the energy of a monomer unit in a coiled conformation ($-120°$, $-120°$), surrounded by planar monomer units is $\Delta U_{12} + \Delta U_{21} \approx -1000$ cal/mole (83), in 1,2-polybutadiene $\approx +1000$ cal/mole (83), and in poly(vinyl chloride) $\approx +1500$ cal/mole (85) (see Section 3.2). The value of ΔU_{22} is actually quite large in all the polymers listed: for polypropylene (83) $\Delta U_{22} \approx 2500$ cal/mole, while for poly-1,2-butadiene it is still greater (83). From the obtained values of ΔU_{ik}, it is possible to calculate, by using eqs. (4.68), (4.69), and (4.71), the probabilities of the various conformations and the average numbers of polymer units in the regular regions of the corresponding chains. The results of these calculations (83) show that, in syndiotactic poly-1,2-butadiene, the planar regions of the chain contain, on the average, almost seven monomer units* and are separated from each other by one monomer unit in coiled conformation. On the other hand, in syndiotactic polypropylene, in which $\Delta U_{12} + \Delta U_{21} < 0$, neighboring monomer units have different (i.e., planar and coiled) conformations more often than identical ones. The structure of such a chain can be conveniently described by the average number of monomer unit pairs

$$\nu(\Omega^{(1)}, \Omega^{(2)}) = w(\Omega^{(1)}, \Omega^{(2)})/w(\Omega^{(1)}, \Omega^{(1)})$$

which have alternating planar and coiled conformations. For polypropylene, we have $\nu(\Omega^{(1)}, \Omega^{(2)}) = 1.8$, i.e., the chains in solution consist of segments of right-handed and left-handed helices corresponding to the

* As was pointed out in Section 3.2, monomer units which are next to monomer units in coiled conformations apparently deviate slightly in this case from a planar structure.

crystal structure and containing on the average 3.6 monomer units. Let us stress that, even though the value of ΔU_{22} is finite in chains of poly-1,2-butadiene and polypropylene, the average number of pairs of neighboring monomer units in coiled conformations is, as before, close to zero ($w(\Omega^{(2)}, \Omega^{(2)}) \sim 10^{-3}$). Therefore, in particular in chains of polypropylene, a junction between segments of right-handed and left-handed helices must contain a pair of neighboring monomer units in planar conformations.

It is possible to calculate with eqs. (4.66), (4.67), and (6.66) the mean dimensions of chains of syndiotactic polypropylene and poly-1,2-butadiene which have the rotational-isomeric structure described above. The results obtained, $(\overline{h^2}/\overline{h^2}_{\text{fr. rot.}})^{1/2} = 2.3$ for polypropylene and $(\overline{h^2}/\overline{h^2}_{\text{fr. rot.}})^{1/2} = 3.0$ for poly-1,2-butadiene (83), are greater than the experimental values for the corresponding atactic polymers [1.8 (91) and 1.7 (92), respectively]. The discrepancy between theory and experiment in this case also (by analogy with isotactic polymers) can be eliminated, apparently, by taking into account the fact that, on the average, monomer units do not have a perfectly planar structure because of torsional oscillations. Let us note that in the case of syndiotactic polystyrene for which, as has been pointed out above, $\Delta U_{12} + \Delta U_{21} \ll kT$, the theory is in good agreement with experiment even without taking torsional oscillations into account (see pp. 192–193).

The cited results show that the rotational-isomeric theory of the dimensions and dipole moments of stereoregular macromolecules of type $(—CH_2—CHR—)_n$ explain quantitatively their properties in solution. This, along with the results presented in Chapter 3 of the direct investigation of the conditions of internal rotation in stereoregular macromolecules, confirms the validity of the scheme proposed above of the structure of these macromolecules in solution; according to this scheme, the *short-range one-dimensional order in a chain coincides with the long-range one-dimensional order in the crystal state, while the principal mechanism of coiling of the chain is rotational isomerization.* Furthermore, it follows from the presented results that the correlation between the conformations of neighboring monomer units plays an important role, i.e., the short-range order extends over several monomer units. It is essential to point out that though the statistical coiling of macromolecules is related primarily to rotational isomerization and not to torsional oscillations, this does not permit any conclusions concerning the relative contributions of the two mechanisms of thermal motion to other properties of polymer chains. The question of the role of rotational isomerization and torsional oscillations, for example, in the heat capacity of macromolecules and in relaxation processes (in particular in dielectric and mechanical losses), has not yet been studied at all.

Of particular interest is the conformational structure of optically active isotactic polymers described in section 3.3. As has been pointed out, isotactic polymers of type $(\text{—}CH_2\text{—}CHR\text{—})_n$, where R is an optically active side group, have in solution an anomalous optical activity; this points to the predominance in their chains of regions of helices of one direction of turn. This is related to the fact that, in molecules of optically active polymers, the free energies of monomer units which enter into segments of right-handed and left-handed helices are not equal to each other, i.e., $U(\Omega^{(1)}, \Omega^{(1)}) \neq U(\Omega^{(2)}, \Omega^{(2)})$. Furthermore, as follows from the data of Table 3.4, even small differences in these free energies, of the order of 400 cal/mole, result in a practically complete predominance of helical segments of one sign.

This was explained in the paper of Birshtein and Luizi (12) on the basis of eq. (4.69) for the fraction of monomer units that are part of right-handed and left-handed helices. For isotactic polymers which have no optical activity

$$g_{11} \equiv e^{\frac{-U(\Omega^{(1)}, \Omega^{(1)})}{kT}} = g_{22} \equiv e^{\frac{-U(\Omega^{(2)}, \Omega^{(2)})}{kT}} \tag{7.3}$$

as a result of which the parameter q, which enters into eqs. (4.69), is $q \equiv (g_{11} - g_{22})/2g_{11} = 0$, so that $w(\Omega^{(1)}) = w(\Omega^{(2)})$. The conformational structure of such chains is characterized by the single parameter

$$\begin{aligned} p &= \sqrt{g_{12}g_{21}}/\sqrt{g_{11}g_{22}} \\ &= e^{-\frac{U(\Omega^{(1)}, \Omega^{(2)}) + U(\Omega^{(2)}, \Omega^{(1)}) - U(\Omega^{(1)}, \Omega^{(1)}) - U(\Omega^{(2)}, \Omega^{(2)})}{2\,kT}} \end{aligned} \tag{7.4}$$

which is a measure of the cooperativity of conformations of monomer units of the chain [compare eq. (6.36)]. In optically active isotactic chains, $g_{11} \neq g_{22}$, so that $q \neq 0$, and the conformational structure of such chains is characterized, in addition to the parameter p, by the quantity

$$s = g_{22}/g_{11} = e^{-\frac{U(\Omega^{(2)}, \Omega^{(2)}) - U(\Omega^{(1)}, \Omega^{(1)})}{kT}} \tag{7.5}$$

which is a measure of the degree to which the two directions of chain turning are not equivalent.

The dependence of the fraction of monomer units $w(\Omega^{(1)})$ in the helical conformation with the smaller free energy on the quantity s, calculated by eq. (4.69), and on the corresponding energy differences between the helical

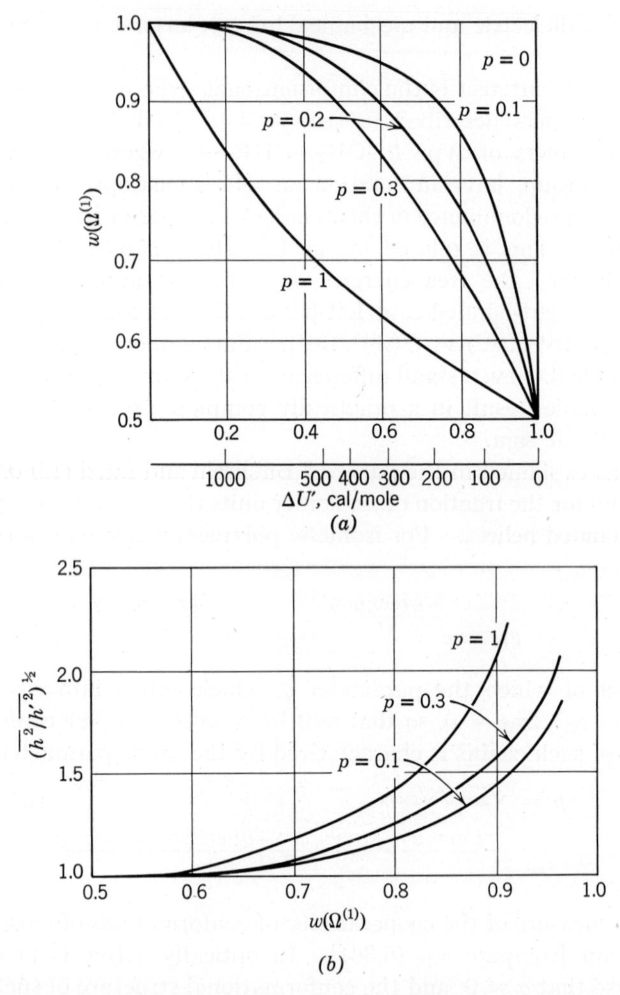

Fig. 7.3. Dependence (a) of the fraction, $w\ (\Omega^{(1)})$, of monomer units on the parameter s and on the energy difference $\Delta U'$ for various values of the parameter p; (b) of $(\bar{h}^2/\bar{h}^{2\prime})^{1/2}$ on the fraction $w(\Omega^{(1)})$ of monomer units in helical regions of a single turning direction. RT is taken as 600 cal/mole.

conformations with different values of the parameter p, are shown in Figure 7.3a. It can be seen from the figure that, at a given value of s, the fraction of monomer units in segments of the more favorable helices increases with an increase in the cooperativity, i.e., with a decrease in p. In the absence of cooperativity, i.e., for $p = 1$, when the conformations of monomer units are independent, eqs. (4.69) give the trivial result: $w(\Omega^{(1)}) = 1/(1 + s)$, and $w(\Omega^{(2)}) = s/(1 + s)$. With full cooperativity, i.e., for $p = 0$, when each molecule consists of a helix of one sign, we have for $s = 1$, $w(\Omega^{(1)}) = w(\Omega^{(2)}) = {}^1/_2$, and for $s < 1$, $w(\Omega^{(1)}) = 1$ and $w(\Omega^{(2)}) = 0$. For values of p typical for isotactic polymers ($p \approx 0.1$–0.2), $w(\Omega^{(1)})$ increases sharply with a decrease of s, so that almost all monomer units are part of segments of helices of one sign, even for values of s which differ comparatively little from unity.

From Figure 7.3*a* it can be seen also that with $\Delta U' = U(\Omega^{(2)}, \Omega^{(2)}) - U(\Omega^{(1)}, \Omega^{(1)}) \approx 400$ cal/mole (i.e., $s = {}^1/_2$) and $p = 0.1$–0.2, $w(\Omega^{(1)}) \approx 0.95$. This explains completely the fact that the experimental values of the molecular rotatory power of poly-(*S*)-3-methyl-1-pentene, poly-(*S*)-4-methyl-1-hexene and poly-(*R*)-3,7-dimethyl-1-octene are close to those calculated for a helix of one sign.

On the other hand, as shown by Birshstein and Luizi (12), this unusual conformational structure of chains of optically active isotactic polymers is not strongly reflected on the degree of coiling in solution. Calculation of $\overline{h^2}$ with eqs. (5.25) and (4.76) results (for conformations $\Omega^{(1)} = (0°, 120°)$ and $\Omega^{(2)} = (-120°, 0°)$ and tetrahedral valence angles) in the expression

$$\overline{h^2} = \frac{4}{3} Nl^2 \frac{(1 - s)(1 - s^3) + p^2 s(3 + 2s + 3s^2)}{p^2 s(1 + s)\sqrt{(1 - s)^2 + 4p^2 s}} \tag{7.6}$$

With $g_{11} = g_{22}$, i.e., $s = 1$, eq. (7.6) becomes

$$\overline{h^2}' = {}^8/_3 Nl^2(1/p) \tag{7.7}$$

which follows from eq. (6.55), which was given earlier (for certain assumptions on the structure of the chain). The dependence of the values of $(\overline{h^2}/\overline{h^2}')^{1/2}$ on the fraction $w(\Omega^{(1)})$ of monomer units in segments of a more favorable helix, calculated from eqs. (7.5), (7.6), and (4.69) with different values of p, is shown in Figure 7.3*b*. It can be seen from this figure that even if the helices of one sign contain 90% of all monomer units, with $p = 0.1$–0.3, the dimensions of the molecule are only 1.5 times greater than those of chains with equal contents of helices of opposite signs.

The theory of the dimensions and dipole moments of isotactic polymers has been compared with experiment also for polymers of the type $(\text{—}CH_2\text{—}CRR'\text{—})_n$, namely, for isotactic poly(methyl methacrylate) (13), which crystallizes in the form of a 5_2 helix (which contains five monomer units and two turns per period) with a step per monomer unit $d = 2.11$ Å (42) (see Table 3.1). Unfortunately, in this case, complete x-ray analysis of the structure has not been carried out, so that the determination of the angles of internal rotation in the crystalline macromolecule requires the introduction of some assumptions on the valence angles in the chain. Birshtein has examined the following models (13): (1) a model in which valence angles are tetrahedral, i.e., $\pi - \alpha_1 = \pi - \alpha_2 = 109°30'$;* two models in which the valence angles are distorted as in polyisobutylene, since the structure of the monomer units of polyisobutylene is close to the structure of monomer units of polymethyl methacrylate, of these model (2) has $\pi - \alpha_1 = \pi - \alpha_2 = 114°$ (43) and model (3) has $\pi - \alpha_1 = 126°$, $\pi - \alpha_2 = 107°$ (44). From eqs. (3.4), we find that, for model (1), $\varphi_1 = 10°$, $\varphi_2 = 140°$, and for models (2) and (3), $\varphi_1 = -20°$, $\varphi_2 = 150°$. Consequently, the conformations of monomer units of isotactic poly(methyl methacrylate) are close to the conformations of monomer units of isotactic polymers of type $(—CH_2—CHR—)_n$. Using eq. (6.50), which does not take into account the torsional oscillations of bonds, and introducing in it the value $d = 2.11$ Å, we find that the experimental value of $(\overline{h^2}/\overline{h^2}_{fr.\,rot.})^{1/2}$ for poly(methyl methacrylate) which is 2.0–2.2, corresponds to $p = 0.3$–0.4 (see Table 1.1). Just as in the case of isotactic macromolecules of type $(—CH_2—CHR—)_n$, this value of p results in a value of $(\overline{\mu^2}/nm^2)^{1/2}$ which coincides with the experimental value 0.81–0.87 (34–36), if the more realistic models (2) and (3) are used and if it is considered that the $COOCH_3$ group has a *cis* conformation relative to the C—O bond (45).†

7.2. Conformations of Macromolecules with Symmetric Side Groups

Polymers of the type of poly(methyl methacrylate) with a general formula $(—CH_2—CRR'—)_n$, where R and R′ are bulky side groups, occupy in a certain sense an intermediate position between polymers with strongly asymmetric side groups of type $(—CH_2—CHR—)_n$ and polymers with symmetric side groups of type $(—CH_2—CR_2—)_n$. The theoretical investigation of conformations of these polymers presents a more complicated problem, since in this case all conformations of monomer units result in overlap of bulky groups (see section 3.2).

Nevertheless, comparison with experiment of the equations for the dimen-

* For the meaning of angles $\pi - \alpha_1$ and $\pi - \alpha_2$ see Figure 6.1.

† In the indicated calculations, it was assumed that there is no rotation about the C—C bond in the side group. Furthermore, in the case of model (2), there is agreement with experiment if the C═O bond is directed in the direction opposite to the α-methyl group, while in the case of model (3), it is directed both in the direction of the α-methyl group and in the opposite direction. In the case of model (1), the theoretical value of $(\overline{\mu^2}/nm^2)^{1/2}$ is in disagreement with the experimental value.

sions and dipole moments of macromolecules with symmetric side groups can again give some information on their conformational structure.

Ptitsyn and Sharonov (2) have applied the rotational isomeric theory of macromolecule dimensions to polyisobutylene, $[-CH_2-C(CH_3)_2-]_n$. These authors took as their starting position the consideration that the conformations of monomer units in solution, in this case also, must be close to the conformations in the crystal state. The latter conformations have been investigated by the x-ray method in a number of studies (43,44, 46–49); furthermore, it was established (43,48,49) that molecules of polyisobutylene crystallize in the form of 8_5 helices with a step per monomer unit of $d = 2.33$ Å (see Table 3.1). Considering, in accordance with Bunn (48) and Liquori (43), that all the chain elements are rotated by identical angles, we obtain from eq. (3.4): $\pi - \alpha_1 = \pi - \alpha_2 = 114°$ (45) and $\varphi_1 = \varphi_2 \ (= \varphi) = 82°$ (2) (structure 1). According to the more exact crystal structure of polyisobutylene, proposed later by Bunn and Holmes (44), $\pi - \alpha_1 = 126°$, $\pi - \alpha_2 = 107°$, $\varphi_1 = 102°30'$ and $\varphi_2 = 51°$ (structure 2).* For the symmetry conditions for chains with symmetric side groups given in section 3.3, we find that, in structure 1, the monomer units in free macromolecules of polyisobutylene have conformations $(+82°, +82°)$ and $(-82°, -82°)$, while, in structure 2, they have conformations $(102°30', 51°)$; $(-102°30', -51°)$; $(51°, 102°30')$ and $(-51°, -102°30')$.

Neglecting correlations between the conformations of neighboring monomer units and using eq. (6.12), Ptitsyn and Sharonov have obtained, for structure 1:

$$\overline{h^2} = 2Nl^2 \left(\frac{1 + \cos \alpha}{1 - \cos \alpha}\right)\left(\frac{1 + \cos \varphi}{1 - \cos \varphi}\right) \approx 6.3Nl^2 \qquad (7.8)$$

(since, in this case, $\Delta = 1$), from which $(\overline{h^2}/\overline{h^2}_{\text{fr. rot.}})^{1/2} = 1.8$. Furthermore, the result is practically the same if torsional oscillations are taken into account. This theoretical value is quite close to the experimental values of 1.7–1.8 obtained by a number of authors from the intrinsic viscosity of polyisobutylene in Θ-solvents: benzene (50,51), phenetole (51) and a mixture of cyclohexane with methyl ethyl ketone (52). (In the earlier work of Kunst (53) a somewhat larger value, 2.3, was obtained by the method of light scattering.) The quantity $(\overline{h^2}/\overline{h^2}_{\text{fr. rot.}})^{1/2}$ calculated in this way is quite sensitive to the value of the angle of internal rotation φ: agreement with experiment is obtained only with $\varphi \approx 70$–$80°$; other

* The values of valence angles in the main chain of polyisobutylene obtained from x-ray data are not in agreement with the values of the angles determined by optical anisotropy (55,66) under the assumption that the valence-optical scheme is valid.

values of φ result in a sharp disagreement between theory and experiment. Later, Birshtein, Ptitsyn, and Sokolova (54), using structure 2, obtained $(\overline{h^2}/\overline{h^2}_{\text{fr. rot.}}) = 2.5$ by applying eq. (6.8) (in this case, $\eta = 0.206$; $\zeta = -0.136$; $\xi = 0.757$); this is in somewhat poorer agreement with the majority of experimental data. It is possible that, contrary to the case found with polymers of type $(\text{—CH}_2\text{—CHR—})_n$ in which only the conformations of monomer units that exist in the crystal structure are formed in the free chains, in polyisobutylene it is necessary to take into consideration also other conformations with similar energies. Thus, according to the calculations of Liquori and co-workers (63), each monomer unit of the polyisobutylene chain can have six almost isoenergetic conformations:* conformations (+95°, +95°) and (−95°, −95°) which correspond to the crystal structure of the chain, and conformations (135°, 25°), (−135°, −25°), (25°, 135°), and (−25°, −135°) which are almost equal in energy. Using eqs. (6.8) and (6.12), we obtain for this set of conformations and for valence angles $\pi - \alpha_1 = \pi - \alpha_2 = 114°$ and $\pi - \alpha_1 = 126°$, $\pi - \alpha_2 = 107°$ values of $(\overline{h^2}/\overline{h^2}_{\text{fr. rot.}})^{1/2}$ of 1.4_5 and 1.8_5, respectively. The second value is close to the experimental one.

All the theoretical values of $\overline{h^2}/\overline{h^2}_{\text{fr. rot.}}$ cited above for polyisobutylene chains were obtained with correlations between the conformations of monomer units neglected, so that the averaging was carried out over practically isoenergetic states. This is consistent with the experimental fact that both the dimensions (50–52) and the optical anisotropy (55) of polyisobutylene molecules are rather weak functions of temperature. This conformational structure of polyisobutylene chains is confirmed also by the almost total absence of energetic effects during its stretching. As is shown in section 8.2, the ratio of the energetic resilient force, f_e, which arises during stretching of the polymer (at constant volume) to the total elastic force f is equal to (56–60):

$$f_e/f = T(d \ln \overline{h^2}/dT) \tag{7.9}$$

Investigation of the energetic elasticity of polyisobutylene has shown (61) that $T(d \ln \overline{h^2}/dT) = -0.03 \pm 0.02$ (see Table 8.2). The value of this quantity, which is close to zero, also can be obtained from a direct measure of the intrinsic viscosity of polyisobutylene in various Θ solvents (50–52). This means that the actual conformations of monomer units of

* Volkenshtein (65) pointed out earlier the existence of a large number of almost isoenergetic conformations of the monomer units of polyisobutylene.

polyisobutylene molecules have similar energies and that correlation between the conformations of neighboring monomer units is not great.*

Another example of a chain with symmetric side groups is polydimethylsiloxane, $[\text{—Si(CH}_3)_2\text{—O—}]_n$, which has been studied in detail recently by Flory and co-workers (103–105). The valence angles $\pi - \alpha_1$ and $\pi - \alpha_2$ of the main chain differ greatly from each other: $\pi - \alpha_1 = 109°30'$, and $\pi - \alpha_2 = 140–148°$ (67–69,106). Measurements of the intrinsic viscosity of solutions in various ideal solvents (70,100,104,107) have shown that, in all cases except one, $(\overline{h^2}/\overline{h^2}_{\text{fr. rot.}})^{1/2}$ if approximately 1.4† [if in the calculation of $\overline{h^2}_{\text{fr. rot.}}$ the length of the Si—O bonds are taken as 1.64 Å, $\pi - \alpha_1 = 109°30'$, and $\pi - \alpha_2 = 143°$ (105)]. In a mixed solvent with a rather low cohesion energy density (mixtures of C_8F_{18} and $CCl_2F\text{-}CCl_2F$ in a 1:2 ratio at 22.5°) $(\overline{h^2}/\overline{h^2}_{\text{fr. rot.}})^{1/2} = 1.5$ (104). From data on the energetic elasticity of polydimethylsiloxane (103) it follows, according to eq. (7.9), that $T(d \ln \overline{h^2}/dT) \approx 0.27$; this is consistent with data obtained from measurements of the dependence of the intrinsic viscosity of polydimethylsiloxane solutions in nonideal athermal (see p. 205) solvents (103); according to these data $T(d \ln \overline{h^2}/dT) \approx 0.24$.‡

The values of the dimensions and also, apparently, of dipole moments, $(\overline{\mu^2}/nm^2)^{1/2} \approx 1$ (54) of polydimethylsiloxane chains appear to indicate that these molecules are highly flexible. However, in chains with alternating valence angles, such as polydimethylsiloxane, the values of $(\overline{h^2}/\overline{h^2}_{\text{fr. rot.}})^{1/2}$ and $(\overline{\mu^2}/nm^2)^{1/2}$ are determined not only by the conditions of internal rotation but also by the values of the valence angles [see eqs. (6.10) and (6.11)] (93). Examination of the expression for $\overline{h^2}$ of polydimethylsiloxane chains shows that, as a result of the alternating values of the valence angles, the dimensions of the molecules do not increase without limit with an increase of the fraction of *trans* isomers, but pass through a maximum, after which they decrease to a value of the order of the dimensions of a single bond. Therefore, a value of $\overline{h^2}$ close to $\overline{h^2}_{\text{fr. rot.}}$ can be found not only when the energy differences between rotational isomers are small, but also when they are quite considerable (93); a positive sign of $d \ln h/dT$ indicates that the second situation is true (see section 8.3).

* The equation $T(d \ln \overline{h^2}/dT) = -\Delta U/kT$ which follows from eq. (6.57), gives for the energy of breaking of the polyisobutylene helix a value of ΔU of 20 (61) to 250 cal/mole.

† A somewhat larger value is obtained by Kuwahara et al. (51); this can be explained by the polydispersity of the samples investigated.

‡ In the earlier studies of Ciferri, lower values of $T(d \ln \overline{h^2}/dT)$ were obtained: 0.15 from the energetic elasticity (71,72) and 0.10 from the temperature dependence of $[\eta]$ (73).

A detailed interpretation of the flexibility of polydimethylsiloxane chains is given in the paper of Flory, Crescenzi, and Mark (105). At present, the crystalline conformation of polydimethylsiloxane is not known; there is an indication, however, that this polymer crystallizes in the form of helices (74,75). Considering the internal rotation barriers in similar low molecular weight compounds, the potential barriers in polydimethylsiloxane must be quite small (of the order of several hundred calories per mole); thus, the use of the rotational-isomeric approximation is not quite justified in this case (105). The potential curve, however, can be conditionally divided in this case as well as into a finite number of states; moreover, for the sake of simplicity, states which correspond to internal rotation angles $\varphi = 0, \pm 120°$ were examined by Flory et al. (105) [see also (93)]. The calculations of $\overline{h^2}$ were carried out by the method described in section 6.2, with correlations of internal rotation about neighboring bonds of the polymer chain taken into account. This correlation consists in the absolute prohibition of sequences of internal rotation angles $(+120°, -120°)$ or $(-120°, +120°)$ about neighboring O-Si and Si-O bonds because of the steric repulsion between Si atoms, while, as a result of the electrostatic repulsion of O atoms, the rotational isomer which corresponds to an angle of rotation $\varphi = 120°$ about a O-Si bond must be assigned the usual difference ΔU between the energies of *gauche* and *trans* isomers if it is preceded by rotational isomer $\varphi = 0$ or $\varphi = 120°$, and energy difference $\Delta U'$, if it is preceded by rotational isomer $\varphi = -120°$. A similar situation exists for a rotational isomer which corresponds to an angle of rotation $\varphi = -120°$ about a O-Si bond.

Comparison of experimental data on $(\overline{h^2}/\overline{h^2}_{\text{fr. rot.}})^{1/2} = 1.4$ and $T(d \times \ln \overline{h^2}/dT) = 0.27$ with results of numerical calculations carried out with an electronic computer has shown that $\Delta U = 850$ cal/mole, while $\Delta U' = 1900$ cal/mole. This large energy difference, ΔU, between the *gauche* and *trans* isomers of polydimethylsiloxane has been assigned (105) to an excess of the energy of attraction between the CH_3 groups in a *trans* conformation (when the distance between them is $\sim$3.8 Å) over the energies of attraction of these groups to molecules of the polar solvent.

The conformations of the chains of other polar molecules as well must be determined not only by steric factors but also by dipole–dipole interactions. In the case of polymers with bulky side groups, the latter cannot change the set of possible monomer unit conformations (determined by the stronger steric interactions), but, obviously, can have an effect on the statistical weights of the various conformations. The influence of dipole–dipole interactions on the dimensions of polyhalostyrene macromolecules has been demonstrated directly by Eskin and co-workers. They showed that the dimensions of molecules of poly-3,4-dichlorostyrene, the side groups of which have a considerable total dipole moment, exceed considerably the dimensions of polystyrene molecules (76), while the dimensions of poly-2,5-dichlorostyrene molecules, in which the total dipole moment of the side groups is equal to zero, are close to the dimensions of polystyrene molecules (77). The increase in the dimensions of polar macromolecules relative to nonpolar ones as a result of dipole–dipole interactions of the side groups, has been established in a less exact manner in a study of poly-(vinyl chloride) (78). A quantitative theory of the effect of dipole–dipole interactions on the conformations of molecules meets with serious difficulties (see section 2.2), since the interactions between polar bonds at such close distances evidently cannot be regarded as the interactions between point dipoles.

Finally, Hoeve (79) and Nagai and Ishikawa (84) have applied the mathematical method developed above to the calculation of the value of $\overline{h^2}$ of polyethylene molecules, taking into account correlations between the rotations of neighboring elements. Since each element is characterized by three rotational isomers (*trans* isomer, $\varphi = 0°$ and *gauche* isomers, $\varphi = \pm 120°$), matrix G (see section 4.1) is, in this case, a third-order matrix, while matrix W (see section 5.1) is a ninth-order matrix; as a result, in the general case, the calculations could be brought to completion only with the use of an electronic computer (79).

If the rotations about neighboring elements were independent, the only parameter determining the conformational structure of the chain would be the energy difference ΔU between the *gauche* and *trans* isomers. From an analysis of models, it has been concluded (79,84) that the correlation between rotations about neighboring elements can be reduced to an additional energy increase for sequences of angles $\varphi_1 = 120°$, $\varphi_2 = -120°$ or $\varphi_1 = -120°$, $\varphi_2 = 120°$. In fact, it is easy to see that such sequences of angles correspond to a conformation in which two CH_2 groups of the main chain ($k - 2$ and $k + 2$) lie on one side of a plane drawn through the three C atoms of the main chain which separate them ($k - 1$, k, and $k + 1$). This results in an overlap of the electron clouds of CH_2 groups similar to the overlap of, for example, CH_3 groups in the planar conformation of isotactic polypropylene (see section 3.2). To be consistent with this, rotational isomer $\varphi_2 = 120°$, which follows rotational isomer $\varphi_1 = -120°$ (or vice versa), was assigned energy $\Delta U'$ (larger than ΔU), while the energies of all other sequences were taken as equal to the sum of the energies of individual bonds.

Hoeve (79) assigned to the quantity ΔU a value of 500 cal/mole, which follows from spectroscopic data (94,95) and data on the heat capacity of paraffins higher than n-butane (96), while energy $\Delta U'$ was regarded as the parameter of the problem. In another version of the theory, developed by Nagai and Ishikawa (84), it was assumed that $\Delta U' = \infty$, while the parameter was taken as the ratio of the statistical weights of *gauche* and *trans* isomers, which is a function of ΔU. In this last case, it was possible to obtain for $\overline{h^2}$ of a polyethylene chain the analytical expression:

$$\overline{h^2} = Nl^2 \frac{2(\lambda - g)}{2\lambda - 1 - g}\left[\frac{\dfrac{(\lambda - 1)^2 t_1}{2g} - 2(\lambda - 1)t_2 + t_3}{t_1 t_3 - 2g t_2^2} - 1\right] \tag{7.10}$$

where

$$t_1 = 1 - c - \zeta[c + (2 - c)\psi]$$
$$t_2 = -c - \zeta[c + (1 - c)\psi]$$
$$t_3 = 1 - gc - g\zeta[2c + (1 - c)\psi]$$
$$\zeta = \frac{\sin^2\alpha}{\lambda \cos\alpha[1 + c + (1 - c)\psi]}$$
$$\psi = \cos\alpha\left\{\frac{g\cos\varphi}{\lambda} + \frac{g^2 \sin\varphi}{\lambda^2\left[1 + \left(\dfrac{g\cos\varphi}{\lambda}\right)\right]}\right\} \tag{7.11}$$
$$c = \cos\frac{\alpha}{\lambda}$$
$$\lambda = {}^1/_2[1 + g + (1 + 6g + g^2)^{1/2}]$$
$$g = e^{\frac{-\Delta U - T\Delta S}{kT}}$$

is the ratio of the statistical weights of *gauche* and *trans* isomers. ΔU and ΔS are the energy and entropy differences of *gauche* and *trans* isomers, $\pi - \alpha$ is the valence angle, and φ is the absolute value of the angle of internal rotation corresponding to the *gauche* isomers (in actual calculations, the authors took $\pi - \alpha = 109°30'$ and $\varphi = 120°$).

Both versions of the theory were compared with the experimental value of $(\overline{h^2}/\overline{h^2}_{\text{fr. rot.}})^{1/2} \approx 1.8$ obtained from the dimensions of polyethylene molecules in α-chloronaphthalene* (97–99), and with the values of the derivative $d \ln \overline{h^2}/dT \approx -1.2 \times 10^{-3}$ deg.$^{-1}$, obtained from the energetic

* α-Chloronaphthalene is not an ideal solvent for polyethylene; therefore, the quantity $(\overline{h^2}/\overline{h^2}_{\text{fr. rot}})^{1/2}$ was evaluated by excluding the effect of long-range interactions.

force of elasticity with the use of eq. (7.9) (61) and measured directly from the temperature dependence of the intrinsic viscosity of polyethylene solutions in nonideal athermal* solvents (80) (see sections 8.2,8.3). In the paper of Hoeve (79), in which it was assumed that $\Delta U = 500$ cal/mole and $\Delta S = 0$, agreement with experimental data on $\overline{h^2}$ and $d \ln \overline{h^2}/dT$ could be obtained by assigning an energy $\Delta U' \approx 2300$ cal/mole to a rotational isomer $\varphi_2 = 120°$ which follows a rotational isomer $\varphi_1 = -120°$ (or vice versa).

In the paper of Nagai and Ishikawa, in which it was assumed that $\Delta U' = \infty$, the value of ΔU determined from $d \ln \overline{h^2}/dT$ by eq. (7.10) was found to be 820 ± 50 cal/mole (for $\Delta S = 0$). This value of ΔU (with $\Delta S = 0$ and at 140°C.) corresponds to the quantity $(\overline{h^2}/\overline{h^2}_{\text{fr. rot.}})^{1/2} = 2$; this is close to the experimental value cited above. Reasonable values of ΔU and $\overline{h^2}/\overline{h^2}_{\text{fr. rot.}}$ are obtained also for small positive values of ΔS. The influence of torsional oscillations on $\overline{h^2}$ was examined also (84), and it was shown that they have little effect on $\overline{h^2}$ and $d\overline{h^2}/dT$ at amplitudes up to 16°.

Values of ΔU and $\Delta U'$ for polyethylene, calculated by Borisova (81) on the basis of semiempirical potentials of interaction between C and H atoms are cited in Chapter 3. These values of $\Delta U = 600$ cal/mole and $\Delta U' = 2100$–2400 cal/mole are quite consistent with the results obtained from a comparison with experiment of the calculations of Hoeve and Nagai and Ishikawa. Thus, the conformational structure of polyethylene chains is known at the present time with a high degree of precision.

References

1. Ptitsyn, O. B., and Yu. A. Sharonov, *Zh. Tekhn. Fiz.*, **27**, 2744 (1957); *Soviet Phys.-Tech. Phys.*, **2**, 2544 (1957).
2. Ptitsyn, O. B., and Yu. A. Sharonov, *Zh. Tekhn. Fiz.*, **27**, 2762 (1957).
3. Nagai, K., *Busseiron Kenkyu*, **4**, 65 (1958).
4. Nagai, K., *J. Chem. Phys.*, **30**, 660 (1959).
5. Birshtein, T. M., and O. B. Ptitsyn, *Zh. Tekhn. Fiz.*, **29**, 1048 (1959); *Soviet Phys.-Tech. Phys.*, **4**, 954 (1959).
6. Birshtein, T. M., Candidate Dissertation, Institut Vysokomolekulyarnykh Soedinenii, Akad. Nauk SSSR, Leningrad, 1960.
7. Birshtein, T. M., and O. B. Ptitsyn, *Vysokomol. Soedin.*, **2**, 628 (1960).
8. Rossi, C., and V. Magnasco, *Makromol. Chem.*, **41**, 45 (1960).
9. Mori, T., *J. Phys. Soc., Japan*, **15**, 1482, 1638, 2118 (1960).
10. Mori, T., *Busseiron Kenkyu*, **9**, 473 (1961); *ibid.*, **10**, 36 (1961).

* As is known, in athermal solvents (with a zero heat of solution), the coefficient of swelling of a macromolecule as a result of long-range interactions is independent of temperature.

11. Corradini, P., and G. Allegra, *Atti Accad. Nazl. Lincei, Rend. Classe Sci. Fis. Mat. Nat.*, [8] **30,** 516 (1961).
12. Birshtein, T. M., and P. Luizi, *Vysokomol. Soedin.*, **6,** 1238 (1964).
13. Birshtein, T. M., *Vysokomol. Soedin.*, **5,** 1675 (1963).
14. Birshtein, T. M., and O. B. Ptitsyn, *Zh. Fiz. Khim.*, **28,** 213 (1954).
15. Birshtein, T. M., and O. B. Ptitsyn, *Zh. Tekhn. Fiz.*, **24,** 1998 (1954).
16. Natta, G., F. Danusso, and G. Moraglio, *Makromol. Chem.*, **20,** 37 (1956).
17. Peaker, F. W., *J. Polymer Sci.*, **22,** 25 (1956).
18. Danusso, F., and G. Moraglio, *J. Polymer Sci.*, **24,** 161 (1957).
19. Ang, F., *J. Polymer Sci.*, **25,** 126 (1957).
20. Krigbaum, W. R., D. K. Carpenter, and S. Newman, *J. Phys. Chem.*, **62,** 1586 (1958).
21. Trossarelli, L., E. Campi, and G. Saini, *J. Polymer Sci.*, **35,** 205 (1959).
22. Ciampa, G., *Chim. Ind. (Milan)*, **38,** 298 (1956).
23. Ang, F., and H. Mark, *Monatsh. Chem.*, **88,** 427 (1957).
24. Chiang, R., *J. Polymer Sci.*, **28,** 235 (1958).
25. Danusso, F., and G. Moraglio, *Makromol. Chem.*, **28,** 250 (1958).
26. Kinsinger, J. B., and R. E. Hughes, *J. Phys. Chem.*, **63,** 2002 (1959).
27. Parrini, P., F. Sebastiano, and G. Messina, *Makromol. Chem.*, **38,** 27 (1960).
28. Tsvetkov, V. N., V. S. Skazka, and N. M. Krivoruchko, *Vysokomol. Soedin.*, **2,** 1045 (1960).
29. Flory, P. J., *Principles of Polymer Chemistry*, Cornell Univ. Press, Ithaca, N. Y., (1953).
30. Ptitsyn, O. B., *Usp. Fiz. Nauk*, **69,** 371 (1959); *Soviet Phys.-Usp.*, **2,** 797 (1959).
31. Ptitsyn, O. B., *Vysokomol. Soedin.*, **3,** 1673 (1961).
32. Kinsinger, J. B., and R. A. Wessling, *J. Am. Chem. Soc.*, **81,** 2908 (1959).
33. Krigbaum, W. R., and A. Roig, *J. Chem. Phys.*, **31,** 544 (1959).
34. Bacskai, R., and H. A. Pohl, *J. Polymer Sci.*, **42,** 151 (1960).
35. Pohl, H. A., R. Bacskai, and W. P. Purcell, *J. Phys. Chem.*, **64,** 1701 (1960).
36. Salovey, R., *J. Polymer Sci.*, **50,** S7 (1961).
37. Borisova, N. P., and T. M. Birshtein, *Vysokomol. Soedin.*, **5,** 279 (1963).
38. Krigbaum, W. R., and D. K. Carpenter, *J. Phys. Chem.*, **59,** 1166 (1955).
39. Burshtein, L. L., Candidate Dissertation, Institut Vysokomolekulyarnykh Soedineii Akad. Nauk SSSR, Leningrad, 1957.
40. Natta, G., P. Corradini, and P. Ganis, *Makromol. Chem.*, **39,** 238 (1960).
41. Krigbaum, W. R., and P. J. Flory, *J. Polymer Sci.*, **11,** 37 (1953).
42. Stroupe, J. D., and R. E. Hughes, *J. Am. Chem. Soc.*, **80,** 2341 (1958).
43. Liquori, A. M., *Acta Cryst.*, **8,** 345 (1955).
44. Bunn, C. W., and D. R. Holmes, *Discussions Faraday Soc.*, **25,** 95 (1958).
45. Mizushima, S., *Stroenie Molekul i Vnutrennee Vrashchenie* IL, Moscow, 1957, originally published as *S. Mizushima, Structure of Molecules and* Internal *Rotation*, New York, Academic Press, 1954.
46. Brill, R., and F. Halle, *Naturwiss.*, **26,** 12 (1938).
47. Fuller, C. S., C. J. Frosch, and N. R. Pape, *J. Am. Chem. Soc.*, **62,** 1905 (1940).
48. Bunn, C. W., *J. Chem. Soc.*, **1947,** 297.
49. Lenne, H., *Kolloid-Z.*, **137,** 65 (1954).
50. Fox, T. G, and P. J. Flory, *J. Am. Chem. Soc.*, **73,** 1909 (1951).

51. Kuwahara, N., M. Kaneko, Y. Miyake, and J. Furuichi, *J. Phys. Soc. Japan*, **17**, 568 (1962).
52. Bawn, C. E. H., and R. D. Patel, *Trans. Faraday Soc.*, **52**, 1669 (1956).
53. Kunst, E. D., *Rec. Trav. Chim.*, **69**, 125 (1950).
54. Birshtein, T. M., O. B. Ptitsyn, and E. A. Sokolova, *Vysokomol. Soedin.*, **1**, 852 (1959).
55. Stein, R. S., F. H. Holmes, and A. V. Tobolsky, *J. Polymer Sci.*, **14**, 443 (1954).
56. Volkenshtein, M. V., and O. B. Ptitsyn, *Zh. Tekhn. Fiz.*, **25**, 662 (1955).
57. Volkenshtein, M. V., and O. B. Ptitsyn, Mezinaroudui Symposium Makromolekularui Chemie, Praha, Oct. 9–15, 1957, *Documentation*, **1**, No. 44.
58. Flory, P. J., C. A. J. Hoeve, and A. Ciferri, *J. Polymer Sci.*, **34**, 337 (1959).
59. Ptitsyn, O. B., *Fiz. Tverd. Tela*, **1**, 923 (1959).
60. Volkenshtein, M. V., and O. B. Ptitsyn, *Fiz. Tverd. Tela Sb.*, **1**, 259 (1959).
61. Ciferri, A., C. A. J. Hoeve, and P. J. Flory, *J. Am. Chem. Soc.*, **83**, 1015 (1961).
62. Hoeve, C. A. J., *J. Chem. Phys.*, **32**, 888 (1960).
63. De Santis, P., E. Giglio, A. M. Liquori, and A. Ripamonti, *Nuovo Cimento*, **26**, 616 (1962).
64. Bunn, C. W., *Adv. Colloid Sci.*, **2**, 95 (1946).
65. Volkenshtein, M. V., *Zh. Fiz. Khim.*, **26**, 1072 (1952).
66. Tsvetkov, V. N., V. E. Bychkova, S. M. Savvon, and N. K. Nekrasov, *Vysokomol. Soedin.*, **1**, 1407 (1959); *Polymer Sci. USSR*, **1**, 584 (1960) (abstract).
67. Steinfink, H., B. Post, and J. Fankuchen, *Acta Cryst.*, **8**, 420 (1955).
68. Larsson, K., *Arkiv Kemi*, **16**, 203 (1961).
69. Aronson, J. R., R. C. Lord, and D. W. Robinson, *J. Chem. Phys.*, **33**, 1004 (1960).
70. Flory, P. J., L. Mandelkern, J. B. Kinsinger, and W. B. Schultz, *J. Am. Chem. Soc.*, **74**, 3364 (1952).
71. Ciferri, A., *J. Polymer Sci.*, **45**, 528 (1960).
72. Ciferri, A., *Trans. Faraday Soc.*, **57**, 846 (1961).
73. Ciferri, A., *Trans. Faraday Soc.*, **57**, 853 (1961).
74. Ohlberg, R. M., L. E. Alexander, and E. L. Warrick, *J. Polymer Sci.*, **27**, 1 (1958).
75. Roth, W. I., and D. Harker, *Acta Cryst.*, **1**, 34 (1948).
76. Eskin, V. E., and L. N. Andreeva, *Vysokomol. Soedin.*, **3**, 435 (1961).
77. Eskin, V. E., and K. Z. Gumargalieva, *Vysokomol. Soedin.*, **2**, 265 (1960).
78. Martin Guzman, G., and J. M. G. Fatou, *Anales Real. Soc. Espan. Fis. Quim.* (*Madrid*), **B55**, No. 1, 31 (1959).
79. Hoeve, C. A. J., *J. Chem. Phys.*, **35**, 1266 (1961).
80. Flory, P. J., A. Ciferri, and R. Chiang, *J. Am. Chem. Soc.*, **83**, 1023 (1961).
81. Borisova, N. P., *Vysokomol. Soedin.*, **6**, 135 (1964).
82. Krigbaum, W. R., J. E. Kurz, and P. Smith, *J. Phys. Chem.*, **65**, 1984 (1961).
83. Borisova, N. P., and T. M. Birshtein, *Vysokomol. Soedin.*, **6**, 1234 (1964).
84. Nagai, K., and T. Ishikawa, *J. Chem. Phys.*, **37**, 496 (1962).
85. Fordham, J. W. L., *J. Polymer Sci.*, **39**, 321 (1959).
86. Allegra, G., P. Ganis, and P. Corradini, *Makromol. Chem.*, **61**, 225 (1963).
87. Krause, S., and E. Cohn-Ginsberg, *Polymer*, **3**, 565 (1962).
88. Natta, G., P. Corradini, and P. Ganis, *J. Polymer Sci.*, **58**, 1191 (1962).
89. Borisova, T. I., L. L. Burshtein, and G. P. Mikhailov, *Vysokomol. Soedin.*, **4**, 1479 (1962).

90. Mikhailov, G. P., and L. L. Burshtein, *Vysokomol. Soedin.*, **6,** 1713 (1964).
91. Danusso, F., and G. Moraglio, *Rend. Inst. Lombardo Sci. Lettere*, **A93,** 666 (1959).
92. Cleland, R. L., *J. Polymer Sci.*, **27,** 349 (1958).
93. Ptitsyn, O. B., *Vysokomol. Soedin.*, **5,** 1219 (1963).
94. Sheppard, N., and G. J. Szasz, *J. Chem. Phys.*, **17,** 86 (1949).
95. Mizushima, S., and H. Okazaki, *J. Am. Chem. Soc.*, **71,** 3411 (1949).
96. Person, W. B., and G. C. Pimentel, *J. Am. Chem. Soc.*, **75,** 532 (1953).
97. Henry, P. M., *J. Polymer Sci.*, **36,** 3 (1959).
98. Chiang, R., *J. Polymer Sci.*, **36,** 91 (1959).
99. Tung, L. H., *J. Polymer Sci.*, **36,** 287 (1959).
100. Schulz, G. V., and A. Haug, *Z. Physik. Chem. (Frankfurt)*, **34,** 328 (1962).
101. Krause, S., and E. Cohn-Ginsberg, *J. Phys. Chem.*, **67,** 1479 (1963).
102. Kinsinger, J. B., and R. E. Hughes, *J. Phys. Chem.*, **67,** 1922 (1963).
103. Mark, J. E., and P. J. Flory, *J. Am. Chem. Soc.*, **86,** 138 (1964).
104. Crescenzi, V., and P. J. Flory, *J. Am. Chem. Soc.*, **86,** 141 (1964).
105. Flory, P. J., V. Crescenzi, and J. E. Mark, *J. Am. Chem. Soc.*, **86,** 146 (1964).
106. Liebau, F., *Acta Cryst.*, **14,** 1103 (1961).
107. Haug, A., and G. Meyerhoff, *Makromol. Chem.*, **53,** 91 (1962).

Chapter 8

CONFORMATIONS OF MACROMOLECULES AND MECHANICAL PROPERTIES OF POLYMERS

8.1. Theory of Stretching of Macromolecules

The previous chapters were devoted to a quantitative treatment of the flexibility of macromolecules and its relation to the chemical and stereochemical structure of the chain. As discussed in detail above, the presence of a large number of internal degrees of freedom in a macromolecule results in the presence in polymer chains of an intramolecular entropy which is a function of their end-to-end distance. Because of this, the stretching of a polymer chain (change of its end-to-end distance) results in an elastic force of entropic origin. In Chapter 5, it was shown that in model chains consisting of n freely jointed elements of length r the distribution of end-to-end distances of the chain $\mathbf{h}$ can be expressed by the normal (Gaussian) law (1):

$$W(\mathbf{h})d\mathbf{h} = (3/2\pi nr^2)^{3/2}e^{-3h^2/2nr^2}d\mathbf{h} \tag{8.1}$$

It follows from this that the free energy of such a chain as a function of the projection in any given direction, x, of the vector which connects the ends of the chain is expressed by the equation:

$$F(x) = \text{const} + {}^3/_2kT(x^2/nr^2) \tag{8.2}$$

Consequently, the mean elastic force which acts between the ends of a freely jointed chain kept at a distance x from each other is given (2) by eq. (8.3).

$$\bar{f} = (3kT/nr^2)x \tag{8.3}$$

In the case of a freely jointed chain, the quantities n and r clearly do not depend on the temperature, so that the free energy of the chain F and the elastic force f are proportional to temperature. This means that *in this case the elastic force has a purely entropic origin.*

Equations (8.1) and (8.2) are the basis of the statistical theory of high elasticity developed by Guth and Mark (2) from the thesis that the stretching of a macromolecule by an external force changes only its entropy but not its energy. Later, this theory was extended by Kuhn (3–6), Wall (7–9), Treloar (10,11), Flory (12–15), and a number of other authors (7–22) to polymers in the bulk state, and it accounted for the principal laws of the high elasticity of polymers. We shall not dwell here on the classical theory of high elasticity developed in the papers cited above, since it has been presented in detail in a large number of monographs and review articles (23–27). Let us mention only that, in this theory, a highly elastic polymer is regarded as a network of linked macromolecules, each of which is deformed by an external force according to eq. (8.3). It is assumed also that interaction between individual polymer chains in the network is practically independent of the shape of the sample (at constant volume), while it is a strong function of the sample volume. In other words, a sample of a highly elastic polymer has a large *resilience of volume,* i.e., a large modulus of compressibility from all directions (just as any liquid or any amorphous solid body); however, it has a very small *resilience of shape,* i.e., it has a large modulus of displacement which is entirely determined by the entropic resilience of individual polymer chains. Thus, a change in the shape of highly elastic samples is related to the overcoming not of large energetic forces which maintain a constant value of the volume of the sample, but of rather weak entropic forces which prevent the uncoiling of macromolecules. This explains immediately the low values of the modulus of elasticity of rubber during one-dimensional and two-dimensional deformations and its approximate proportionality to temperature; this has led to the universal acceptance of the classical theory of high elasticity. The mathematics of the theory was considerably improved later [see, in particular, the paper of James and Guth (22)], but its physical assumptions, which were analyzed in detail in the paper of Boggs (28), have remained essentially the same. While the gas theory of high elasticity is not in full agreement with experiment (see below, section 7.3), it is only very recently that several studies have appeared (29–33) in which an attempt has been made to go beyond the limits of this theory, i.e., to take into account the dependence of the interaction of the macromolecules in the lattice on the shape of the sample being deformed.

The classical theory of high elasticity results in the expression for the force of resilience which arises during a change in the shape of the sample (with a one-dimensional deformation) given in eq. (8.4):

$$f = (KkT/V^{2/3})[L - (V/L^2)] = (KkT/V^{1/3})[\alpha - (1/\alpha^2)] \qquad (8.4)$$

where L is the length of the stretched sample in the direction of the elongation, V is the volume of the unstretched sample (which can be considered as cubic, for the sake of simplicity), $\alpha = L/L_0 = L/V^{1/3}$ is the ratio of the length of the stretched sample in the direction of stretching to that of the unstretched sample, and K is a coefficient equal in order of magnitude to the number of chains in the lattice of the sample; K is essentially a function of the structures of the chains and of the lattice. The first terms in the parentheses in the right-hand part of eq. (8.4) reflects the proportionality between the elastic force and deformation in an individual chain [see eq. (8.3)], and the second term takes into account the essential incompressibility of polymers, as a result of which each polymeric chain which is part of the lattice subjected to one-directional deformation undergoes not only stretching in the direction of the acting force, but also compression in the two directions perpendicular to it.

The dependence of the deformation α of the sample on the applied force f, predicted by eq. (8.4), has been verified experimentally many times. The theory describes correctly the general character of this dependence, as well as the order of magnitude of the modulus of elasticity.

A number of authors (11,34–40) have observed a systematic deviation of the theory from experiment not only in the region of large deformations, in which these deviations are related to the inapplicability of the initial Gaussian distribution of chain lengths (see section 5.2), but also in the region of moderate deformations. While the recent investigations of Priss (41) and Ciferri and Flory (42) have shown that part of these deviations is related to an incomplete attainment of equilibrium conditions during deformation, it is almost certain that such deviations remain even after equilibrium is reached.

How do the results of the theory of high elasticity change if we pass from model freely jointed chains to real macromolecules with fixed valence angles and restricted internal rotation, which result in energetically nonequivalent conformations of monomer units? In section 5.2 it was shown that the normal (Gaussian) distribution of the end-to-end distance of the chain is preserved also for macromolecules with fixed valence angles and restricted internal rotation, i.e., for them, just as for freely jointed chains:

$$W(\mathbf{h})d\mathbf{h} = \left(\frac{3}{2\pi\overline{h^2}}\right)^{3/2} e^{-3h^2/2\overline{h^2}}\, d\mathbf{h} \tag{8.5}$$

where $\overline{h^2}$ is the mean-square end-to-end distance of the chain, calculated with short-range interactions taken into account.* The criterion of the

* Long-range interactions result in a non-Gaussian distribution function $W(\mathbf{h})$; we do not consider them here since they (just as intermolecular interactions) have a small effect on the law of deformation of highly elastic polymers in the bulk state.

validity of distribution function (8.5) is the small size of the stiff portion of the chain relative to the entire contour length of the chain. (This is dealt with in greater detail in section 5.2.) It follows from eq. (8.5) that, for real macromolecules as well, the dependence of the free energy of the chain on the projection χ of the vector **h** on the given direction has the form

$$F(x) = \text{const} + {}^3/_2kT(x^2/\overline{h^2}) \tag{8.6}$$

From this, the mean elastic force which acts between the ends of a chain kept at a distance x from each other is

$$\bar{f} = (3kT/\overline{h^2})x \tag{8.7}$$

Equations (8.5)–(8.7) for real macromolecules, just as equations (8.1)–(8.3) for model freely jointed chains, are obviously valid only as long as the distance between the chain ends is small in relation to the maximal length of the stretched chain. For freely jointed chains with large n, but with h comparable to nr, distribution function $W(\mathbf{h})$ is expressed by eq. (5.45) which gives:

$$\bar{f} = \frac{kT}{r}\,\mathfrak{L}^{-1}\left(\frac{h}{nr}\right)\frac{x}{h} \tag{8.8}$$

where $\mathfrak{L}^{-1}$ is the reciprocal of a Langevin function [see eq. (5.46)]. With $h \ll nr$, $\mathfrak{L}^{-1}(h/nr) \approx 3h/nr$, and eq. (8.8) becomes eq. (8.3), while with $h \rightarrow nr$, eq. (8.8) gives $\bar{f} \rightarrow \infty$. Distribution function (5.45) is, strictly speaking, not applicable to real (but not freely-jointed) macromolecules; however, the dependence of the elongation on the force applied can be calculated easily for them also if the problem is reversed, i.e., if, instead of calculating the mean force which acts in the chain with fixed ends, we calculate the mean end-to-end distance of the chain present in the field of the given force. This corresponds to transition from an ensemble of the isothermal–isochoric type to an ensemble of the isothermal–isobaric type. These two approaches are clearly, completely equivalent (with a precision limited only by thermal fluctuations).

The question of the stretching of a real macromolecule by external force, **f**, has been examined by Volkenshtein and Ptitsyn (43). Following their paper, let us write out the partition function of a polymer chain which is under the action of a stretching force, **f**, applied to its ends; it has the form:

$$Z_n(\mathbf{f}) = \int \cdots \int e^{-U(\Omega_1,\ldots,\Omega_n)/kT+(\mathbf{f},\,\mathbf{h})/kT} \prod_{j=1}^{n} d\Omega_j$$

$$= \int \cdots \int e^{-U(\Omega_1,\ldots,\Omega_n)/kT+(1/kT)\sum_{j=1}^{n}(\mathbf{f},\mathbf{r}_j)} \prod_{j=1}^{n} d\Omega_j \tag{8.9}$$

where $\mathbf{r}_j$ are the vectors of the lengths of monomer units, while the integration is carried out over the conformations of all n monomer units. Comparing eq. (8.9) with an expression for the distribution function of macromolecules according to their lengths in the absence of an external force

$$W(\mathbf{h})d\mathbf{h} = \frac{1}{Z_n^0}\int \cdots \int\limits_{\left(\mathbf{h}-\frac{1}{2}d\mathbf{h} \leqq \sum_{j=1}^{n} \mathbf{r}_j \leqq \mathbf{h}+\frac{1}{2}d\mathbf{h}\right)} e^{-\frac{U(\Omega_1,\ldots,\Omega_n)}{kT}} \prod_{j=1}^{n} d\Omega_j \quad (8.10)$$

we obtain

$$Z_n(\mathbf{f}) = Z_n^0 \int W(\mathbf{h}) e^{(\mathbf{f},\mathbf{h}/kT)} d\mathbf{h} \quad (8.11)$$

In eqs. (8.10) and (8.11), $Z_n{}^0$ is the partition function of the chain in the absence of an external force, obtained from eq. (8.9) with $f = 0$. Going over to spherical coordinates in eq. (8.11) and integrating over the angles, we obtain

$$Z_n(\mathbf{f}) = Z_n^0 4\pi \int_0^{h_{\max}} W(h)h^2 \frac{\operatorname{sh}(\chi h)}{\chi h}\, dh = Z_0 \overline{\left(\frac{\operatorname{sh}(\chi h)}{\chi h}\right)} \quad (8.12)$$

where $\chi = f/kT$, and the averaging is carried out in the absence of external force.

From eq. (8.12) we obtain the following expression for the mean projection of the chain length on the direction of the external force:

$$\bar{x} = \frac{\partial \ln Z_n(\mathbf{f})}{\partial \chi} = \frac{1}{\chi} \cdot \frac{\overline{\operatorname{sh}(\chi h)\mathfrak{L}(\chi h)}}{\overline{(1/\chi h)\operatorname{sh}(\chi h)}} = \sum_{k=1}^{\infty} c_k \chi^{2k-1} \quad (8.13)$$

where $\mathfrak{L}$ is a Langevin function, i.e., $\mathfrak{L}(x) = \operatorname{cth} x - 1/x$, and

$$c_k = \frac{2k}{(2k+1)!}\overline{h^{2k}} - \sum_{l=1}^{k-1} c_{k-l} \frac{\overline{h^{2l}}}{(2l+1)!} \quad (8.14)$$

Writing out the first few terms of the series in the right-hand side of eq. (8.14), we obtain:

$$\bar{x} = \frac{f}{kT}\cdot\frac{\overline{h^2}}{3} + \left(\frac{f}{kT}\right)^3 \left[\frac{1}{30}\overline{h^4} - \frac{1}{18}(\overline{h^2})^2\right] + \left(\frac{f}{kT}\right)^5 \times \left[\frac{1}{840}\overline{h^6} - \frac{1}{120}\overline{h^4}\cdot\overline{h^2} + \frac{1}{108}(\overline{h^2})^3\right] + \ldots \quad (8.15)$$

It is obvious that there is a close relationship between the partition function of the chain in a field of external force $Z_n(\mathbf{f})$, which is a three-dimensional Laplace transformation of the distribution function $W_n(\mathbf{h})$, and the three-dimensional Fourier transformation of this function, expressed by us before as $A_n(\boldsymbol{\rho})$ (see section 5.2). In fact, comparison of eqs. (5.40) and (8.11) shows that $Z_n(\mathbf{f})$ coincides with $A_n(\boldsymbol{\rho})$ when $\boldsymbol{\rho} = -i\mathbf{f}/kT$. Accordingly, the coefficients c_n in expansion (8.13) are related to the coefficients g_{2n}, defined by eqs. (5.57), by the equalities

$$c_n = 2ng_{2n}$$

Expansion (8.15) shows that, with small external forces, the stretching of any chain can be described by the expression

$$\bar{x} = (f/kT)(\overline{h^2}/3) \tag{8.16}$$

which is equivalent to eq. (8.7); with greater external forces, however, non-Gaussian terms, defined by the higher moments of distribution function $W(\mathbf{h})$, begin to play a role. The coefficient of $(f/kT)^3$, i.e., the quantity $\overline{h^3}/30 - (\overline{h^2})^2/18$, has been calculated recently by Miyake and Sakakibara (44) for a number of simple model chains. In their paper it is shown that, for example in the case of a chain with fixed valence angles and independent restricting potentials of rotation of neighboring bonds which result in the presence of *trans* and *gauche* rotational isomers in each bond this coefficient increases sharply with an increase in the energy difference ΔU between the *gauche* and *trans* isomers: from $^1/_3Nl^2$ with $\Delta U = 0$ to $\sim 10^4Nl^2$ with $\Delta U \approx 1000$ cal/mole (where l is the length of a bond). It follows from this that the non-Gaussian terms of expansion (8.15) can play a considerable role in the deformation of real macromolecules.

Miyake and Sakakibara (44) also stressed that the first non-Gaussian term in eq. (8.15) for real chains does not coincide with the first non-Gaussian term in eq. (8.8) for freely jointed chains. Furthermore, curves of the stretching of model chains, the elements of which occupy mutually correlated positions in a one-dimensional lattice (43) and a square two-dimensional (45) lattice are quite close to the curves of the stretching of freely jointed chains with "favorable values" of n and r which satisfy the conditions $nr^2 = \overline{h^2}$ and $nr = h_{\max}$ (see section 5.2).

8.2. Rotational Isomerization of Macromolecules during Stretching and Energetic Effects in Stretched Polymers in the Bulk State

In the preceding section it has been shown that, when deformations are not very large, distribution function (8.5) and, consequently, expressions

(8.6) for the free energy of the chain and eq. (8.7) for the elastic force are valid for any macromolecule which is sufficiently long in relation to its rigid portion. The meaning of these expressions, however, is different for chains with free and restricted internal rotations. In fact, in the case of a chain with restricted internal rotation, the quantity $\overline{h^2}$ is a function of temperature, and, as a result, the change in the free energy of the chain during its deformation [see eq. (8.6)] is not proportional to temperature, i.e., it is not reduced to a change in the entropy alone. Consequently, the *elasticity of real polymer chains does not have a purely entropic origin; not only the entropy but also the energy of the chain changes during deformation.*

This conclusion was first reached by Volkenshtein and Ptitsyn (43,46,47), primarily from the considerations of models based on the rotational-isomeric mechanism of flexibility of macromolecules proposed by Volkenshtein (48,49). These considerations were that the stretching of a macromolecule must be accompanied not only by the redistribution of the given number of rotational isomers of various types (for example, *trans* and *gauche* isomers) along the chain, but also by the transition of rotational isomers which correspond to more tightly coiled conformations of the chain into rotational isomers which correspond to more elongated conformations.* While this redistribution process is, obviously, related not to the change in the chain energy, but only to a decrease of its entropy, the transition of some rotational isomers into others changes not only the entropy but also the energy of the chain. As has been shown by Volkenshtein and Ptitsyn for a one-dimension model (46) and in the general form (47), in the case of small deformations (i.e., in a linear approximation in x) this transition is not accompanied by a change in the free energy (the changes in the energy and entropy compensate each other), so that the total elastic force is determined only by the redistribution of the rotational isomers along the chain. We shall not dwell here in detail on these problems, since they have been presented in detail elsewhere (25).

The expression for the energetic force, i.e., the force determined by the change in the energy of the chain during its deformation, can be obtained, of course, without invoking any assumptions on models of the mechanism of flexibility of macromolecules. Using the definition of the energetic force:

$$f_e = (\partial U/\partial x)_T = (\partial F/\partial x)_T + T(\partial S/\partial x)_T = f + T(\partial S/\partial x)_T \quad (8.17)$$

(where U and S are the energy and entropy of the chain, respectively) and

* The existence of such a transition was established later by spectroscopic methods (see section 8.4).

introducing into it the thermodynamic equality $(\partial S/\partial x)_T = -(\partial f/\partial T)_x$, we obtain

$$f_e = f - T(\partial f/\partial T)_x \tag{8.18}$$

Substitution of eq. (8.7) for the elastic force f into eq. (8.18) gives

$$f_e = fT(d \ln \overline{h^2}/dT) \tag{8.19}$$

Equation (8.19) shows that the sign of the energetic force depends on the sign of $d\overline{h^2}/dT$. If the minimum in the potential energy corresponds to maximally stretched conformations of the chain (as is true in most cases), the dimensions of the macromolecule decrease with an increase in temperature, and the energetic force is negative. This is easy to understand since, in such a case, stretching of the chain is accompanied by an increase in the fraction of monomer units in energetically more favorable stretched conformations, i.e., by a decrease in the energy of the chain. On the other hand, if the minimum in the free energy corresponds to coiled conformations of the chain, the dimensions of the macromolecules increase with an increase in temperature, and the energetic force is positive (stretching is accompanied by an increase in the fraction of energetically less favorable stretched conformations, i.e., by an increase in the energy of the chain). Furthermore, evaluations of the magnitude of the energetic force for a number of simple models of polymer chains (see section 8.3) show that in many cases the energetic force can be comparable in absolute value to the total elastic force.

The applicability of eq. (8.19) also to the intramolecular energetic force which arises during the stretching of polymers in the bulk state, has been demonstrated in the studies of Flory, Hoeve, and Ciferri (50) and Ptitsyn (51) [see also (52, 53)]. In this case, the total energy change contains a contribution related to changes in the volume of the sample, which always accompany each deformation.* In order to eliminate these trivial intermolecular effects which are considered in the theory of liquids, the change in the energy of the sample should be examined when it is stretched at constant volume, i.e., the quantity $(\partial U/\partial L)_{V,T}$ (where U is the energy of the sample) should be examined. This quantity is not necessarily equal to the energetic force determined by purely intramolecular effects, since, generally speaking, the energy of the intermolecular interaction can be a function

* While the change in the volume of the sample during high elastic deformation, described by the quantity $(\partial V/\partial L)_{p,T}$, is small, the energetic force related to it may be large, because of the very large value of the derivative $(\partial U/\partial V)_{p,T}$ which describes the dependence of the energy of the sample on its volume.

not only of the volume of the sample but also of its shape. The usual "gas" theory of high elasticity, however, does not take this dependence into account, so that, within the limits of this theory, the change in the energy which accompanies the deformation of the sample at constant volume is related entirely to the change in the conformations of the polymer chains and, consequently,

$$f_e = (\partial U/\partial L)_{V,T} = f - T(\partial f/\partial T)_{V,L} \quad (8.20)$$

[compare eq. (8.18)].

Substituting into eq. (8.20) eq. (8.4), which is given by the classical theory of high elasticity,* we obtain

$$f_e = -fT(\partial \ln K/\partial T)_V \quad (8.21)$$

Different versions of the lattice theory of high elasticity, developed by Flory (15), Kubo (16), and James and Guth (20,22,54) result in the same temperature dependence of the coefficient K:

$$K \approx G\overline{r^2}/\overline{h^2} \quad (8.22)$$

where G is the number of chains in the sample included in the active part of the lattice (i.e., those which are deformed during the deformation of the sample), $\overline{r^2}$ is the mean-square end-to-end distance of the chain in an isotropic sample with volume V, while $\overline{h^2}$ is the mean-square distance between the ends of a free chain in an ideal solvent.

Substituting eq. (8.22) into eq. (8.21), we obtain an expression for the intramolecular energetic elastic force in the sample which is identical with eq. (8.19) for the energetic elastic force in an individual chain.

We see that the theory, which takes into account the change in the conformations of macromolecules during their stretching, predicts the existence of large intramolecular energetic effects during the stretching of polymers in bulk. How can this prediction of the theory be checked by experiment? Equation (8.20) is not an adequate basis for such an experiment, since it requires measurement of the elastic force at different temperatures but at constant volume; this involves tremendous difficulties. In the studies of Elliott and Lippmann (55) and Gee (34) [see also (56)], the approximate thermodynamic equality was proposed

$$(\partial f/\partial T)_{V,L} \approx (\partial f/\partial T)_{p,\alpha} \quad (8.23)$$

* It is understood that taking into consideration the rotational isomerization of the macromolecules during stretching does not change eq. (8.4) for the total elastic force of the sample, since this does not change eq. (8.7) for the total elastic force of each individual chain.

(where α is the ratio of the length of the stretched sample to the length of an unstretched sample at the temperature of the experiment), i.e.,

$$f_e \approx f - T(\partial f/\partial T)_{p,\alpha} \tag{8.24}$$

According to the results of Gee (34) and Flory (56), eqs. (8.23) and (8.24) must be valid with a precision up to the term

$$\Delta \approx \frac{fT\beta}{3}\left[\frac{\kappa/\beta}{(\kappa/\beta)_L} - 1\right] \ll \frac{fT\beta}{3} \tag{8.25}$$

where $\beta = d \ln V/dT$ is the coefficient of volume expansion of the sample, κ is its coefficient of compressibility, while subscript L refers to the stretched sample. Equation (8.24) has been widely used for many years. For example it was used to conclude, on the basis of experimental data (34,57) on natural rubber (*cis*-polyisoprene) for which $f - T(\partial f/\partial T)_{p,\alpha} \approx 0$, that natural rubber is an "ideal" polymer (58), i.e., its elasticity is of a purely entropic character ($f_e = 0$). Furthermore, investigations of synthetic rubbers, for example GR-S (butadiene–styrene copolymer) (58,59), have shown that in this case $f - T(\partial f/\partial T)_{p,\alpha} < 0$; moreover, the absolute value of this quantity increases with an increase in α attaining approximately $f/3$ at $\alpha = 2.8$.

Since 1959, new interesting results have appeared in this area. First, investigations of the thermodynamic properties of highly elastic radiation-crosslinked polyethylene carried out by Flory, Hoeve, and Ciferri (50), have shown that, for this polymer, $f - T(\partial f/\partial T)_{p,\alpha} \neq 0$, i.e. it possesses a considerable energetic force. Second, the studies of Khazanovich (60,61) and Flory (62,63) pointed out that eq. (8.24) contradicts the statistical theory of high elasticity. In fact, since in eq. (8.22) $\overline{r^2} \sim V^{2/3}$, it follows from eqs. (8.4) and (8.22) that

$$\begin{aligned} f_e &= f - T(\partial f/\partial T)_{p,\alpha} + f\beta T/3 \\ &= f - T(\partial f/\partial T)_L - f\beta T/(\alpha^3 - 1) \end{aligned} \tag{8.26}$$

where $\beta = d \ln V/dT$ is the coefficient of volume expansion of an isotropic sample. The difference between eqs. (8.24) and (8.26) is explained by the fact (60–63) that, in the derivation of eq. (8.24), the calculation of the coefficient which characterizes the anisotropy of the compressed sample was carried out on the basis of an intuitional generalization of the theory of infinitely small deformations which does not apply to the large deformations that are characteristic of highly elastic polymers. In actuality, the evaluation of this coefficient must be carried out on the basis not of the classical theory of infinitely small deformations, but of the statistical theory of high elasticity, which results in eq. (8.26) instead of eq. (8.24) (62,63). The difference between these equations is not negligibly small, since the experimental error in the determination of the quantity $f - T \times (\partial f/\partial T)_{p,\alpha}$ is not greater than one quarter of $f\beta T/3$.

Consequently, the equality of $f - T(\partial f/\partial T)_{p,\alpha}$ to zero does not mean that $f_e = 0$.

The thermomechanical properties of polyethylene (64), polyisobutylene (64), and polydimethylsiloxane (65,66,83) in the highly elastic state have been studied in detail in the papers of Flory and co-workers with the aim of determining f_e/f. The polyethylene samples were crosslinked by irradiation, the polyisobutylenes (more precisely, butyl rubber, i.e., of a copolymer of isobutylene with 2% isoprene) were crosslinked by chemical means, and the polydimethylsiloxane was crosslinked by both methods. The temperature dependence of the relative tension σ (of the stretching force relative to a cross-sectional area of unstretched sample) was studied at a constant length of the sample. Within experimental error, the dependence of σ on temperature turned out to be linear in all cases; from the experimental slopes of $(\partial\sigma/\partial T)_{p,L}$ and the values of σ/T averaged over the experimental temperature range values of $[\partial \ln (f/T)/\partial \ln T]_{p,L}$ necessary for an evaluation of f_e/f were calculated by the equation

$$\frac{f_e}{f} = -\left(\frac{\partial \ln (f/T)}{\partial \ln T}\right)_{p,L} - \frac{\beta T}{\alpha^3 - 1} \tag{8.27}$$

which follows from eq. (8.26). After introducing the correction $\beta T/(\alpha^3 - 1)$ (which decreases rapidly with extent of stretching) for the volume compressibility of the sample, Flory and co-workers obtained values of f_e/f for the various samples investigated. First, it was found that the values of f_e/f obtained are practically independent of the degree of stretching (in agreement with the prediction of the theory). They are also independent of the degree of crosslinking of the samples, of the conditions under which the crosslinking was carried out (melt, unoriented amorphous state, unoriented and oriented crystal state), of whether a pure or swollen polymer was studied, and of the solvent in which the swelling took place.

Let us illustrate what has been said above in Table 8.1, in which are collected data on the values of f_e/f obtained by Ciferri, Hoeve and Flory (64) for samples of low-pressure polyethylene crosslinked under various conditions and subjected to swelling and stretching to different extents. The samples were obtained by irradiation of various commercial polyethylenes: the highly oriented crystalline fibers of Marlex-50 (samples

TABLE 8.1

Results of Thermomechanical Investigation of Various Polyethylene Samples[a]

Sample no.	Method of crosslinking	Irradiation dose, Mr	State of sample during crosslinking	Solvent	Volume fraction of polymer	α	$\left(\frac{\partial \sigma}{\partial T}\right)_{p,L} \times 10^3$, kg/cm² deg	$\left[\frac{\partial \ln (f/T)}{\partial \ln T}\right]_{p,L}$	$\frac{\beta T}{\alpha^3 - 1}$	$-\frac{f_e}{f}$
1	γ-rays	29	Oriented crystal	None	1.00	1.55	3.10	0.30	0.11	0.41
						1.82	3.62	0.27	0.06	0.33
						2.09	4.61	0.41	0.04	0.45
						2.46	5.18	0.37	0.02	0.39
						2.96	6.20	0.43	0.02	0.45
2	γ-rays	58	Oriented crystal	None	1.00	1.43	5.30	0.30	0.16	0.46
						1.70	7.73	0.34	0.08	0.42
						2.02	9.63	0.36	0.04	0.40
3	γ-rays	100	Oriented crystal	None	1.00	1.40	6.30	0.15	0.18	0.33
						1.54	8.60	0.32	0.11	0.43
						1.68	10.70	0.37	0.08	0.45
						1.79	12.21	0.42	0.06	0.48
						1.86	12.85	0.43	0.06	0.49

4	γ-rays	26	Unoriented crystal	None	1.00	1.75	4.56	0.40	0.07	0.47
						2.02	5.60	0.41	0.04	0.45
						1.80	1.31	0.32	0.07	0.39
				Di-2-ethylhexyl azelate	0.80	1.85	1.32	0.32	0.06	0.38
				n-Dotriacontane	0.50	1.77	0.71	0.58	0.06	0.64
5	γ-rays	39	Unoriented crystal	Di-2-ethylhexyl azelate	0.70	1.41	2.17	0.29	0.18	0.47
6	γ-rays	90	Liquid[b]	None	1.00	1.40	6.03	0.12	0.18	0.30
7	Electron beam	40	Unoriented crystal	Di-2-ethylhexyl azelate	0.30	1.42	7.07	0.38	0.20	0.58
8	Electron beam	40	Unoriented crystal	Di-2-ethylhexyl azelate	0.55	1.13	3.28	−0.25	0.77	0.52
9	Electron beam	40	Unoriented crystal	Di-2-ethylhexyl azelate	0.53	1.28	11.69	−0.02	0.32	0.30
10	Electron beam	40	Unoriented crystal	n-Dotriacontane	0.31	1.12	9.53	0.81	−0.35	0.46
						1.14	15.00	0.68	−0.30	0.38
						1.18	17.95	0.76	−0.22	0.54
11	Electron beam	40	Unoriented crystal	n-Dotriacontane	0.30	1.24	23.90	0.68	−0.16	0.52
						1.33	27.90	0.59	−0.11	0.48

[a] Data of Ciferri, Hoeve, and Flory (64).
[b] At 175°C.

TABLE 8.2
Effects of Stretching on Intramolecular Energy in Elastic Polymers

Polymer	Solvent	Degree of stretching, α	Temperature range, °C	f_e/f	$\frac{d \ln \overline{h^2}}{dT} \times 10^3$, deg^{-1}
Polyethylene[a]	None	1.40–2.96	137–200	−0.42 ± 0.05	−1.0 ± 0.1
	$C_{30}H_{62}$ (v_2 = 0.50)	1.77	120–165	−0.50 ± 0.06	−1.16 ± 0.1
	$C_{32}H_{66}$ (v_2 = 0.30, 0.32)	1.12–1.33	140–180	−0.50 ± 0.06	−1.16 ± 0.1
	Di-2-ethylhexyl azelate (v_2 = 0.30, 0.70, 0.80)	1.41–1.85	120–180	−0.44 ± 0.10	−1.0 ± 0.2
Polyisobutylene[a]	None	1.73–3.75	20–100	−0.03 ± 0.02	−0.08 ± 0.06
	$C_{16}H_{34}$ (v_2 = 0.41, 0.54)	1.67–3.19	17–60	−0.03 ± 0.02	−0.09 ± 0.07
Natural rubber[b]	None	1.10–2.50	−20 to +25	0.13 ± 0.02	0.41 ± 0.04
GR-S (butadiene–styrene copolymer)[c]	None	1.10–2.50	−20 to +25	−0.13 ± 0.06	−0.41 ± 0.2
Polydimethylsiloxane[d]	None	1.34–2.01	40–100	0.27 ± 0.02	0.78 ± 0.16

[a] Data of Ciferri, Hoeve, and Flory (64).
[b] Data of Wood and Roth (57).
[c] Data of Roth and Wood (59).
[d] Data of Mark and Flory (83).

1–3), unoriented crystalline samples of Super-Dylan (samples 4, 5, and 7–11) and a sample of Super-Dylan heated above the melting temperature (sample 6). The values of α were calculated at the highest temperature of the experiment. For samples of polyethylene swollen in *n*-dotriacontane, $C_{32}H_{66}$, the coefficient of volume expansion β was measured at conditions of equilibrium between the swollen sample and the solvent; for polyethylene, unswollen and swollen in di-2-ethylhexyl azelate and *n*-dotriacontane, the values of β were found to be 6.9×10^{-4}, 9.0×10^{-4},* and -3.3×10^{-4} deg^{-1}, respectively. Similar results have been obtained by Ciferri, Hoeve, and Flory (64) for polyisobutylene and Ciferri (66) and Mark and Flory

* *Editor's note:* According to Flory's paper (64), this value is β for di-2-ethylhexyl azelate alone.

(83) for polydimethylsiloxane. The ratio f_e/f was calculated by two methods by Ciferri (66), namely, from $(\partial f/\partial T)_{p,L}$ and from $(\partial f/\partial T)_{p,\alpha}$ [see eq. (8.26)]. The results were found to be identical within experimental error.

The results obtained (64,83) on the energetic effects which accompany the stretching of polyethylene, polyisobutylene and polydimethylsiloxane are summarized in Table 8.2. Experimental data on natural rubber and GR-S (butadiene–styrene copolymer) (57,59)* and treated anew by Ciferri, Hoeve, and Flory (64) (with the use of eq. (8.26)], are also presented in this table. It is evident that almost all the polymers investigated are not at all ideal, i.e., they do not have a purely entropic elasticity but are characterized by a considerable change in the energy of the sample during its deformation. This applies in particular to the most rigid polymer investigated, namely, to polyethylene in which the energetic force (with a negative sign) accounts for close to half of the total elastic force in absolute value. The only polymer for which the energetic effects observed practically do not deviate by more than experimental error from zero is polyisobutylene; this is due to the specificity of the conformational structure of this polymer (see section 7.2).

The values of f_e/f in Table 8.2 are the result of the averaging of experimental data over various samples investigated and various degrees of elongation, α. The values of $d \ln \overline{h^2}/dT$ have been calculated from f_e/f by eq. (8.19), which is based on the fact that the energetic force f_e, normalized to a constant volume of the sample, has a purely intramolecular origin.

8.3. Interpretation of Thermomechanical Curves for Real Types of Polymers

We have seen that the values of f_e/f for all the polymers studied are practically independent of all possible factors which could have an effect on intermolecular interactions. This is strong evidence for the intramolecular character of the energetic effects investigated and confirms the independence of the energy of intermolecular interaction of polymer chains on the shape of the sample (at constant volume). The intramolecular nature of the effects investigated is further confirmed by a comparison of the values of $d \ln \overline{h^2}/dT$ for polyethylene and polydimethylsiloxane given in Table 8.2 with values obtained from the temperature dependence of the

* The data of Wood and Roth (57) on natural rubber are also confirmed by the data of Anthony, Caston, and Guth (67).

intrinsic viscosity of these polymers in nonideal athermal solvents after correction for long-range interactions (68,83). It was found that for polyethylene $d \ln \overline{h^2}/dT \approx -1.2\ (\pm 0.2) \times 10^{-3}\ \text{deg}^{-1}$ (68), while for polydimethylsiloxane $d \ln \overline{h^2}/dT \approx +0.71\ (\pm 0.13) \times 10^{-3}\ \text{deg}^{-1}$;* this is very close to values cited in Table 8.2.

It is pointed out by Ciferri, Hoeve, and Flory (64) that the independence of the ratio of f_e/f of factors which have an effect on intermolecular interactions (in particular the equality of this ratio for swollen and unswollen samples) proves the absence of partial ordering of chains in the amorphous polymers studied, since the necessary weakening of such ordering during swelling should be reflected in the values of f_e. Strictly speaking, however, this does not contradict the possibility of partial ordering of macromolecules in the sample with the condition that the ordering be relatively small and be determined not by the energy of interaction between segments of different chains which is a function of their orientation, but by the entropy of packing of the chains in the deformed sample.† In his theory of polymer crystallization developed in 1956, Flory (70) expressed and proved the very interesting thought that the crystallization of polymers depends not so much on the energy of intermolecular interactions, but on the requirements of the packing of chains with limited flexibility in the given volume of the sample. According to Flory's point of view, polymers crystallize with a decrease in temperature because, during cooling, the stiffness of the chain increases (the number of coiled rotational isomers decreases), and chains which have a sufficiently large amount of stiffness cannot fill the volume available to them in disordered array (keeping the required density of the sample) and thus must take on an ordered conformation, i.e., they must crystallize. The rotational-isomeric theory of crystallization and melting of polymers with limited flexibility developed by Flory relates the temperature of crystallization only to intramolecular interactions;‡ it takes intermolecular interactions into account only as a "background" factor which maintains the actually observed density of the sample.

Considerations of the impossibility of random packing of semirigid macromolecules which results in the spontaneous ordering of chains, are

* In an earlier paper of Ciferri (69), a lower value was obtained, +0.33 (±0.05).

† In such a case, the presence of ordering will not be reflected in the values of f_e, and its effect on the total elastic force f can be small.

‡ The role of intramolecular interactions in the crystallization of polymers was first considered in the theory of Volkenshtein and Ptitsyn (93); in this theory, a single polymeric chain was actually examined and not an entire sample; as a result, the determining influence of the packing of semirigid chains in the given volume of the sample was not taken into account.

of importance, evidently, not only for crystalline, but also for amorphous polymers. Thus it is quite obvious that, even if the polymer cannot crystallize (because its molecules do not have a chemically or stereochemically regular structure), a completely disordered packing of semirigid chains becomes impossible below a given temperature. Gibbs and Di Marzio (71), applying Flory's model to amorphous polymers, reached the conclusion that a noncrystallizing polymer must undergo second-order phase transition at some temperature. Gibbs and Di Marzio equated this with the vitrification of polymers; this is in contradiction to the generally accepted and experimentally firmly proven concepts on the purely relaxational nature of this phenomenon (72). Volkenshtein (25), however, has pointed out that the transition predicted by Gibbs and Di Marzio can be treated as a transition from a totally disordered to a partly ordered state of the system of noncrystallizable macromolecules. The limiting case of such an ordered state is the bunched structure of amorphous polymers, proposed by Kargin, Kitaigorodskii, and Slonimskii (73,74). It is obviously not known whether the transition from a disordered into a partly ordered state is sufficiently cooperative to permit it to be treated as a second-order phase transition. (Up to now there are no experimental data in favor of this assumption.) It is evident, however, that the requirements of the packing of semirigid macromolecules must result, at low temperatures, in the presence of some ordering, even in amorphous polymers (if, of course, they do not crystallize first).

On the other hand, Volkenshtein, Gotlib, and Ptitsyn (30) have shown from an analysis of the experimentally observed deviations from the classical theory of high elasticity (11,34–40) that these deviations cannot be related to changes in the energy of intermolecular interactions. The fact is that these deviations are reduced to the presence in the expression of the elastic force of an additional term which is less dependent on deformation than is required by the gas theory [see eq. (8.4)], while, as has been shown (30), the energetic force, determined by intermolecular interactions, must be a stronger function of the deformation than the elastic force calculated in the gas theory. On the other hand, the simplest model which takes into account the "entropic" packing of macromolecules (a mixture of disordered chains which obey Gaussian statistics and "bundles"), describes satisfactorily deviations from the classical theory of high elasticity (30).

Di Marzio (31,32) has developed recently a quantitative theory of the high elasticity of polymers which takes into account the orientational dependence of the entropy of molecular packing. He calculated (without any new parameters) the entropy of packing of polymer chains as a function of their orientation and he showed (32) that this entropy has a minimal (negative) value in an unstretched sample and during stretching increases to a value close to zero (since in a sample oriented to the limit there is at least one method of chain orientation, namely their parallel distribution). This does not mean that polymer chains spontaneously orient themselves parallel to each other, since the increase in the entropy of packing related to this is considerably smaller than the entropy decrease due to the flexibility of the chain which is taken into account in the gas theory. The increase in the entropy of packing during deformation of the sample, however, results in an additional negative force; as a result of this, the curve of the dependence of tension on sample deformation must be below the curve calculated by the gas theory; this is in agreement with experiment. The dependence of the additional elastic force on deformation, given by the theory of Di Marzio (32), is in qualitative agreement with experiment. At the same time, the magnitude of the correction term calculated by Di Marzio is only one-tenth to one-half of the observed deviation of the gas theory from experiment. This is in agreement with the conclusions of Priss (41) and Ciferri and Flory (42), according to whom the major part of the deviation is the result of incomplete attainment of equilibrium.

We see that the deviations from the gas theory of high elasticity, observed in experiments, can be explained by entropic and not energetic effects. If this is so, the energetic force, normalized to a constant volume of the sample, must have a purely intramolecular origin; this explains the fact that the results of Ciferri, Hoeve, and Flory (64,66) are independent of factors that affect intermolecular interactions of the chains (see Tables 8.1 and 8.2).

The considerations presented above justify the attempt to interpret the values of f_e/f obtained by these authors on concepts involving changes of conformations of macromolecules during stretching, i.e., with equation (8.19) (47,50,64–66,75,83,84,96). Such an interpretation was actually carried out on the basis of the rotational-isomeric model of flexibility of macromolecules, so that the change of the energy of the deformed sample at constant volume was related to rotational isomerization of polymer chains during stretching.

As the simplest model of a macromolecule, let us examine a chain with symmetric side groups and independent rotations about neighboring bonds, characterized by rotational isomers (0, $\pm 120°$) with statistical weights 1 and $g = e^{-\Delta U/kT}$. For such a chain (see section 1.2):

$$\overline{h^2} = Nl^2\left(\frac{1 + \cos\alpha}{1 - \cos\alpha}\right)\left(\frac{1 + \eta}{1 - \eta}\right) \quad (8.28)$$

where, within the rotational-isomeric approximation, the mean cosine of the angle of internal rotation (48,49) is

$$\eta = (1 - g)/(1 + 2g) \quad (8.29)$$

Substituting eq. (8.29) into eq. (8.28), we obtain

$$\overline{h^2} = Nl^2\left(\frac{1 + \cos\alpha}{1 - \cos\alpha}\right)\frac{2 + g}{3g} \quad (8.30)$$

from which (47)

$$f_e/f = T(d \ln \overline{h^2}/dT) = -2/(2 + g)\cdot(\Delta U/kT) \quad (8.31)$$

where ΔU is the energy difference between the *gauche* and *trans* isomers. If $\Delta U \approx kT$, then $f_e \approx f$. Furthermore, if $\Delta U > 0$, then $f_e < 0$, since stretching of the chain increases the contents of the more favorable *trans* isomers.

Using eq. (8.31), Flory, Hoeve, and Ciferri (50) found from measurements of f_e/f that in polyethylene $\Delta U \simeq 500$ cal/mole (compare Fig. 8.1 from which $\Delta U/kT \approx 0.55$; with $T = 440°$K, this gives $\Delta U = 500$ cal/mole). This value of ΔU is in agreement with the value obtained from the temperature dependence of infrared spectra of n-paraffins (76) and polyethylene (77,78) (see section 2.1). Later, Hoeve (79) and Nagai and Ishikawa (94) interpreted the experimental values of the dimensions of polyethylene molecules in solution and values of f_e/f with the use of a more realistic model which takes into account correlations between the internal rotations of neighboring elements, i.e., the low probability of sequences ($+120°$, $-120°$) and ($-120°$, $+120°$) [see also Borisova (80); for more details see section 7.2].

In the case of chains with alternating valence angles, $\pi - \alpha_1$ and $\pi - \alpha_2$ (for example, polydimethylsiloxane), using eq. (6.15) (with $\eta^{(1)} = \eta^{(2)} = \eta$) and considering that rotational isomers (0, $\pm$ 120°) arise during rotation about each bond just as in polyethylene, so that $\eta = (1 - g)/(1 + 2g)$, where $g = e^{-\Delta U/kT}$, we obtain

$$\overline{h^2} = Nl^2\frac{(1 + \cos\alpha_1)(1 + \cos\alpha_2)}{\sin\alpha_1 \sin\alpha_2}\left[\frac{3g(2 + g)}{\chi(2 + 2g + 5g^2) - 2(1 - g)(1 + 2g)}\right] \quad (8.32)$$

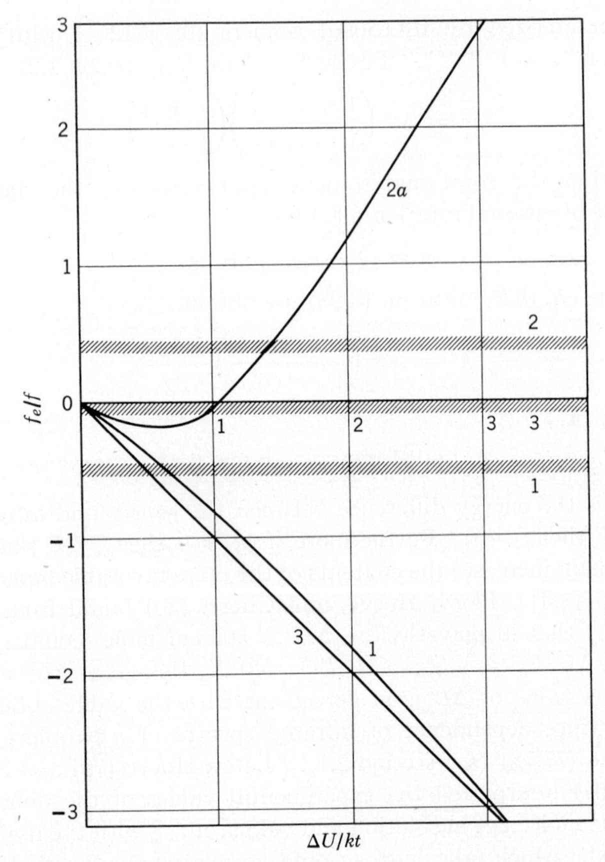

Fig. 8.1. Dependence of the energetic force on the energy difference between rotational isomers. Theoretical curves: (*1*) polyethylene [eq. (8.31)]; (*2*) polydimethylsiloxane [eq. (8.33) with $\pi - \alpha_1 = 150°$; (*3*) polyisobutylene [eq. (8.34)]. Shaded lines: experimental data for the corresponding polymers, with experimental error taken into account (see Table 3.5).

from which (75) we obtain

$$\frac{f_e}{f} = T\frac{d \ln \overline{h^2}}{dT} = -\frac{2}{2+g}\cdot\frac{\Delta U}{kT}\cdot\frac{1+\eta^2-2\eta\chi}{(1+\eta^2)\chi-2\eta} \tag{8.33}$$

where

$$\chi = \frac{1 - \cos\alpha_1, \cos\alpha_2}{\sin\alpha_1 \sin\alpha_2}$$

When $\alpha_1 = \alpha_2$, $\chi = 1$ and eq. (8.33) becomes eq. (8.31), as should have been expected. It follows from eq. (8.33) that, while in polyethylene the energetic force is negative at any positive ΔU, in polymers with alternating valence angles (for example, in polydimethylsiloxane) $f_e < 0$ with $\eta < \chi - \sqrt{\chi^2 - 1}$ and $f_e > 0$ with $\eta > \chi - \sqrt{\chi^2 - 1}$. This is related to the fact that the dimensions of such chains do not increase without limit with a decrease of the fraction of coiled isomers, but pass through a maximum and then decrease to a value of the order of the dimensions of a single bond [see eq. (8.32)].

The dependence of f_e/f on $\Delta U/kT$ according to eq. (8.33) with $\pi - \alpha_2 = 109° 33'$ and $\pi - \alpha_1 = 150°$ is shown in Figure 8.1, taken from the paper of Ptitsyn (75) (curve *2*).

For the sake of comparison, a similar dependence is shown for $\alpha_2 = \alpha_1$, i.e., according to eq. (8.31) (curve *1*). It can be seen from the figure that the experimental value of f_e/f for polydimethylsiloxane (see Table 8.2) corresponds to $\Delta U/kT = 1.3$ (with $\pi - \alpha_1 = 150°$), whence $\Delta U \simeq 850$ cal/mole (75). This value of ΔU results in dimensions for the polydimethylsiloxane molecule close to those observed experimentally, as is shown in Section 7.2. A more detailed treatment of the data requires that correlations between rotations about neighboring bonds be taken into account (84) (see section 7.2). Thus, a positive sign of the energetic force in polydimethylsiloxane can be explained quite naturally by the inequality of the valence angles in this chain and, contrary to the opinion of Ciferri (65,66) it does not require for its interpretation any specific assumptions about the conditions of internal rotation.

In the case of polymers with symmetric side groups and correlated conformations of neighboring monomer units we obtain (75) from eqs. (6.57) and (6.36):

$$f_e/f = T(d \ln \overline{h^2}/dT) = -\Delta U/kT \tag{8.34}$$

where ΔU is the energy difference between different and identical conformations of neighboring monomer units (see curve *3* on Fig. 8.1). Consequently, in this case also $f_e < 0$ with $\Delta U > 0$. Application of eq. (8.34) to the experimental value of f_e/f for polyisobutylene (see Table 8.2) gives $\Delta U = 20$ cal/mole (64,75).* As has been shown in section 7.2, a small value of ΔU is in agreement with the experimental data on the dimensions of polyisobutylene molecules in solution as well as with the fact that the

* This value of ΔU was obtained (64) from the equation of Hoeve (81) for $\overline{h^2}$ of polyisobutylene, which consists of the first two terms of the expansion of eq. (6.57) in series in $\Delta U/kT$.

dimensions and the optical anisotropy of these molecules are rather weak functions of temperature.

Equations (6.57) and (6.36) are also valid for $\overline{h^2}$ of isotactic polymers of the type $(—CH_2—CHR—)_n$ in the rotational-isomeric approximation. Therefore, eq. (8.34) is valid in this approximation for isotactic polymers, as well (75). Experimental and theoretical evaluations of ΔU in these polymers (see sections 3.3 and 7.1) show that, in the rotational-isomeric approximation, the energetic force must be quite considerable in this case. This result can be changed considerably, however, if the effect of torsional oscillations is taken into account; as has been shown in section 7.1 these can change considerably the mean values of the angles of rotation of the helix in polymers with asymmetric side groups, and thus they can have an effect on $\overline{h^2}$. Even a small displacement of the mean values of the angles of rotation with a change in temperature can make a substantial contribution to the temperature dependence of dimensions of macromolecules and thus to the energetic force (95). It is this fact which apparently explains the essential absence of energetic effects during the stretching of isotactic poly-1-butene (96) and poly-1-pentene (82).

Let us note that small values of f_e/f have been obtained as well in the case of syndiotactic polyacrylates (82). On the other hand, considerable energetic effects in polymethacrylates were found (82).

We see that the thermomechanical method of investigating rotational isomerization of macromolecules gives quite valuable results, which, in many cases, can be treated quantitatively. It can be stated that at the present time the concepts of the purely entropic nature of the elasticity of polymers have been refuted both theoretically and experimentally and that they can be regarded only as a very rough approximation of reality. Energetic effects which arise during stretching can be neglected only in some special cases.

8.4. Other Methods of Studying Rotational Isomerization of Macromolecules during Stretching

The experimental results on the energetic effects which accompany the stretching of high elastic polymers, presented in the previous section, are a convincing verification of the concepts of the rotational isomerization of macromolecules during stretching developed by Volkenshtein and Ptitsyn (23,46,47). An even more direct confirmation of these concepts is found in the papers of Volchek, Nikitin and Volkenshtein (85–89) as well as of other authors (90,91) reporting investigations of the stretching of polymers by means of polarized infrared spectroscopy. In these studies, a considerable change of the intensities of a number of bands was found during the stretching of such polymers as poly(vinyl acetate) (85), polyethylene (85), vulcanized natural rubber (86), gutta-percha (87), isotactic polypropylene (87,89), poly(vinyl chloride) (90), and Terylene (91). The results of some of these studies (85–90) are summarized in Table 8.3, taken in part from the dissertation of Volchek (92).

TABLE 8.3
Intensity Changes of Infrared Spectral Bands during Stretching of Polymers

Polymer	Band investigated, cm^{-1}	Change of intensity during stretching	Remarks	Refs.
Polyethylene	1460	Increases by 30%	Intensity decreases during melting	85
Poly(vinyl acetate)	1250 950	Increases by 20%	Intensity increases in relation to the 1740 cm^{-1} band	85
Natural rubber	1130	Increases by 13%	Intensity increases with a decrease in temperature	86
Gutta-percha	865	Decreases	Characteristic of the less stretched α form of gutta-percha	
	754	Appears during stretching	Characteristic of the more stretched β form of gutta-percha	87
Isotactic polypropylene	2845	Increases by 30%	Intensity increases in relation to the 2926 cm^{-1} band	88
	974	Increases	Intensity increases in relation to the 1460 cm^{-1} band. This 974 cm^{-1} band is characteristic of intramolecular short-range order (helical conformation of the chain)	89
Poly(vinyl chloride)	693	Decreases	Corresponds to the C—Cl valence vibration of the gauche isomer	90

As is evident from Table 8.3, in many cases, bands which increase or decrease in intensity with stretching can be related with certainty to rotational isomers which correspond to more stretched or more coiled chain conformations, respectively. For example, in the case of poly(vinyl chloride) (90), it has been shown that the band at 693 cm^{-1}, which decreases in intensity with stretching, belongs to the gauche isomer of the main chain; this has been confirmed by direct calculation (97). In the case of isotactic polypropylene (89), the band which increases in intensity during stretching is absent from atactic samples and characterizes the intramolecular short-range order (the helical conformation of the chain). In the case of gutta-percha (87), it was possible to identify two examined bands with two crystalline forms of the polymer, i.e., with two different conformations of the macromolecules stabilized by a cooperative intermolecular interaction. As could have been expected, the intensity of the band which corresponds to the less stretched α form decreases, while that of the band which corresponds to the more stretched β form increases during the stretching of gutta-percha. In the case of polyethylene (85) and natural rubber (86), the conformational correspondence of the bands investigated is less clear; comparison of their behavior during stretching and lowering of the sample temperature, however, leaves no doubt that they belong to more stretched conformations of the chain which are also the most favorable ones from the energetic point of view. This can be seen from the fact that the intensity of the band at 1460 $cm.^{-1}$ in polyethylene increases during melting, indicating that it is related to the crystalline stretched conformation of the chain, while in natural rubber, the intensity of the band at 1130 cm^{-1} increases with a decrease in temperature, i.e., it is related to the conformation which corresponds to the energy minimum of the chain. All these results prove quite conclusively that the stretching of macromolecules is actually accompanied by a transition of those rotational isomers which correspond to the less stretched conformations of the chain into rotational isomers which correspond to the more stretched conformations.

Let us present an elementary calculation (51) of the change in infrared absorption spectra of polymers during stretching which is valid for polymers which do not crystallize during stretching and for the simplest case in which only two energetically nonequivalent types of rotational isomers are possible in the chain (for example, *trans* and *gauche* isomers in polyethylene and identical and different conformations of neighboring monomer units in isotactic polymers), to which correspond different frequencies in the infrared spectrum. When the sample is stretched to the extent α, the relative change in the optical density, $D(\alpha)$, of the band in the infrared absorption spectrum attributable to the more coiled rotational isomer (which corresponds to the shorter chain length), is equal to

$$\Delta(\alpha) = \frac{D_0 - D(\alpha)}{D_0} = \frac{N_0 - N(\alpha)}{N_0} = \frac{U_0 - U(\alpha)}{U_0} \tag{8.35}$$

where $D_0 = D_{\alpha=1}$ is the optical density of the band under examination in the unstretched sample, $N(\alpha)$ is the number of the more coiled isomers in the sample, $U(\alpha)$ is the total energy of all the coiled rotational isomers (which is equal to the intramolecular potential energy of the sample, if the energy of the *trans* isomer is taken as zero for the sake of simplicity). Since for the absorption band under examination $D(\alpha) \leqslant D_0$, then $0 \leqslant \Delta(\alpha) \leqslant 1$.

Using the equation

$$U(\alpha) = U_0 + \int_L^L (\partial U/\partial L)_{V,T} dL \tag{8.36}$$

and introducing into it expression (8.19) for $f_e = (\partial U/\partial L)_{V,T}$ and expression (8.4) for f and integrating, we obtain

$$U(\alpha) = U_0 + \frac{1}{2} KkT \frac{d \ln \overline{h^2}}{d \ln T}\left(\alpha^2 + \frac{2}{\alpha} - 3\right) \tag{8.37}$$

Introducing eq. (8.37) into eq. (8.35) and considering that

$$U_0 = nGu_0 \tag{8.38}$$

where G is the number of active chains in the network, n is the number of monomer units in one chain (between crosslinks) and u_0 is the intramolecular potential energy per monomer unit, we obtain

$$\Delta(\alpha) = A[\alpha^2 + (2/\alpha) - 3] \tag{8.39}$$

where

$$A = -(KkT^2/2nGu_0)(d \ln \overline{h^2}/dT) \tag{8.40}$$

Since $K \approx G$ [see eq. (8.22), where $\overline{r^2} \approx \overline{h^2}$], then

$$A \approx -\frac{1}{N}\cdot\frac{kT^2}{u_0}\cdot\frac{d \ln \overline{h^2}}{dT} = \frac{\Psi}{N} \tag{8.41}$$

where $N = 2n$ is the number of bonds in a chain of the network (between crosslinks) and $\Psi = (-kT^2/u_0)(d \ln \overline{h^2}/dT)$ is a coefficient which depends on the flexibility of the chains. Since $d\overline{h^2}/dT < 0$ when $u_0 > 0$ and vice versa, then in all cases $\Psi > 0$, and, consequently, $A > 0$. The coefficient Ψ can be calculated easily for the simplest models of macromolecules examined above (51). For a chain with symmetric side groups and independent rotations about neighboring bonds, which result in rotational isomers (0°, ±120°), with statistical weights 1 and $g = e^{-\Delta U/kT}$, respectively,

$$u_0 = [4g/(1 + 2g)]\Delta U \tag{8.42}$$

and, consequently [taking eq. (8.31) into account],

$$\Psi = [(1 + 2g)/2g(2 + g)] \tag{8.43}$$

For an isotactic chain of type $(-CH_2—CHR—)_n$ and also for a chain with symmetric side groups and monomer unit rotational isomers $(+\varphi, +\varphi)$ and $(-\varphi, -\varphi)$:

$$u_0 = [p/(1 + p)]\Delta U \tag{8.44}$$

(where ΔU is the energy difference between different and identical conformations of neighboring monomer units), and, consequently [taking eq. (8.34) into account],

$$\Psi = (1 + p)/p \tag{8.45}$$

Equations (8.43) and (8.45) show that the coefficient Ψ and, consequently, also the relative change of the intensity of the absorption band $\Delta(\alpha)$ increase without limit with an increase in the energy difference ΔU between the more coiled and less coiled conformations. In this case, however, the large relative change in the intensity is related to the low intensity of the corresponding band in the unstretched sample (because of the small fraction of coiled conformations), so that when ΔU is very large it is almost impossible to see bands that correspond to coiled rotational isomers. When the values of the statistical weights of the coiled conformations are reasonable (when $\Delta U \approx kT$), the value of Ψ is of the order of several units, according to eqs. (8.43) and (8.45). According to eq. (8.43), Ψ increases from $^1/_2$ to 3 as the value of g decreases from 1 to $^1/_{10}$, while, according to eq. (8.45), it increases from 2 to 11 as the value of p decreases from 1 to $^1/_{10}$. Since for normal degrees of vulcanization, the number of elements $N \sim 10^3$, then for polymers with symmetric side groups and for isotactic polymers, coefficient A in eq. (8.39) is of the order of magnitude of 10^{-3}. Consequently, in the case of most polymers, a considerable change in the intensity of an infrared spectral band can occur only for $\alpha \sim 10$; this has been confirmed experimentally (85).* Equations (8.43) and (8.45) show that changes in the infrared absorption spectra can be observed also in those cases in which the energy of the chain does not change during stretching, since different rotational isomers of monomer units have identical energies. This is natural since, if the rotational isomers differ from each other spectroscopically, the infrared spectrum should change during stretching even when the energies of the rotational isomers are equal.† This

* When $\alpha \approx 10$, it is already necessary to take into account the non-Gaussian character of the curve of the dependence of tension on deformation [see eq. (8.8)]; this, however, will not change the estimate of the order of magnitude presented before.

† It follows from this, for example, that the infrared spectrum of an amorphous polymer can change during stretching even in the case when it does not change with a change in temperature.

makes the spectroscopic method of studying rotational isomerization of the chain during stretching more general in a certain sense than the thermomechanical method.

A third effect related to the phenomenon of rotational isomerization during stretching, which has been predicted theoretically but, up to now, has not been studied experimentally, is the dependence of the heat capacity of polymers on their deformation. Volkenshtein and Ptitsyn (47) have shown that the heat capacity of a polymer chain at constant length must decrease during stretching. This is easy to understand since part of the heat capacity of a polymer chain is related to rotational isomerization processes, while fixing of the length of the stretched chain puts limits on the sets of rotational isomers possible and decreases rotational isomerization during heating.* Later, on the basis of this, Ptitsyn (75) calculated the change in the heat capacity of polymers in bulk during stretching. The intramolecular energy of polymer chains is expressed by eq. (8.37), as we have seen already. Differentiation of this equation at constant V and L gives

$$C_{V,L} = C_V^0 - {}^1/_2 Kk\left(\alpha^2 + \frac{2}{\alpha} - 3\right)\left[\left(\frac{d\ln\overline{h^2}}{d\ln T}\right)^2 - 2\frac{d\ln\overline{h^2}}{d\ln T} - \frac{d^2\ln\overline{h^2}}{(d\ln T)^2}\right] \quad (8.46)$$

where C_V^0 is the value of C_V in an unstretched sample. For the case of the simple models of a polymer chain examined above we obtain for a chain with symmetric side groups and independent rotations about neighboring elements (rotational isomers 0°, ±120°):

$$C_{V,L} = C_V^0 - Kk\left(\alpha^2 + \frac{2}{\alpha} - 3\right)\left(\frac{\Delta U}{kT}\right)^2 \frac{2-g}{(2+g)^2} \quad (8.47)$$

and for an isotactic chain of type $(\text{—CH}_2\text{—CHR—})_n$ and a chain with symmetric side groups and rotational isomers $(+\varphi, +\varphi)$ and $(-\varphi, -\varphi)$:

$$C_{V,L} = C_V^0 - {}^1/_2 Kk\left(\alpha^2 + \frac{2}{\alpha} - 3\right)\left(\frac{\Delta U}{kT}\right)^2 \quad (8.48)$$

Equations (8.47) and (8.48) show that the heat capacity of a polymer in bulk at constant length must decrease with stretching of the sample.

* We are examining here the heat capacity of macromolecules in the rotational-isomeric approximation; all the conclusions of this section, however, are valid qualitatively also for the part of the heat capacity which is related to torsional oscillations.

The change in heat capacity per cubic centimeter of the sample (with $\Delta U \approx kT$) is equal in order of magnitude to:

$$|\Delta C_V| \approx Kk\alpha^2/V \approx Gk\alpha^2/V \approx 10^{-4}\alpha^2 \text{ cal/cm}^3\text{-deg} \quad (8.49)$$

Consequently, when $\alpha \approx 10$, $|\Delta C_V| \approx 10^{-2}$ cal/cm^3-deg, which exceeds experimental error by one order of magnitude. For the sake of comparison, let us note that the intramolecular heat capacity related to the rotational isomerization of the chain (for a chain with rotational isomers 0°, ±120°) is equal to

$$C_0 = \frac{dU_0}{dT} = nGk \frac{4g}{(1+2g)^2}\left(\frac{\Delta U}{kT}\right)^2 \quad (8.50)$$

Consequently, when $\Delta U \approx kT$, $C_0 \approx 10^{-4}n$ cal/cm^3-deg, i.e., when $n \approx 10^2$–10^3, $C_0 \approx 10^{-2}$–10^{-1} cal/cm^3-deg. In this way, the change in heat capacity during stretching can be comparable to the total value of that fraction of the heat capacity which is determined by the rotational isomerization.*

In actuality the heat capacity is measured, of course, not at constant volume, but at constant pressure; the change of these quantities with stretching, however, can be easily related to each other by eq. (8.4), which is the equation of state of a highly elastic polymer. From eq. (8.37) we obtain, remembering that $K \sim V^{2/3}$:

$$C_{V,L} - C_V^0 = C_{p,L} - C_p^0 - KkT(d \ln \overline{h^2}/d \ln T)(\beta/\alpha) \quad (8.51)$$

where $\beta = d \ln V/dT$ is the coefficient of volume expansion of the polymer. The difference between $|\Delta C_V|$ and $|\Delta C_p|$ is, thus, of the order of magnitude of $KkT\beta/\alpha$, i.e., it is $\alpha^3/\beta T$ times smaller than $|\Delta C_V|$. The factor $\alpha^3/\beta T$ is equal approximately or $10\alpha^3$ (since $\beta \approx 5 \times 10^{-4}$ deg^{-1}). Consequently, it is possible to consider that $\Delta C_V \approx \Delta C_p$ with a sufficient degree of accuracy even for $\alpha \approx 2$.

8.5. Concluding Remarks on the Conformations of Macromolecules Which Do Not Have a Secondary Structure

In the preceding chapters, the conformations of typical, i.e., nonbiological polymers have been examined. These molecules, unlike biopolymer molecules and their synthetic analogs, do not have a secondary structure deter-

* It is evident that $|\Delta C_V|$ is always smaller than C_0, since α^2 cannot be larger than n. When $\alpha^2 \approx n$, it is necessary, of course, to take into account the non-Gaussian character of the dependence of tension on deformation.

mined by a cooperative system of intramolecular hydrogen bonds and expressed by the presence of one-dimensional long-range order in free chains. In the following chapters, we shall examine in detail the theory of the secondary structure of biopolymer molecules; at this point, we shall summarize briefly the main results on the conformational structure of "ordinary" macromolecules.

Up to quite recently, our information on the conformations of free macromolecules without secondary structure was limited to the concept that they exist in the form of statistical coils. The picture has changed drastically as a result of the theoretical and experimental investigations of recent years and we have now reliable quantitative information on the structure and flexibility of polymer chains. First of all, the crystal structures of a large number of polymers of different structures have been determined and investigated. The progress in this area is related, on one hand, to the successful synthesis of stereoregular polymers and the investigation of their structures by the x-ray method and, on the other hand, to the development of semiempirical methods of calculating potential curves that characterize intramolecular interactions. Such calculations, carried out most recently for a large number of polymers, have made it possible to calculate theoretically conformations of macromolecules which correspond to the minimum in the potential energy. In all cases these conformations were found to coincide practically with the crystal structures of the chains investigated. It was shown in this way that the crystal structures of polymers are determined not by intermolecular but by intramolecular interactions.

This result leads immediately to the important conclusion that, in free macromolecules, there must be a one-dimensional short-range order which corresponds to the one-dimensional long-range order in crystalline chains. Such a conclusion is confirmed not only by the calculations of intramolecular potential curves, mentioned above, but also by direct spectroscopic and polarimetric experiments. It was established, furthermore, that the short-range order in free polymer chains encompasses several neighboring monomer units, so that the molecule is a one-dimensional cooperative system in which the conformation of each monomer unit is a function of the conformations of neighboring monomer units.

Calculations of intramolecular potential curves make possible the evaluation of two possible mechanisms in which short-range order in macromolecules can be disturbed: torsional oscillations and rotational isomerization. These calculations show that all the polymers investigated have two or several conformations of each monomer unit which are similar in energy, i.e., two or several rotational isomers; furthermore, in each such conformation there can be torsional oscillations about the equilibrium position within a limited (usually small) angular interval. It was possible to evaluate also the energies of various sequences of conformations of neighboring monomer units. The results of these calculations make it possible to visualize quite well the conformational structure of typical macromolecules. It was found that polymer chains consist of regular segments with a structure close to the crystal, but disturbed to some extent by torsional oscillations. The segments can be either regions of enantiomorphous helices (if the polymer has a helical structure in the crystal state), or regions of a planar chain (if the crystal structure of the polymer is planar), separated by monomer units in nonplanar conformations. The average length of the regular sequence is usually small, comprising several (not more than ten) monomer units; this indicates the important rôle of rotational isomerization in the mechanism of flexibility of the chain.

These theoretical results can be compared with experimental data on the thermodynamic flexibility (i.e., degree of coiling) of polymer chains in solution and in the highly elastic state, for example, with data on the average dimensions and average dipole moments of macromolecules in solution, on the temperature dependence of the dimensions, on energetic effects during the stretching of a polymer in bulk, etc. The development of a statistical theory relating the parameters of the flexibility of macromolecules with given physical properties requires the use of the mathematical apparatus of the statistical physics of one-dimensional cooperative systems (for example, the matrix method of the Ising model). Comparison of such a theory with experiment has resulted in good agreement and permitted evaluation of the relative role of two possible mechanisms of flexibility in the statistical coiling of macromolecules. It was found in all the cases examined that the observed coiling of the chains is almost entirely determined by rotational isomerization, while torsional oscillations play a secondary role.

In this way, during the last few years, the conformational structure and the thermodynamic flexibility of typical macromolecules have received a quite complete quantitative characterization and theoretical interpretation. It is evident that the significance of these results transgresses by far the limits of the physics of individual macromolecules which is essentially the topic of this book. According to modern concepts, the thermodynamic rigidity of polymer chains determines the processes of their spontaneous ordering in the bulk state and in concentrated solutions (for example, crystallization processes). This interesting field, related to the investigation of supermolecular structures of polymers, is still awaiting further investigations which, one can suppose, will be based to a large extent on the current progress in the field of investigation of the flexibility of individual polymer chains.

Calculations of intramolecular potential curves permit one to evaluate not only energy differences between various conformations of chain regions but also the heights of potential barriers which separate the conformations. This leads us to the much more complicated problem of the kinetic flexibility of macromolecules, i.e., the rate of change of their conformations. There is still much that is unclear in this area; first of all, the relative roles of intramolecular and intermolecular interactions have not been established in various relaxation processes in macromolecules and in polymers in bulk. In a number of cases, however, experiment shows that polymers which have a high thermodynamic flexibility also have a high kinetic flexibility; this lets us hope that the approach outlined above will be successful also in the interpretation of differences in the relaxation properties of polymers.

References

1. Kuhn, W., *Kolloid-Z.*, **68,** 2 (1934).
2. Guth, E., and H. Mark, *Monatsh. Chem.*, **65,** 93 (1934).
3. Kuhn, W., *Kolloid-Z.*, **76,** 258 (1936).
4. Kuhn, W., and H. Kuhn, *Helv. Chim. Acta*, **29,** 1615, 1634 (1946).
5. Kuhn, W., and F. Grün, *J. Polymer Sci.*, **1,** 183 (1946).
6. Pasternak, U. R., and W. Kuhn, *Helv. Chim. Acta*, **31,** 340 (1948).
7. Wall, F. T., *J. Chem. Phys.*, **10,** 132 (1942).
8. Wall, F. T., *J. Chem. Phys.*, **10,** 485 (1942).
9. Wall, F. T., *J. Chem. Phys.*, **11,** 527 (1943).
10. Treloar, L. R. G., *Trans. Faraday Soc.*, **39,** 36, 241 (1943).
11. Treloar, L. R. G., *Trans. Faraday Soc.*, **40,** 59 (1944).
12. Flory, P. J., and J. Rehner, *J. Chem. Phys.*, **11,** 512 (1943).
13. Flory, P. J., *Chem. Rev.*, **35,** 51 (1944).
14. Wall, F. T., and P. J. Flory, *J. Chem. Phys.*, **19,** 1435 (1951).
15. Flory, P. J., *J. Am. Chem. Soc.*, **78,** 5222 (1956).
16. Kubo, R., *J. Phys. Soc. Japan*, **2,** 51 (1947).
17. Guth, E., and H. M. James, *Ind. Eng. Chem.*, **33,** 624 (1941).
18. James, H. M., and E. Guth, *Phys. Rev.*, **59,** 111 (1941).
19. James, H. M., and E. Guth, *Ind. Eng. Chem.*, **34,** 1365 (1942).
20. James, H. M., and E. Guth, *J. Chem. Phys.*, **11,** 455 (1943).
21. James, H. M., and E. Guth, *J. Chem. Phys.*, **15,** 669 (1947).
22. James, H. M., and E. Guth, *J. Polymer Sci.*, **4,** 153 (1949).
23. Alfrey, T., *Mekhanicheskie Svoistva Vysokopolimerov*, IL, Moscow, 1952 (originally published as *Mechanical Behavior of High Polymers*, Interscience, New York, 1948).
24. Treloar, L. R. G., *Fizika Uprugosti Kauchuka*, IL, Moscow, 1953 (originally published as *Physics of Rubber Elasticity*, Clarendon Press, Oxford, 1949).

25. Volkenshtein, M. V., *Konfigurationnaya Statistika Polimernykh Tsepei*, Izdatel'stvo Akad. Nauk SSSR, Moscow, 1959 (published in translation as *Configurational Statistics of Polymeric Chains*, Interscience, New York, 1963).
26. Treloar, L. R. G., in *The Rheology of Elastomers*, P. Mason and N. Wookey, Eds., Pergamon Press, London, 1958, p. 1–16.
27. Ciferri, A., *J. Polymer Sci.*, **54**, 149 (1961).
28. Boggs, F. W., *J. Chem. Phys.*, **20**, 632 (1952).
29. Volkenshtein, M. V., *Dokl. Akad. Nauk SSSR*, **125**, 523 (1959).
30. Volkenshtein, M. V., Yu. Ya. Gotlib, and O. B. Ptitsyn, *Vysokomol. Soedin.*, **1**, 1056 (1959).
31. Di Marzio, E. A., *J. Chem. Phys.*, **35**, 658 (1961).
32. Di Marzio, E. A., *J. Chem. Phys.*, **36**, 1563 (1962).
33. Boggs, F. W., *J. Chem. Phys.*, **36**, 1733 (1962).
34. Gee, G., *Trans. Faraday Soc.*, **42**, 585 (1946).
35. Flory, P. J., *Ind. Eng. Chem.*, **38**, 417 (1946).
36. Flory, P. J., N. Rabjohn, and M. C. Schaffer, *J. Polymer Sci.*, **4**, 225 (1949).
37. Rivlin, R. S., and D. W. Saunders, *Phil. Trans. Roy. Soc., London*, **A243**, 251 (1951).
38. Rivlin, R. S., and D. W. Saunders, *Trans. Faraday Soc.*, **48**, 200 (1952).
39. Blackwell, R., *Trans. Inst. Rubber Ind.*, **28**, 75 (1952).
40. Gumbrell, S. M., L. Mullins, and R. S. Rivlin, *Trans. Faraday Soc.*, **49**, 1495 (1953).
41. Priss, L. S., Candidate Dissertation, NIIShP, Moscow, 1959.
42. Ciferri, A., and P. J. Flory, *J. Appl. Phys.*, **30**, 1498 (1959).
43. Volkenshtein, M. V., and O. B. Ptitsyn, *Zh. Tekhn. Fiz.*, **25**, 649 (1955).
44. Miyake, A., and M. Sakakibara, *J. Phys. Soc. Japan*, **17**, 164 (1962).
45. Birshtein, T. M., *Zh. Tekhn. Fiz.*, **28**, 2493 (1958).
46. Volkenshtein, M. V., and O. B. Ptitsyn, *Dokl. Akad. Nauk SSSR*, **91**, 1313 (1953).
47. Volkenshtein, M. V., and O. B. Ptitsyn, *Zh. Tekhn. Fiz.*, **25**, 662 (1955).
48. Volkenshtein, M. V., *Dokl. Akad. Nauk SSSR*, **78**, 879 (1951).
49. Volkenshtein, M. V., *Zh. Fiz. Khim.*, **26**, 1072 (1952).
50. Flory, P. J., C. A. J. Hoeve, and A. Ciferri, *J. Polymer Sci.*, **34**, 337 (1959).
51. Ptitsyn, O. B., *Fiz. Tverd. Tela*, **1**, 923 (1959).
52. Volkenshtein, M. V., and O. B. Ptitsyn, Mezinarodni Symposium Makromolekularni Chemie, Praha, Oct. 9–15, 1957; *Documentation*, **1**, No. 44.
53. Volkenshtein, M. V., and O. B. Ptitsyn, *Fiz. Tverd. Tela Sb.*, **1**, 259 (1959).
54. James, H., private communication.
55. Elliott, D. R., and S. A. Lippmann, *J. Appl. Phys.*, **16**, 50 (1945).
56. Flory, P. J., *Principles of Polymer Chemistry*, Cornell Univ. Press, Ithaca, N. Y., 1953.
57. Wood, L. A., and F. L. Roth, *J. Appl. Phys.*, **15**, 781 (1944).
58. Peterson, L. E., R. L. Anthony, and E. Guth, *Ind. Eng. Chem.*, **34**, 1349 (1942).
59. Roth, F. L., and L. A. Wood, *J. Appl. Phys.*, **15**, 749 (1944).
60. Khazanovich, T. N., Candidate Dissertation, Moscovskii Gosudarstvennyi Pedagogicheskyi Institut im. V. P. Potemkina, Moscow, 1959.
61. Khazanovich, T. N., *J. Appl. Phys.*, **30**, 948 (1959).
62. Flory, P. J., A. Ciferri, and C. A. J. Hoeve, *J. Polymer Sci.*, **45**, 235 (1960).
63. Flory, P. J., *Trans. Faraday Soc.*, **57**, 829 (1961).
64. Ciferri, A., C. A. J. Hoeve, and P. J. Flory, *J. Am. Chem. Soc.*, **83**, 1015 (1961).
65. Ciferri, A., *J. Polymer Sci.*, **45**, 528 (1960).

66. Ciferri, A., *Trans. Faraday Soc.*, **57,** 846 (1961).
67. Anthony, R. L., R. H. Caston, and E. Guth, *J. Phys. Chem.*, **46,** 826 (1942).
68. Flory, P. J., A. Ciferri, and R. Chiang, *J. Am. Chem. Soc.*, **83,** 1023 (1961).
69. Ciferri, A., *Trans. Faraday Soc.*, **57,** 853 (1961).
70. Flory, P. J., *Proc. Roy. Soc. (London)*, **A234,** 60 (1956).
71. Gibbs, J. H., and E. A. Di Marzio, *J. Chem. Phys.*, **28,** 373, 807 (1958).
72. Kobeko, P. P., *Amorfnye Veshchestva* (Amorphous Substances), Izdatel'stvo Akad. Nauk SSSR, Moscow, 1952.
73. Kargin, V. A., A. I. Kitaigorodskii, and G. L. Slonimskii, *Kolloidn. Zh.*, **19,** 131 (1957).
74. Kargin, V. A., *Coll. Czechoslovak Chem. Comm. (Suppl.)*, **22,** 50 (1957).
75. Ptitsyn, O. B., *Vysokomol. Soedin.*, **5,** 1219 (1963).
76. Sheppard, N., and G. J. Szasz, *J. Chem. Phys.*, **17,** 86 (1949).
77. Novak, I. I., *Zh. Tekhn. Fiz.*, **24,** 18 (1954).
78. Novak, I. I., *Zh. Tekhn. Fiz.*, **25,** 1854 (1955).
79. Hoeve, C. A. J., *J. Chem. Phys.*, **35,** 1266 (1961).
80. Borisova, N. P., *Vysokomol. Soedin.*, **6,** 135 (1964).
81. Hoeve, C. A. J., *J. Chem. Phys.*, **32,** 888 (1960).
82. Tobolsky, A. V., D. W. Carlson, and N. Indictor, *J. Polymer Sci.*, **54,** 175 (1961).
83. Mark, J. E., and P. J. Flory, *J. Am. Chem. Soc.*, **86,** 138 (1964).
84. Borisova, N. P., *Vysokomol. Soedin.*, in press.
85. Nikitin, V. N., M. V. Volkenshtein, and B. Z. Volchek, *Zh. Tekhn. Fiz.*, **25,** 2486 (1955).
86. Nikitin, V. N., B. Z. Volchek, and M. V. Volkenshtein, *Trudy 10-ogo Soveshchaniya Po Spektroskopii* (Transactions of the 10th Conference on Spectroscopy), Izdatel'stvo of Lvov Univ., Vol. 1, 1960, p. 411.
87. Volchek, B. Z., and V. N. Nikitin, *Zh. Tekhn. Fiz.*, **28,** 1753 (1958).
88. Volchek, B. Z., and Zh. N. Roberman, *Vysokomol. Soedin.*, **2,** 1157 (1960).
89. Volchek, B. Z., *Vysokomol. Soedin., Carbotsepnye soedineniya (Carbochain Compounds)* 260 (1963).
90. Shimanouchi, T., S. Tsuchiya, and S. Mizushima, *J. Chem. Phys.*, **30,** 1365 (1959).
91. Miyake, A., *J. Polymer Sci.*, **38,** 497 (1959).
92. Volchek, B. Z., Candidate Dissertation, Institut Vysokomoleukulyarnikh Soedinenii, Akad. Nauk SSSR, Leningrad, 1961.
93. Volkenshtein, M. V., and O. B. Ptitsyn, *Dokl. Akad. Nauk SSSR*, **86,** 677 (1952).
94. Nagai, K., and T. Ishikawa, *J. Chem. Phys.*, **37,** 496 (1962).
95. Birshtein, T. M., and O. B. Ptitsyn, *Vysokomol. Soedin.*, in press.
96. Mark, J. E., and P. J. Flory, *J. Phys. Chem.*, **67,** 1396 (1963).
97. Boitsov, V. G., and Yu. Ya. Gotlib, *Opt. Spektroskopiya Sb.*, **2,** 128 (1963).

Chapter 9

THEORY OF CONFORMATIONAL TRANSITIONS IN POLYPEPTIDE CHAINS

9.1. Helix–Coil Transitions in Molecules of Biopolymers

During the last decade the physics of macromolecules has received a strong impetus for development from the direction of biology. After it had become evident that many life processes are based on the behavior of individual macromolecules of proteins and nucleic acids, the investigation of these biologically active macromolecules became one of the most important areas of polymer physics. Moreover, it was established immediately that the molecules of native proteins and nucleic acids, as well as those of their synthetic analogs (polypeptides and polynucleotides), differ quite considerably in their conformational structure from the ordinary biologically inactive polymers which we have examined in the preceding chapters. A strictly regular structure is found in the latter only in the crystalline state, while in solution they are present in the form of coils.

The statistical coiling of individual macromolecules of ordinary polymers can be explained by the fact that the forces of intramolecular interaction operating in them are insufficient to maintain in the chain a long-range order, such order being disturbed by the rotational isomerization and torsional oscillations of the units. On the other hand, in biologically active polymers, an important role is played by the intramolecular hydrogen bonds which determine the stabilization of the rigid chain structure. This stabilization is determined by the cooperative nature of the hydrogen bonds, expressed by the fact that the equilibrium constant for each hydrogen bond is strongly dependent on the presence or absence of hydrogen bonds in neighboring monomer units (this is discussed in greater detail in section 9.2). Hydrogen bonds certainly can be present as well in ordinary biologically inactive polymers. In these polymers, however, they do not have a cooperative character and, thus, do not result in the presence of long-range order in the chains.*

According to the terminology proposed by Linderstrøm-Lang (1), the molecules of ordinary polymers in solution do not have a secondary structure, while the molecules of biologically active polymers and their synthetic analogs can have one. In this terminology, the primary structure of a macromolecule refers to the number and position of chemical bonds in the molecule, while the secondary structure refers to the regular spatial helical structure with a definite periodicity, stabilized by hydrogen bonds. A great number of studies has been devoted to the investigation of the secondary structures of biologically active macromolecules; these investigations served to determine the parameters of the helical conformations for a large number of synthetic polypeptides and polynucleotides, as well as for natural nucleic acids and proteins. In the last case, the tertiary structure, i.e. the mutual positions of helical and nonhelical segments as determined by the interactions of chain side groups, in particular by S—S bonds, also plays an important role. The best known examples of secondary structures are found in the α-helix of Pauling and Corey (2,3) for polypeptides and the double helix of Crick and Watson (4) for deoxyribonucleic acid (DNA). At the present time, these structures have been confirmed by a vast amount of experimental data.

Reviews of the vast literature devoted to the elucidation of the secondary structures of various biologically active polymers can be found, for example, in the papers of Leach (5), Rich (6,7), Kendrew (8), Katchalski and Steinberg (9) and other authors. We shall concentrate our attention on the theory of the common properties of biologically active polymers which have a secondary structure. As will become obvious from the following discussion, these common properties are determined by the behavior of a macromolecule as a linear cooperative system and their theory may be developed by using methods similar to those that have been developed above for ordinary macromolecules.

A single macromolecule with secondary structure is essentially a one-

* At the present time, there is a large number of experimental results which indicate that the stability of the polypeptide helices and, especially, of the double helices of nucleic acids is maintained not only by intramolecular hydrogen bonds but also by the forces of van der Waals interactions (dipole–dipole and dispersion) which act between the hydrophobic groups (45,53–55). The important role of van der Waals interactions in the stabilization of the nucleic acid double helices has been demonstrated also in the calculations of De Voe and Tinoco (44). As long as this fact does not alter significantly the mathematical apparatus of the presented theory, for the sake of simplicity, we shall speak only of hydrogen bonds in the present discussion.

dimensional crystal. Just as a regular crystal, such a one-dimensional ordered system can undergo a sharp transition with change in temperature or solvent composition; such a transition is similar to a phase transition, i.e., the molecule "melts" going over into the structure of a statistical coil which is typical for ordinary macromolecules. Helix–coil transitions were described in 1954 by Doty, Holtzer, Bradbury, and Blout (10) in molecules of the synthetic polypeptide, poly-γ-benzyl-L-glutamate, which assumes a helical or coiled conformation depending on the composition of the solvent; later, these transitions were the subject of a detailed experimental and theoretical investigation. The most important experimental investigations in this realm have been carried out by Doty and his school.

Helix–coil transitions occur with a change in the temperature of the solution, in the solvent composition, and also in the pH of the solution (in the case of macromolecules with ionizable groups). These transitions usually occur within a quite narrow, although finite, temperature interval (or within a narrow interval of change in solvent composition or change in pH). As has been shown by Doty (11,58) for molecules with a high degree of polymerization, the transitions do not take place according to the all-or-none principle, i.e., in the region of transition each molecule contains both segments in which the hydrogen bonds have been broken already and segments in which such bonds are still present. Reviews of methods of investigation of helix–coil transitions and of the experimental data obtained can be found in the recently published monograph of Bresler (59), as well as in a large number of papers (5,9,11,12,45–47). We shall point out only that the majority of the methods used for studying the transitions make it possible to determine the fraction of monomer units which are bonded by hydrogen bonds, or a quantity close to it, namely the fraction of monomer units present in the helical conformation.

The physical basis of transitions such as the helix–coil is the fact that the state of a macromolecule in which the monomeric units take part in intramolecular hydrogen bonds is usually more favorable energetically, while the state of a free macromolecule is favorable entropically because of its flexibility. As a result, the free energies of these two states vary in different manner with change in temperature, in solvent composition (for example, if the solvent molecules can form hydrogen bonds with the macromolecules) or in solution pH (if the ionization of monomer units introduces an additional energetic effect). The transition temperature occurs at the point at which the free energies of the two states are identical. The cooperative nature of the transition, which manifests itself in the narrowness of its interval, is determined, as has already been pointed out above, by the strong dependence of the change in free energy of the molecule during hydrogen bond formation in one of the monomer units on the presence or absence of hydrogen bonds in neighboring monomer units. This cooperativeness probably has a purely entropic character, at least in the case of polypeptides (see section 9.2).

The general methods of the statistics of one-dimensional cooperative systems have been presented in Chapter 4. It is evident that the theory of helix–coil transitions of biologically active macromolecules and synthetic analogs can be built on the basis of the same methods, as long as these molecules can be considered as examples of such systems. After the studies of Schellman (13,14), Rice, Wada, and Geiduschek (15), Zimm and Bragg (16), Gibbs and Di Marzio (17), and Rice and Wada (18) had laid the foundations of the helix–coil transition theory, this problem was investigated in detail in a large number of other theoretical studies (19–32,48–51). The statistical theory of these transitions has been developed along with the thermodynamic approach, which had been used in the early studies of Schellman and Rice and co-workers. In this theory, the calculation of the partition function of a macromolecule was carried out both by a matrix method similar to that presented in Chapter 4 (16,17,23–25,27–32) and by an alternate, somewhat more cumbersome method, namely, the so-called "method of the largest term" (19–22,26,48,49). A new interesting method of calculating directly the transition curve has been proposed in the studies of Lifson and Zimm (50) and Lifson (51). This method is based on the formal introduction of the grand canonical ensemble, i.e., of an ensemble which encompasses macromolecules of all possible degrees of polymerization. The most complete theoretical analysis of helix–coil transitions is given in a series of papers by Zimm and co-workers which deal with transitions in uncharged (16,23) and charged (27) polypeptide chains, as well as with transitions of synthetic polynucleotides and DNA (28).* All these studies are based on the application of the matrix method of the Ising model (see Chapter 4). Using the same method, Nagai (24, 25,29), and Lifson and Roig (30) have also examined helix–coil transitions in polypeptides; Nagai (24,25,29) has calculated the dimensions of polypeptide molecules in the transition region; and Birshtein has examined helix–coil transitions in polypeptide chains under load (31) as well as titration curves of polynucleotides in the transition region (32).

* See also the paper of Zimm, Doty, and Iso (33), in which experimental data on helix–coil transitions in polypeptides are treated on the basis of the theory of Zimm and Bragg.

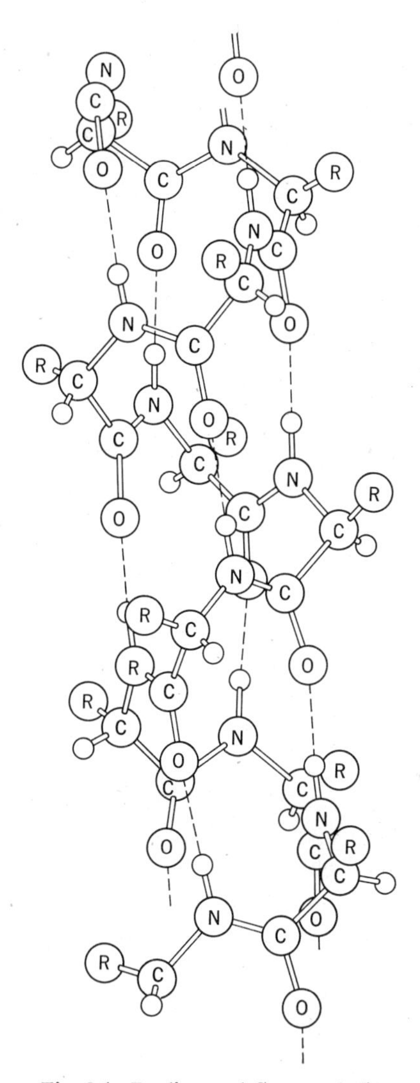

Fig. 9.1. Pauling and Corey α-helix.

9.2. Conformational Partition Function of a Polypeptide Chain

In this section, as well as those that follow, we shall present the theory of helix–coil transitions in polypeptide molecules developed in the cited studies and based on the matrix method of the Ising model for a one-dimensional cooperative system. In doing this, we shall follow principally the papers of Zimm (16,23,27). The molecules of synthetic polypeptides have the general formula (—CO—CHR—NH—)$_n$. A typical secondary structure of such molecules, stabilized by intramolecular hydrogen bonds, is the Pauling and Corey α-helix (2,3); in it, all the planar peptide groups* are positioned in such a way that their planes are tangent to a cylinder the axis of which coincides with the helix axis (Fig. 9.1). In this structure a hydrogen bond may be formed between the oxygen atom of the carboxyl group of each monomer unit with the hydrogen atom of the NH group of the fourth preceding monomer unit (Fig. 9.2). These hydrogen bonds are approximately parallel to the axis of the helix, they overlap with each other and, thus, hold together the different turns of the helix. As has been shown by Mizushima (52,56), the α-helix is characterized by angles of

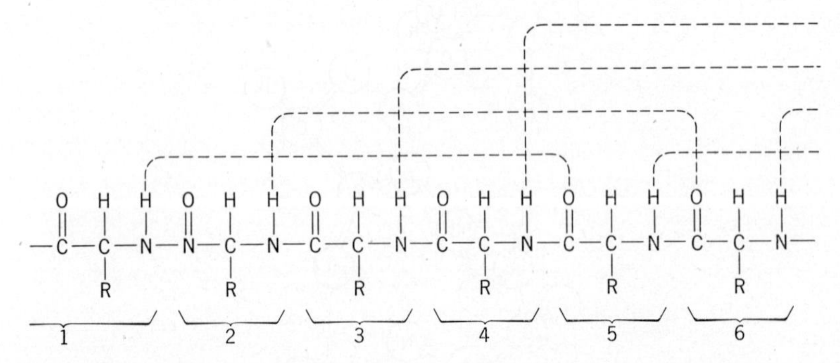

Fig. 9.2. Schematic representation of hydrogen bonds in a Pauling and Corey α-helix.

internal rotation close to 120° about the —CO—CHR— and —CHR—NH— bonds of the main chain; this corresponds to one of the possible energy minima of the monomer units. The geometric structure of the α-helix is characterized by a turn of 100° about its axis and a step of 1.5 Å along its axis per monomer unit. Therefore, one complete turn of the helix about its axis takes place per 3.6 monomer units and encompasses a displacement of 5.4 Å along the axis.

The conformational partition function of the polypeptide chain is determined, just as in the cases examined earlier, by the conformations of all its monomer units. From Figures 9.1 and 9.2 it is seen that these conformations are not independent of each other, as a result of the presence in the

* As is known, the N—C bond of a peptide group has a partial double bond character, and rotation about it is almost completely restricted. As a result, the peptide —N—C— group has a planar *trans* structure.
H O

chain of intramolecular hydrogen bonds. In fact, the formation of a hydrogen bond, for example, between the oxygen atom of the C=O group of the ith monomer unit and the hydrogen atom of the NH group of the (i-4)th monomer unit imposes a strict restriction on the conformations of three consecutive monomer units. Furthermore, it can be seen from Figure 9.2 that the breaking of one or two hydrogen bonds in a segment of the chain of bonded monomer units does not enable the corresponding monomer units to come out of the helical conformation. The realization of conformational degrees of freedom becomes possible only when the number of consecutive nonbonded monomer units is equal to or greater than three. These two effects lead to the interdependence of monomer unit conformations, i.e., to the cooperative nature of the system. As a first approximation (absolutely sufficient for the interpretation of facts known at the present time) it is possible to consider that any other interdependence between the conformations of monomer units (for example, one determined by van der Waals interactions between free monomer units) is absent and the polypeptide chain can be looked upon as broken into flexible —CO—CHR—NH— sections, consisting of two bonds separated from each other by stiff peptide bonds, —NH—CO—.

Averaging over all the conformations of the macromolecule can be carried out in two stages: first, over all the conformations of monomer units with a given distribution of the intramolecular hydrogen bonds and then over all possible distributions of the hydrogen bonds. Furthermore, only the second stage of averaging is cooperative and requires the application of the statistics of one-dimensional cooperative systems.* In the first stage, it is necessary to take into account also all the possible states of the solvent molecules which are consistent with the given distribution of intramolecular hydrogen bonds in the macromolecules. The necessity of averaging the conformational partition function of the macromolecule over the states of the solvent has been pointed out already in section 5.1, which was concerned with macromolecules devoid of secondary structure. It should be stressed that the state of macromolecules capable of forming hydrogen bonds can exert a quite strong influence on the state of the solvent, the molecules of which are often capable of competing for hydrogen bonds with the groups of the chain. Therefore, the *physical interpretation of the parameters of the helix–coil transition theory* introduced below *can, in the general case, not be carried out without taking into account*

* See section 7.1, in which the averaging was carried out in similar manner, first, over the noncooperative torsional oscillations of the bonds, and then, over the cooperative conformations of monomer units.

*changes in the state of the solvent.** From the point of view of the statistical physics of cooperative transitions, we shall be interested only in the second stage of the averaging, in which it can be assumed that the thermodynamic functions of each monomer unit have been calculated already, taking into account all possible conformations of monomer units and all the possible states of the solvent which are consistent with the given distribution of the intramolecular hydrogen bonds.

Following the approach of Zimm and Bragg (23), we shall distinguish between the following two states of each monomer unit, indicating them by the indices $\mu_i = 0$ or 1: (*1*) the state in which the carboxylic group oxygen atom is bonded by a hydrogen bond to the NH hydrogen atom of the fourth preceding monomer unit of the chain ($\mu_i = 1$, bonded monomer unit); (*2*) the state in which such a hydrogen bond is absent ($\mu_i = 0$, free monomer unit).

As will be shown below, as long as the conformations of each quartet of consecutive monomer units are essentially interdependent, and the formation of hydrogen bonds is related to changes in the conformations of monomer units, the free energy of the chain, as a function of the states of monomer units μ_i, has the form

$$F(\mu_1, \mu_2, \ldots, \mu_n) = \sum_{i=1}^{n} F(\mu_{i-3}, \mu_{i-2}, \mu_{i-1}, \mu_i) \tag{9.1}$$

where n is the degree of polymerization. (As before, in Chapters 4–6, we neglect end effects, assuming that $n \gg 1$.) Since the correlation between the states of the monomer units is determined entirely by intramolecular hydrogen bonds, the thermodynamic functions of a free monomer unit are independent of the states of the preceding units, i. e.,

$$F_{\text{free}} \equiv F(\mu_{i-3}, \mu_{i-2}, \mu_{0-1}, 0) \tag{9.2}$$

The free energy of the ith bonded monomer unit is dependent on the states of the preceding monomer units. Let us designate the free energy of a bonded unit which follows a bonded unit by

$$F_{\text{bonded}} \equiv F(\mu_{i-3}, \mu_{i-2}, 1, 1) \tag{9.3}$$

The independence of the quantity defined in this way from the states of the (i-2)th and (i-3)th monomer units is due to the fact that the restriction, imposed by the bonded state of the (i-1)th unit on the conformations of the

* This is covered in greater detail at the end of Section 9.3. More complicated cases, in which the helix–coil transition is related to a change in *solvent composition*, are examined in Sections 10.1 and 10.2.

(i-2)th and (i-3)th units, is taken into account in the calculation of the free energy of the (i-1)th monomer unit. Thus, the bonding of the ith unit (with the condition that the (i-1)th is bonded) imposes additional restrictions only on the conformation of the ith unit (see Fig. 9.2).

As a result, the free energy change which accompanies an increase by one of the region of bonded monomer units at the expense of a neighboring unbonded monomer unit is equal to

$$\Delta F \equiv F_{\text{bonded}} - F_{\text{free}} = F(\mu_{i-3}, \mu_{i-2}, 1, 1) - F(\mu_{i-3}, \mu_{i-2}, 1, 0) \quad (9.4)$$

The quantity ΔF contains both a ΔH component, determined by the change in energy, and a $T\Delta S$ component, determined by the change in entropy for an increase in the number of intramolecular hydrogen bonds by one (by means of an increase of the region of bonded monomer units):

$$\Delta F = \Delta H - T\Delta S \quad (9.5)$$

The value of ΔH can be essentially reduced to the change in energy when two hydrogen bonds between the macromolecule and solvent molecules are broken and an intramolecular hydrogen bond and a hydrogen bond between the solvent molecules are formed instead. It should be pointed out that intermolecular hydrogen bonds do not have a sharp cooperative character and, as a result, the number of bonded groups is a smooth function of temperature. For example, according to the theoretical evaluation of Nemethy and Scheraga (61), in the case of water the fraction of unbroken hydrogen bonds amounts to about 50% of the maximal number of bonds possible. On the other hand, intramolecular hydrogen bonds are highly cooperative, so that in the helical conformation of the chain all groups capable of forming them are in a bonded state. Therefore, even when the energies of the intra- and intermolecular hydrogen bonds are equal, intramolecular bonding may be predominant (55). In fact, this is usually (but not always) found to be so. The value of ΔS includes the decrease in entropy during the rigid restriction of monomer unit conformations which is imposed by the formation of an intramolecular hydrogen bond and is usually also negative.

Additional free energy (relative to ΔF) must be expended during the formation of a hydrogen bond in a monomer unit that follows three non-bonded monomer units. This additional free energy has an entropic origin. In fact, the formation of a hydrogen bond between the oxygen atom of a given monomer unit and the hydrogen atom of the fourth preceding monomer unit requires a rigid conformation of three monomer units (see Fig. 9.2). The hydrogen bonds can be visualized as staples, which overlap with each other, each of which fixes the conformations of three units. Obviously, each consecutive staple fixes the conformation of only one unit, while the first imposed staple fixes the conformations of three units. Therefore

$$F(0, 0, 0, 1) = F_{\text{bonded}} + F_{\text{init.}} \tag{9.6}$$

where $F_{\text{init.}}$ is the additional free energy of initiation of the bonded region; it is determined by the decrease in entropy during the rigid restriction of the conformations of two monomer units.

Each monomer unit of a polypeptide chain has two bonds about which internal rotation is possible. For rough estimates, it is possible to assume that three rotational isomers are possible during rotation about each bond, while the rigid structure of the α-helix, obviously, corresponds to only one isomer. In such a case, $F_{\text{init.}} = -TS_{\text{init.}} \approx 2 \times 300 \times 4 \ln(^1/_3) \approx 2.5$ kcal/mole.* As can be seen, the initiation of a helical region, bonded by hydrogen bonds, is strongly hindered with respect to the growth of an already existing region. This is what produces the cooperative character of the transition.

Finally, we must take into account the impossibility of the occurrence of less than three consecutive nonbonded monomer units in the chain, a fact that has already been mentioned. In fact, in the most common case, in which $\Delta H < 0$ and $\Delta S < 0$, the opening of one or two hydrogen bonds in a region of the chain which consists of bonded monomer units results in an increase in the energy of the system which is not compensated by an increase in its entropy (since the "liberated" monomer units must still maintain a helical conformation as shown in Fig. 9.2). The chain acquires flexibility, and its entropy increases only when the number of consecutive nonbonded monomer units is equal to or greater than three. In accordance with what has been said, let us set

$$F(\mu_{i-3}, 1, 0, 1) = \infty \tag{9.7}$$

$$F(1, 0, 0, 1) = \infty \tag{9.8}$$

Equations (9.2), (9.3), and (9.6)–(9.8) determine completely the free energy of a macromolecule for the model under consideration. It is possible that, in real chains, $F_{\text{init.}}$ is a function of the number of preceding nonbonded atoms, and that there is also an interaction between the hydrogen bonds of neighboring turns of the helix (34); these effects, however, play a secondary role and the existing experimental material is in-

* The value of $F_{\text{init.}}$ cited is, of course, given strictly as an example.

sufficient to detect them. A detailed theoretical analysis (29) has shown that the transition curve is little affected when these effects are taken into account. Setting the free energy of a nonbonded monomer unit equal to zero, it is found, according to eqs. (9.1)–(9.8), that the contribution of a given state of the chain to the partition function, Z is determined by the product of the following factors: (*1*) factor 1 for every monomer unit in the free state ($\mu_i = 0$); (*2*) factor s for every monomer unit in the state ($\mu_i = 1$), where

$$s = e^{-\Delta F/kT} = e^{-(\Delta H - T\Delta S)/kT} \tag{9.9}$$

is the equilibrium constant of the hydrogen bond formation reaction in a monomer unit which follows a bonded monomer unit, i.e., for the increase of the region of bonded monomer units by one, at the expense of the neighboring region of nonbonded units; (*3*) factor σ for every monomer unit in the hydrogen bonded state ($\mu_i = 1$), following three or more nonbonded monomer units ($\mu_{i-1}, \mu_{i-2}, \mu_{i-3} = 0$), where

$$\sigma = e^{-F_{\text{init.}}/kT} \tag{9.10}$$

is the equilibrium constant for the reaction of the formation of one break in a sequence of hydrogen bonds, their total number remaining unchanged. (From the rough estimate of $F_{\text{init.}}$, given above, we obtain for the cooperativeness parameter $\sigma \sim 10^{-2}$); (*4*) factor 0 for every monomer unit in the hydrogen bonded state ($\mu_i = 1$), that follows nonbonded monomer units, if their number is less than three ($\mu_{i-1} = 0$, $\mu_{i-2} = 1$ or $\mu_{i-1} = \mu_{i-2} = 0$, $\mu_{i-3} = 1$.)

In this manner

$$\begin{aligned} Z &= \sum_{\{\mu_i\}} e^{-F\{\mu\}/kT} \\ &= \sum_{\{\mu_i\}} \prod_{i=1}^{n} S^{\mu_i} \sigma^{\mu_i(1-\mu_{i-1})} [1 - \delta\mu_{i,1}\delta\mu_{i-1,0}(1 - \delta\mu_{i-2,0}\,\delta\mu_{i-3,0})] \end{aligned} \tag{9.11}$$

where $\delta_{\alpha\beta}$ is the Kronecker delta, while summation is carried out over all possible sets of $\{\mu_i\}$. As has been shown in section 4.1, the partition function Z of a one-dimensional cooperative system can be expressed in the form

$$Z = \text{Sp } G^n \tag{9.12}$$

as $n \to \infty$, where n is the degree of polymerization, while matrix G is defined by eq. (4.6). In our case, each monomer unit of the chain may have only two states, and the free energy of the chain is expressed in the form (9.1), i.e., it contains components which are a function of the states of four consecutive monomer units [eq. (4.43) with $m = 3$]. As was pointed out in section 4.1, matrix G must be, in this case, a matrix of order $2^m = 8$.

Let us renumber the states of the three monomer units, which index the components of matrix G, in the sequence: 000, 001, 010, 011, 100, 101, 110, 111; then, matrix G can be written in the form of eq. (9.13) (we write out only the nonzero elements):

$G =$

$\mu_{i-3}, \mu_{i-2}, \mu_{i-1}$ \ $\mu_{i-2}, \mu_{i-1}, \mu_i$	000	001	010	011	100	101	110	111
000	1	σs						
001			1	s				
010					1			
011							1	s
100	1							
101			1	s				
110					1			
111							1	s

(9.13)

It is evident that, since column $\mu_{i-2}, \mu_{i-1}, \mu_i = 101$ has no nonzero elements, it can be eliminated along with the corresponding row; we can consider then a matrix of the seventh, rather than eighth, order. The characteristic equation of matrix G has the form:

$$\lambda^2(\lambda - 1)(\lambda - s) = \sigma s \tag{9.14}$$

The roots of eq. (9.14) (and for $n \gg 1$, the largest root of this equation, λ_1) characterize all the statistical properties of the system. Thus, the mean fraction ϑ of hydrogen-bonded monomer units, the mean fraction η of bonded monomer units following free units, and the mean lengths ν_{bonded} and ν_{free} of regions in which all the monomer units are bonded or all the monomer units are not bonded by hydrogen bonds, are given by eqs. (9.15)–(9.18): [compare eqs. (4.18)–(4.20)]:

$$\vartheta = \frac{1}{n}\frac{\partial \ln Z}{\partial \ln s} \simeq \frac{\partial \ln \lambda_1}{\partial \ln s} \tag{9.15}$$

$$\eta = \frac{1}{n}\frac{\partial \ln Z}{\partial \ln \sigma} \simeq \frac{\partial \ln \lambda_1}{\partial \ln \sigma} \tag{9.16}$$

$$\nu_{\text{bonded}} = \vartheta/\eta \tag{9.17}$$

$$\nu_{\text{free}} = (1 - \vartheta)/\eta \tag{9.18}$$

Differentiating eq. (9.14) with respect to the proper parameters, we obtain for our model

$$\vartheta = \frac{\lambda_1(\lambda_1 - 1)}{4\lambda_1^2 - 3(1 + s)\lambda_1 + 2s} \tag{9.19}$$

$$\eta = \frac{\sigma s}{[4\lambda_1^2 - 3(1 + s)\lambda_1 + 2s]\lambda_1^2} \tag{9.20}$$

9.3. Theory of Helix–Coil Transitions in Polypeptide Chains

Equation (9.14), derived in section 9.2, cannot be solved in an analytical form in the general case (for $\sigma \neq 0$). Therefore, making use of the fact that $\sigma \ll 1$ (see above), we shall examine it in the first approximation for $\sigma = 0$. Then, the roots of eq. (9.14) are equal to 1, s, 0, and 0. Then

$$Z = \text{Sp}\, G^n = 1 + s^n \tag{9.21}$$

Equation (9.21) shows that, for $\sigma = 0$,* *the system may exist in only two states, namely, in the entirely helical state, in which all the monomer units are bonded* ($Z_{\text{helix}} = s^n$), *or in the entirely coiled state, in which all the monomer units are free* ($Z_{\text{coil}} = 1$). For $n \gg 1$, eq. (9.21) yields

$$Z = \begin{cases} s^n (s > 1) \\ 1\ (s < 1) \end{cases} \tag{9.22}$$

i.e., with $s > 1$, the overwhelmingly major contribution to the total partition function of the system is made by the entirely helical state, while with $s < 1$ it is made by the entirely coiled state. This means, that at $s = 1$, *a sharp cooperative helix–coil transition takes place.* In fact, the fraction of bonded monomer units is given by

$$\vartheta = \frac{1}{n}\frac{\partial \ln Z}{\partial \ln s} = \frac{s^n}{1 + s^n} \tag{9.23}$$

which gives, for $n \gg 1$

$$\vartheta \approx \begin{cases} 1 & s > 1 \\ 0 & s < 1 \end{cases} \tag{9.24}$$

i.e., the *transition occurs according to the "all-or-none" principal.*

* In this case, it is easy to see that eq. (9.21) follows directly from eq. (9.11).

This result is obvious, since the condition $\sigma = e^{-F_{\text{init.}}/kT} = 0$ corresponds to an infinitely large free energy of initiation of the helical region of the chain (to the exclusion of chain ends); this means that helical and coiled states cannot coexist in the same molecule. This fact leads directly to the introduction of (9.21) for the partition function of the chain.

For finite values of σ, eq. (9.14) can be solved only approximately by expanding λ_1, in series in the small parameter σ. For the regions $(s - 1)^2 \ll \sigma$ and $(s - 1)^2 \gg \sigma$, such an expansion has the form:

$$\lambda_1 = \begin{cases} s + \dfrac{\sigma}{s(s-1)} & \text{For } s > 1,\ (s-1)^2 \gg \sigma \\[2ex] \dfrac{1+s}{2} + \sqrt{\sigma} & \text{For } s \approx 1,\ (s-1)^2 \ll \sigma \\[2ex] 1 + \dfrac{\sigma s}{1-s} & \text{For } s < 1,\ (1-s)^2 \gg \sigma \end{cases} \tag{9.25}$$

From this, using equation (9.15), we obtain:

$$\vartheta = \begin{cases} 1 - \dfrac{\sigma(3s-2)}{s^2(s-1)^2} & \text{For } s > 1,\ (s-1)^2 \gg \sigma \\[2ex] \dfrac{s}{1+s} - \dfrac{2\sqrt{\sigma}}{(1+s)^2} & \text{For } s \approx 1,\ (s-1)^2 \ll \sigma \\[2ex] \dfrac{\sigma s}{(1-s)^2} & \text{For } s < 1,\ (1-s)^2 \gg \sigma \end{cases} \tag{9.26}$$

Equations (9.26) show that, *for finite, but small σ, close to the region where $s = 1$, the transition occurs from an almost completely helical state ($\vartheta = 1$) into an almost completely coiled state ($\vartheta = 0$); this transition takes place, however, not at one point ($s = 1$), but over a certain interval of change of s (i.e., over a certain temperature interval)*, the width of which is determined by the value of σ and can be quite small for small σ. Furthermore, *the transition does not take place according to the all-or-none principle, i.e., helical and coiled regions of the chain coexist in a single molecule in the transition zone.* In fact, eqs. (9.16)–(9.18), (9.25), and (9.26) show that the mean fraction of monomer pairs present at the junction between bonded and nonbonded regions, is not zero at $\sigma \neq 0$,

$$\zeta = 2\eta \approx \begin{cases} \dfrac{2\sigma}{s^2(s-1)} & \text{For } s > 1,\ (s-1)^2 \gg \sigma \\ \dfrac{2\sqrt{\sigma}}{1+s} & \text{For } s \approx 1,\ (s-1)^2 \ll \sigma \\ \dfrac{2\sigma s}{1-s} & \text{For } s < 1,\ (1-s)^2 \gg \sigma \end{cases} \tag{9.27}$$

and the average numbers of consecutive monomer units in bonded and free regions of the chain, ν_{bonded} and ν_{free} in the central part of the transition (i.e., with $s \approx 1$) are equal to

$$\nu_{\text{bonded}} \approx \nu_{\text{free}} \approx 1/\sqrt{\sigma} \tag{9.28}$$

In the hypothetical case in which $\sigma = 0$ the helix–coil transition, which takes place according to the all-or-none principle, is a true first-order phase transition, since the energy of the chain is equal to

$$\begin{aligned} E &= kT^2 \frac{\partial \ln Z}{\partial T} \\ &= nkT \frac{s^n}{1+s^n} \cdot \frac{d \ln s}{d \ln T} \\ &\approx \begin{cases} nkT \dfrac{d \ln s}{d \ln T} & \text{For } s < 1 \\ 0 & \text{For } s > 1 \end{cases} \end{aligned} \tag{9.29}$$

i.e., as $n \rightarrow \infty$ [to which corresponds the last equality in the right-hand side of eq. (9.29)], the energy of the macromolecule changes abruptly at the point $s = 1$. On the other hand, in the real case, with $\sigma \neq 0$, the helix–coil transition, while it is cooperative, is not a true phase transition, even though it takes place over a narrow temperature interval. In fact, it follows from eqs. (9.12) and (9.25) that, in this case and for $n \rightarrow \infty$, the energy of the system is a smooth function of the temperature in the region of transition. Furthermore, the coexistence of helical and coiled regions of the chain in the region of transition does not have the character of a phase equilibrium, i.e., of an equilibrium between two chain regions of any size which touch at one point.

The conclusion that different phases cannot coexist in one-dimensional cooperative systems was reached by Landau and Lifshits (35) from a strictly thermodynamic examination of such systems. Landau and Lifshits examined a linear system formed of consecutive alternating regions of two different "phases" and showed that these regions cannot have any desirable size, i.e., the examined phases are not true phases in the thermodynamic sense. In fact, the free energy of a one-dimensional system F can be expressed as the sum of the free energy F_0 of the additive quantities of the two phases, where

$$F_0 = n\vartheta F_{\text{bonded}} + n(1 - \vartheta)F_{\text{free}} \tag{9.30}$$

and the free energy of the points of contact between the phases. Looking at a linear cooperative system as a dilute "solution" in both phases of m points of contact between the phases, we obtain

$$F = F_0 + mkT \ln (m/en) + m\psi \tag{9.31}$$

where ψ is the "boundary tension" free energy at the contacts between the phases and n is the total number of elements in the system. This gives

$$\partial F/\partial m = kT \ln (m/n) + \psi \tag{9.32}$$

At sufficiently low "concentrations" of m/n (i.e., when the number of segments of different phases is small) ln (m/n) has a large (on the absolute scale) negative value, i.e., $\partial F/\partial m < 0$. Thus, F decreases with an increase in m, and since F tends to a minimum, the number of junctions between the phases increases up to the point at which F reaches a minimum; this is given by the condition $\partial F/\partial m = 0$, i.e.,

$$m/n = e^{-\psi/kT} \tag{9.33}$$

In this manner, the two phases will tend to mix to the point at which they become separated in finite segments, the dimensions of which are determined by condition (9.33), i.e., they end their existence as separate macroscopic phases consisting of as large as possible a number of elements.

For the system examined by us, $m/n = \zeta$, $\psi = F_{\text{init.}}/2$, and eq. (9.33) assumes the form

$$\zeta = e^{-F_{\text{init.}}/2kT} = \sqrt{\sigma} \tag{9.34}$$

which is identical with eq. (9.27) for the midpoint of the transition ($s = 1$).

The problem of phase transitions in one-dimensional systems has been examined in detail also by statistical methods (36,37); it was shown that, with finite interactions in the system ($F_{\text{init.}}$ is finite, i.e., $\sigma \neq 0$), the transitions between states, which differ from each other by the temperature dependence of their free energy, are not truly phase transitions.

However, if the interactions which determine the cooperative nature of the system are sufficiently large ($F_{init.} \gg kT$, i.e., $\sigma \ll 1$), the transition takes place within a quite narrow interval of change of external parameters and may be regarded, in this sense, as a "quasi-melting" of a one-dimensional system.

The shape of the helix–coil transition curve in the region of melting has been investigated in detail with the use of eqs. (9.14)–(9.20) by Zimm and Bragg (23), Nagai (24,25,29), and Lifson and Roig (30). In view of the cumbersome form of these calculations, however, we shall examine the shape of the transition in terms of a somewhat simpler model proposed by Zimm and Bragg (23) which leads to practically the same results, as has been shown by these authors [see also (48)]. Equations (9.2), (9.3), and (9.6)–(9.8) show that the cooperative nature of the interactions in a polypeptide macromolecule capable of helix–coil transitions is determined first by the fact that the initiation of a region of bonded monomer units is not favorable, and second by the fact that the breaking of less than three consecutive hydrogen bonds is not possible. The relation between the states of the ith monomer unit on one hand and those of the (i-2)th and (i-3)th units on the other hand is determined only by the second factor, i.e., by the fact that $F(\mu_{i-3}, 1, 0, 1) = \infty$ and $F(1, 0, 0, 1) = \infty$. If this restriction is not taken into account and it is considered only that the free energies of bonded and free monomer units which follow bonded units differ by the quantity ΔF and the first bonded monomer unit is characterized by an additional free energy, $F_{init.}$, then the free energy of the chain may be written in the form

$$F(\mu_1, \mu_2, \ldots, \mu_n) = \sum_{i=1}^{n} F(\mu_{i-1}, \mu_i) \tag{9.35}$$

This is similar to the situation which exists in ordinary macromolecules [see eq. (4.2)]. The approximate free energy expression, eq. (9.35), makes the examination of the system considerably simpler; furthermore, as shall be evident from what follows, the results based on it reflect all the most characteristic traits of the phenomenon. For the terms of the right-hand side of eq. (9.35) we obtain, in accordance with eqs. (9.2), (9.3), and (9.6),

$$\begin{aligned} F(\mu_{i-1}, 0) &= F_{free} \\ F(1, 1) &= F_{bonded} \\ F(0, 1) &= F_{bonded} + F_{init.} \end{aligned} \tag{9.36}$$

Taking the free energy of the nonbonded monomer units for the reference value of the calculation, we find that, in the model system under investigation, each bonded monomer unit contributes to the partition function a factor s; each free unit, a factor of one; and the first of nonbonded units following one or more free units, an additional factor σ where s and σ are defined by eqs. (9.9) and (9.10), respectively. The partition function of such a system has the form:

$$Z = \sum_{\{\mu_i\}} \prod_{i=1}^{n} s^{\mu_i} \sigma^{\mu_i(1-\mu_{i-1})} = \mathrm{Sp}\, G^n \tag{9.37}$$

where G is a second-order matrix

$$G = \begin{array}{c|cc} \mu_{i-1} \diagdown \mu_i & 0 & 1 \\ \hline 0 & 1 & \sigma s \\ 1 & 1 & s \end{array} \tag{9.38}$$

the secular equation of which has the form

$$(\lambda - 1)(\lambda - s) = \sigma s \tag{9.39}$$

For $\sigma = 1$, the roots of eq. (9.39) are equal to

$$\begin{aligned} \lambda_1 &= 1 + s \\ \lambda_2 &= 0 \end{aligned} \tag{9.40}$$

From this

$$Z = (1 + s)^n \tag{9.41}$$

Thus, in this case the partition function of a macromolecule is equal to the product of the partition functions of the individual monomer units.* This means that cooperativeness is completely absent from the system, i.e., the breaking and formation of hydrogen bonds take place independently in each monomer unit. From eqs. (9.15) and (9.41) we find that, in this case, the fraction of bonded monomer units is equal to

$$\vartheta = s/(1 + s) \tag{9.42}$$

i.e., it is a smooth function of the temperature, in agreement with a unimolecular reaction equation (the helix–coil transition is smeared over a very wide temperature interval).

* For the more general model, examined above, the partition function of the chain is not expressed by eq. (9.41) with $\sigma = 1$, since, in this case, the states of the individual monomer units remain interdependent, due to conditions (9.7) and (9.8).

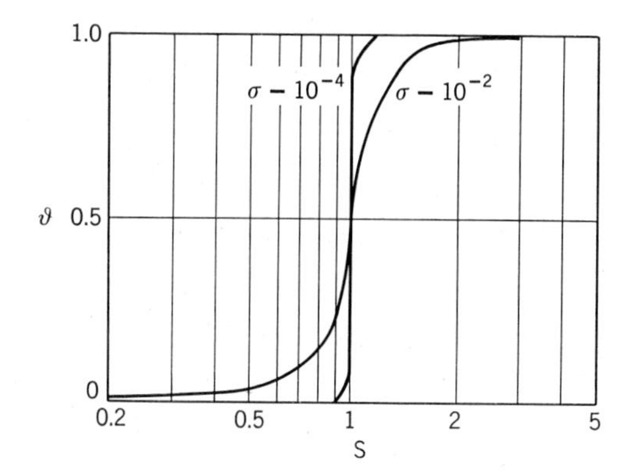

Fig. 9.3. Dependence of the fraction ϑ of monomer units linked by hydrogen bonds in a polymer chain on the equilibrium constant s.

For $\sigma = 0$, the roots of eq. (9.39) coincide with the nonzero roots of the more general equation, eq. (9.14); as a result, eqs. (9.21)–(9.24) are obeyed as before, indicating that the helix–coil transition takes place at the point $s = 1$, in accordance with the all-or-none principle. In the general case, in which $0 \leqq \sigma \leqq 1$, using equations (9.15)–(9.18) and differentiating eq. (9.39) with respect to the corresponding parameters, we obtain:

$$\vartheta = (\lambda_1 - 1)/(2\lambda_1 - 1 - s) \tag{9.43}$$

$$\eta = \sigma s/[\lambda_1(2\lambda_1 - 1 - s)] \tag{9.44}$$

$$\nu_{\text{bonded}} = \lambda_1/(\lambda_1 - s) \tag{9.45}$$

$$\nu_{\text{free}} = \lambda_1/(\lambda_1 - 1) \tag{9.46}$$

where λ_1 is the largest root of eq. (9.39):

$$\lambda_1 = \frac{1 + s}{2} + \sqrt{\frac{(1 - s)^2}{4} + \sigma s} \tag{9.47}$$

Figure 9.3 shows the dependence on s of the fraction of bonded monomer units ϑ, calculated with eqs. (9.43) and (9.47) for two values of σ, namely, 10^{-2} and 10^{-4}. It can be seen easily that the transition takes place over a variation in s from $1 + \sqrt{\sigma}$ to $1 - \sqrt{\sigma}$ (38). In this interval, λ_1 changes from $1 + (\sqrt{5}/2 + 1/2)\sqrt{\sigma}$ to $1 + (\sqrt{5}/2)\sqrt{\sigma}$, and ϑ from $^1/_2(1 + 1/\sqrt{5}) = 0.72$ to $^1/_2(1 - 1/\sqrt{5}) = 0.28$. As s varies from $1 + 2\sqrt{\sigma}$ to $1 - 2\sqrt{\sigma}$, ϑ varies from 0.85 to 0.15. Substitution of the value $s = 1$

$\pm \sqrt{\sigma}$ into the equation $s = e^{-(\Delta H - T\Delta S)/kT}$ gives the temperature interval of the transition as

$$\Delta T = \frac{|\Delta H|}{k} \cdot \frac{\ln (1 + \sqrt{\sigma}) - \ln (1 - \sqrt{\sigma})}{[\ln (1 + \sqrt{\sigma}) - (\Delta H/kT_m)][\ln (1 - \sqrt{\sigma}) - (\Delta H/kT_m)]} \quad (9.48)$$

where T_m (the melting temperature) is the midpoint of the transition; it is defined by the condition that $s(T_m) = 1$; $-\Delta H$ is the heat of the helix–coil transition. For $\sigma \ll 1$, we obtain (38):

$$\Delta T/T_m = 2\sqrt{\sigma}(kT_m/|\Delta H|) \quad (9.49)$$

The average lengths of the regular sequences of bonded and free monomer units in the transition region are proportional to $1/\sqrt{\sigma}$ [see eq. (9.28)]. Furthermore, in the region in which the main part of the helix–coil transition takes place, i.e., over a decrease of s from $1 + \sqrt{\sigma}$ to $1 - \sqrt{\sigma}$, ν_{bonded} decreases from $1.62/\sqrt{\sigma}$ to $0.62/\sqrt{\sigma}$ and ν_{free} increases from $0.62/\sqrt{\sigma}$ to $1.62/\sqrt{\sigma}$. The values of ν_{bonded} and ν_{free} differ drastically outside of the transition region. Thus, for $s > 1$, when $(s - 1)^2 \gg \sigma$,

$$\lambda_1 \approx s + [\sigma s/(s - 1)]$$

$$\vartheta = 1 - [\sigma s/(s - 1)^2]$$

$$\nu_{\text{bonded}} = (s - 1)/\sigma$$

$$\nu_{\text{free}} = s/(s - 1)$$

while for $s < 1$, when $(1 - s)^2 \gg \sigma$,

$$\lambda_1 \approx 1 + [\sigma s/(1 - s)]$$

$$\vartheta = [\sigma s/(1 - s)^2]$$

$$\nu_{\text{bonded}} = 1/(1 - s)$$

$$\nu_{\text{free}} = (1 - s)/\sigma s$$

In the approximate treatment, when σ is small, the possibility of breaking less than three consecutive hydrogen bonds is small in the region of $s < 1$, in which there are primarily long sequences which do not contain hydrogen bonds. Thus, for $\sigma \ll 1$, the results of the approximate treatment based on eqs. (9.43)–(9.47) coincide, in the region of $s < 1$, with the results obtained above with the more exact model [see eqs. (9.25)–(9.27)]. In the region of $s > 1$ the two methods give results which differ somewhat quantitatively. The approximate method results in a smaller fraction of bonded monomer units (since it permits the breaking of additional hydrogen bonds) and a larger probability of junctions (since permitting the breaking of one and two hydrogen bonds decreases the mean dimensions of the coiled regions). For $\sigma \ll 1$, however, these differences are, on the whole, not large, so that the approximate method can be used successfully not only for the qualitative, but also for the quantitative characterization of the helix–coil transition.

Let us compare the expressions for the temperature dependence of the fraction of bonded monomer units in a completely noncooperative chain [eq. (9.42)] and a completely cooperative chain [eq. (9.23)]. We see that, in the first case, the fraction of bonded monomer units varies with a change in temperature according to the equation of the unimolecular reaction of a single monomer unit, while, in the second case, it follows the equation of a unimolecular reaction in which n monomer units participate simultaneously (this is what leads, as $n \rightarrow \infty$, to an abrupt increase of ϑ from 0 to 1 as soon as the equilibrium constant of the reaction reaches unity). As a result, it is possible to assume (21,39,48) that in the intermediate cases as well, i.e., for real macromolecules, the temperature dependence of the fraction of bonded monomer units must obey the equation of a unimolecular reaction, which involves the simultaneous participation of a number of monomer units larger than unity but smaller than n:

$$\vartheta = \tilde{s}/(1 + \tilde{s}) \tag{9.50}$$

The effective equilibrium constant

$$\tilde{s} = e^{-(\Delta H_{\text{eff.}} - T\Delta S_{\text{eff.}})/kT} \tag{9.51}$$

is a function of the number of monomer units that participate in the reaction. From this point of view, the temperature dependence of ϑ in the transition region is determined by the effective heat of transition $-\Delta H_{\text{eff.}}$, and the usefulness of eqs. (9.50) and (9.51) is determined by the extent to which the actual function $\vartheta(T)$ in the transition region can be approximated by these equations with $\Delta H_{\text{eff.}}$ independent of temperature. Using eqs. (9.50) and (9.43), we obtain

$$\tilde{s} = \vartheta/(1 - \vartheta) = (\lambda_1 - 1)/(\lambda_1 - s) \tag{9.52}$$

from which

$$\Delta H_{\text{eff.}} = \frac{-d \ln \tilde{s}}{d(1/kT)} = \frac{-d \ln s}{d(1/kT)} \cdot \frac{d \ln \tilde{s}}{d \ln s}$$

$$= \Delta H \frac{1 + s}{2\lambda_1 - 1 - s} = \Delta H \tilde{\nu} \frac{1 + s}{2} \tag{9.53}$$

where $\Delta H = -d \ln s/d(1/kT)$ [see eq. (9.9)], and

$$\tilde{\nu} = 2\nu_{\text{bonded}}\nu_{\text{free}}/(\nu_{\text{bonded}} + \nu_{\text{free}}) \tag{9.54}$$

is the "reduced" length of a region of the chain, in which all the monomer units are in an identical state (bonded or free). In the transition region, the quantity $[(1 + s)/2]\tilde{\nu} \simeq \tilde{\nu}$ lies within the limits of $0.9/\sqrt{\sigma}$ (at the endpoints of the transition) and $1/\sqrt{\sigma}$ (at the midpoint of the transition), i.e., the reduced length of this region of the chain is a weak function of temperature. Consequently, in the transition region, $\Delta H_{\text{eff.}} \approx$ const., i.e., the equilibrium constant $\tilde{s}$ is an exponential function of $1/kT$, and $\tilde{\nu}$ is the average number of monomer units in which the breaking or formation of hydrogen bonds takes place simultaneously (39). The fraction of hydrogen bonds (in the transition interval), then, turns out to be a linear function of the reciprocal of the temperature. In fact, it follows from equations (9.50) and (9.53) that, in the transition interval, where $\tilde{s} \approx 1$ and $\tilde{\nu} = 1/\sqrt{\sigma}$:

$$d\vartheta/d(1/kT) = -(d\vartheta/d \ln \tilde{s})\Delta H_{\text{eff.}} = -\Delta H/4\sqrt{\sigma} \tag{9.55}$$

On the other hand, outside the region of transition, the effective equilibrium constant $\tilde{s}$ is not an exponential function of $1/kT$, i.e., the dependence of $\Delta H_{\text{eff.}}$ on temperature becomes considerable. Examination of this dependence reveals that, in the region of transition (at $s \approx 1$), $|\Delta H_{\text{eff.}}|$ has a maximum equal to $|\Delta H|/\sqrt{\sigma}$ [see eq. (9.55), while, with departure from the region of transition in either direction, the value of $[(1 + s)/2]\tilde{\nu}$ falls to unity and the effective heat of transition, $-\Delta H_{\text{eff.}}$, becomes equal to the heat of transition of a single monomer unit, $-\Delta H$.

Let us pass now to the comparison of the above theory with experiment. Figure 9.4 [see (48)] gives the experimental dependence of the fraction of hydrogen bonds ϑ in the interval of transition on the reciprocal of the temperature for the three polypeptides that have been studied up to now, namely, poly-γ-benzyl-L-glutamate (40), partly ionized poly-L-glutamic acid (42), and partly ionized poly-L-lysine (58). Poly-γ-benzyl-L-glutamate is an uncharged polypeptide. In the case of the other two polymers, even though they are partly charged, the investigation of the helix–coil transition was carried out at a constant pH of the medium; as a result, even in these cases, the transition is completely determined by the temperature change and, consequently, may be interpreted in terms of the above theory, in which the properties of the solvent are considered as constant in the process of transition.

The first notable feature in Figure 9.4 is that, in molecules of poly-γ-benzyl-L-glutamate, the helix–coil transition takes place not with an increase but a decrease of the temperature. This means that, in this case, ΔH is positive, i.e., the heat of the helix–coil transition, equal to $-\Delta H$, is negative (the helical state is energetically less favorable than the coiled state). Furthermore, the transition entropy, equal to $-\Delta S$, is also negative (since $\Delta S = \Delta H/T_m$), i.e., the helical state is entropically more favorable than the coiled state. It is evident that this observation cannot be explained without considering the effect of the solvent: the entropy of the macromolecule itself must increase and not decrease during the helix–coil transition. Such an increase, however, can be compensated for by a decrease in entropy during the formation of polymer–solvent hydrogen bonds and the accompanying change in the structure of the solvent.* In the two other polymers investigated, the helix–coil transition occurs with an increase in temperature; this corresponds to negative ΔH and ΔS, i.e., to a positive heat and entropy of transition.

Passing over to a quantitative interpretation of the experimental data, let us note first of all that, in all three cases, the fraction of hydrogen bonds in the transition interval is a linear function of $1/T$, in accordance with the predictions of the theory [see eq. (9.55)]. This is confirmed by the fact that, in the transition interval, the effective equilibrium constant $\tilde{s}$ is an almost exponential function of temperature, i.e., the transition obeys the equation of a unimolecular reaction for $\tilde{\nu}$ monomer units with an effective heat of transition independent of temperature. The quantity $\Delta H/\sqrt{\sigma}$ can be determined from the shape of the ϑ versus $1/T$ curves, in accordance with eq. (9.55). The separate determination of ΔH and σ requires the availability of additional experimental data. Such data, obtained by

* Recently, Baur and Nosanow (57), having taken into account the possibility of various energetic states of monomer units in a coiled chain, showed that, at sufficiently high temperatures, because of an increase in the occupation of high energy levels, the coiled state may become more favorable than the helical state, even if the opposite situation is true at the usual temperatures. Thus, at very high temperatures, a second helix–coil transition may taken place in principle in polymers of the type of poly-γ-benzyl-L-glutamate; therefore, the helical state is stable only in the region between the two transitions. Let us note, however, that according to the estimate of Baur and Nosanow (57), the temperature of the second transition for poly-γ-benzyl-L-glutamate is too high ($\approx$700–1000°K) for this transition to be observed in actuality.

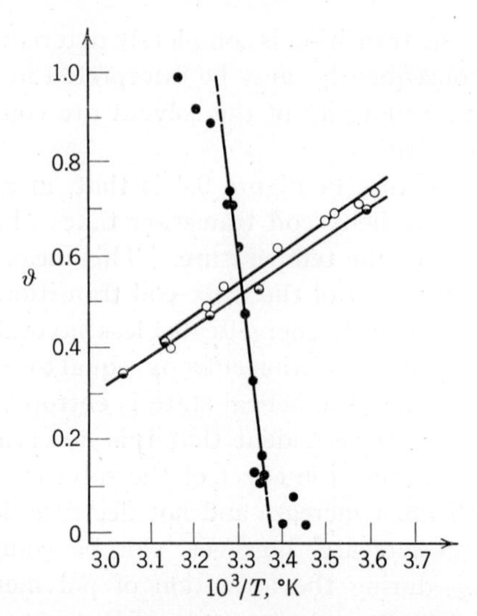

Fig. 9.4. Dependence of the fraction ϑ of monomer units linked by hydrogen bonds on the reciprocal temperature: (●) poly-γ-benzyl-L-glutamate; (○) poly-L-lysine; ◓ poly-L-glutamic acid. The solvents are listed in Table 9.1.

Doty (33,40), are related to the dependence of the transition temperature of poly-γ-benzyl-L-glutamate on the degree of polymerization of the sample.

The theory of helix–coil transitions presented above is valid for polypeptide chains sufficiently long ($n \gg 1$), to permit end effects to be neglected. Zimm and Bragg (23) and Lifson and Roig (30) have developed, however, also a theory of helix–coil transitions in polypeptide chains with any degree of polymerization. They showed that a decrease in the degree of polymerization broadens the transition and shifts it into the direction of larger values of s, i.e., it stabilizes the coiled conformation.* At low degrees of polymerization, where the number of monomer units is less than the average number of consecutive bonded or free units, ν_{bonded} and ν_{free} calculated at $n \gg 1$, the helix–coil transition occurs simultaneously for all the monomer units of the given chain; in this process, however, half of the chains are in the helical state and half in the coiled state at the midpoint

* This is explained by the fact that in a polypeptide chain, consisting of n amino acid residues, the maximum number of hydrogen bonds that may be formed is $n - 4$; this imposes restrictions on the conformations of $n - 2$ monomer units. The two remaining nonhelical monomer units, at small n, serve as initiators of the coiled conformation, as a result of the cooperative nature of the system. As a result, helix formation is possible only for $n > n_0$, where n_0 is that value of n which satisfies the condition that $(s - 1)^2/s^n = \sigma$.

of the transition. The experimental melting curves of poly-γ-benzyl-L-glutamate samples of various degrees of polymerization (n = 1500, 46 and 26) (33,40) (Fig. 9.5) confirm the main conclusion of the theory according to which a decrease in the degree of polymerization shifts the transition toward larger values of s.

Quantitative comparison of theory with the experimental curves for different n carried out by Zimm, Doty, and Iso (33) [see also (23)], made possible the separate determination of the parameters ΔH and σ. The

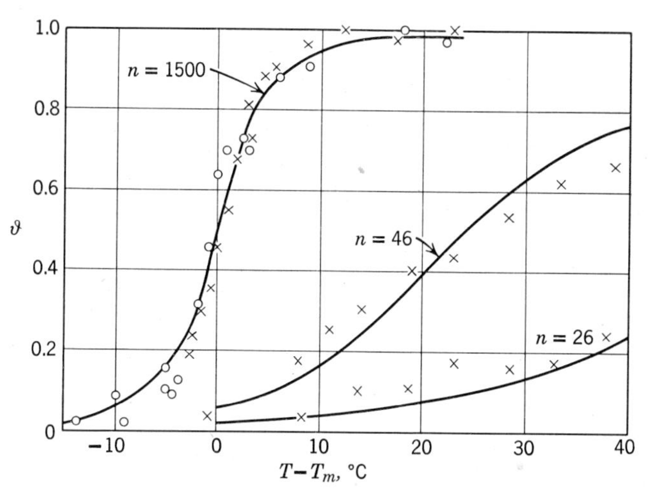

Fig. 9.5. Temperature dependence of the fraction ϑ of monomer units linked by hydrogen bonds in solutions of poly-γ-benzyl-L-glutamate of various degrees of polymerization n in a mixture of dichloroacetic acid with 1,2-dichloroethane: (O) ratio of solvent components = 4:1 (T_m = 28.7°C for n = 1500); ($\times$) ratio of solvent components = 7:3 (T_m = 11.8°C for n = 1500); (——) theoretical curves for $\sigma = 2 \times 10^{-4}$, ΔH = 890 cal/mole.

best agreement between theory and experiment was obtained with $\Delta H = +890 \pm 130$ cal/mole and $\sigma = 2 \times 10^{-4}$.

In the two other polymers studied, poly-L-glutamic acid and poly-L-lysine, helix–coil transitions take place over a much wider temperature interval than in poly-γ-benzyl-L-glutamate. This can be explained [see eq. (9.40)], either by the small heat of transition $|\Delta H|$ or by the small degree of cooperativeness, i.e., by large values of σ. The fact, however, that helix–coil transitions occur in both ionizable polymers over a narrow range of the pH of the medium (see section 10.2), points to a high degree of cooperativeness of the system, i.e., to small values of σ.

As a result, the evaluation of the heat of transition in these polymers is carried out on the basis of the hypothesis of Zimm and Bragg (23) that the value of σ has a relatively weak dependence on the actual polymer–solvent pair.

Accordingly, in a number of studies (27,48,57,58), it has been assumed that for poly-L-glutamic acid and poly-L-lysine σ is also equal to 2×10^{-4},* and ΔH was determined from experimental data on the temperature dependence of the transition. The values of ΔH (and also of $\Delta S = \Delta H/T_m$) determined by Applequist (48) from the shapes of the curves of Figure 9.4 for $\sigma = 2 \times 10^{-4}$ are given in Table 9.1.

TABLE 9.1

Thermodynamic Data on Helix–Coil Transitions in Synthetic Polypeptides

Polypeptide	Solvent	Degree of polymerization	$\Delta H/\sqrt{\sigma}$, kcal/mole	ΔH, cal/mole	ΔS, cal/deg-mole
Poly-γ-benzyl-L-glutamate[a]	Dichloroacetic acid + 1,2-dichloroethane (4:1)	1600	70 ± 14	1000 ± 200	3.2 ± 0.6
Poly-L-glutamic acid (67% ionized)[b]	0.2M aqueous NaCl + dioxane (2:1); pH 5.90 at 25°C	260	−5.0 ± 0.5	−70 ± 7	−0.23 ± 0.02
Poly-L-lysine (20% ionized)[c]	Water; pH 10.10 at 22°C	1500	−5.3 ± 0.5	−75 ± 7	−0.25 ± 0.02

[a] Data of Doty and Yang (40).
[b] Data of Doty et al. (42).
[c] Data of Applequist and Doty (58).

Similar ΔH values have been obtained also in other studies. The value of ΔH for poly-γ-benzyl-L-glutamate is in good agreement with the calculation of Zimm, Doty, and Iso (33), as could be expected. Negative, but very small, values of ΔH have been obtained for the two other polymers. According to Applequist and Doty (58), the small values of ΔH in poly-L-glutamic acid and poly-L-lysine can be explained by the fact that in the helix–coil transition, not only hydrogen bonds change, but also interactions between the hydrophobic groups of the chain, as well as the electrostatic interactions of the charged groups. The simultaneous change of all these

* Zimm and Rice (27) have shown that the value $\sigma \approx 10^{-4}$ is in satisfactory agreement with potentiometric titration curves of poly-L-glutamic acid (see section 10.2).

interactions can lead to an almost complete compensation of energetic effects.

9.4. Changes in Polypeptide Chain Dimensions during Helix–Coil Transitions

In the preceding discussion (sections 9.2 and 9.3) of helix–coil transitions in polypeptide chains, the states of monomer units were classified according to a "physical" criterion, i.e., according to the presence or absence of a hydrogen bond. In many cases, for example in the calculation of chain dimensions, it is the geometric structure of the macromolecule which is of interest. In such cases, in the calculation of the partition function of the chain, it is proper to examine the states of monomer units present in the helical ($\epsilon_i = 1$) and coiled ($\epsilon_i = 0$) states, as has been done by Nagai (24,25,29) [see also Lifson and Roig (30)]. Here coiled conformation refers to the result of the averaging over all rotational isomers of a monomer unit in a statistical coiled chain. As before (see section 9.2), the free energy of the chain is given by the sum of terms, each of which is a function of the conformations of four consecutive monomer units [see eq. (9.1)]. By analogy with eqs. (9.2), (9.3), and (9.6)–(9.8), we obtain:

$$
\begin{aligned}
&F(\epsilon_{i-3}, \epsilon_{i-2}, 0, 0) = F(1, 1, 1, 0) \equiv F_{\text{free}} \\
&F(\epsilon_{i-3}, 1, 1, 1) \equiv F_{\text{bonded}} \\
&F(\epsilon_{i-3}, \epsilon_{i-2}, 0, 1) = F(\epsilon_{i-3}, 0, 1, 1) \equiv {}^1/_2 F_{\text{init.}} \qquad (9.56) \\
&F(\epsilon_{i-3}, 0, 1, 0) = \infty \\
&F(0, 1, 1, 0) = \infty
\end{aligned}
$$

where the quantities F_{free}, F_{bonded}, and $F_{\text{init.}}$ are again determined by eqs. (9.2), (9.3), and (9.6). The second of eqs. (9.56) means that, for hydrogen bond formation, it is necessary that three consecutive monomer units exist in a rigid helical conformation, i.e., state 1, 1, 1 is necessary (see Figs. 9.1 and 9.2). In states 0, 1 and 0, 1, 1, one or two monomer units are present in a rigid helical conformation, respectively. The fourth and fifth of eqs. (9.56) mean that these monomer units must be followed by a monomer unit bonded by a hydrogen bond to the third preceding unit (states 0, 1, 0 and 0, 1, 1, 0 are impossible). The third of eqs. (9.56) assigns the free energy of initiation of a helical region of the chain, $F_{\text{init.}}$, equally to two monomer units present in the beginning of such a region which has a rigid helical conformation but is not bonded by a hydrogen bond to the preceding units.

Setting, as before, $F_{\text{free}} = 0$, we find that the contribution of a given state of the chain to the partition function of the macromolecule is determined by the product of the following factors: (*1*) factor 1 for each monomer unit in the coiled conformation ($\epsilon_i = 0$); (*2*) factor s for each unit in the helical conformation ($\epsilon_i = 1$), following two units in the helical conformation ($\epsilon_{i-2} = \epsilon_{i-1} = 1$); (*3*) factor $\sqrt{\sigma}$ for each monomer unit in the helical conformation ($\epsilon_i = 1$), if at least one of the two preceding units is not present in the helical conformation ($\epsilon_{i-1}\epsilon_{i-2} = 0$); (*4*) factor 0 for each monomer unit in the coiled conformation, which follows monomer units in the helical conformation, if their number is less than three ($\epsilon_i = 0$, $\epsilon_{i-1} = 1$, $\epsilon_{i-2}\epsilon_{i-3} = 0$).

We have

$$Z = \sum_{\{\epsilon_i\}} \prod_{i=1}^{n} s^{\epsilon_{i-2}\epsilon_{i-1}\epsilon_i} \sigma^{(\epsilon_i/2)(1-\epsilon_{i-2}\epsilon_{i-1})} [1 - \delta\epsilon_{i,0}\epsilon_{i-1}(1 - \epsilon_{i-2}\epsilon_{i-3})] \tag{9.57}$$

The summation is carried out over all possible sets of $\{\epsilon_i\}$, where $\epsilon_i = 0, 1$. Factors s and σ are, as before, defined by eqs. (9.9) and (9.10).

In this case, as well, $Z = \text{Sp}\, G^n$, where matrix G has the form given in eq. (9.58).

$$G = \begin{bmatrix} 1 & \sqrt{\sigma} & \cdot & \cdot & \cdot & \cdot & \cdot \\ \cdot & \cdot & \sqrt{\sigma} & \cdot & \cdot & \cdot & \cdot \\ \cdot & \cdot & \cdot & \cdot & \cdot & \cdot & s \\ 1 & \sqrt{\sigma} & \cdot & \cdot & \cdot & \cdot & \cdot \\ \cdot & \cdot & \sqrt{\sigma} & \cdot & \cdot & \cdot & \cdot \\ \cdot & \cdot & \cdot & 1 & \sqrt{\sigma} & \cdot & \cdot \\ \cdot & \cdot & \cdot & \cdot & \cdot & 1 & s \end{bmatrix} \tag{9.58}$$

(Only the nonzero elements have been written out, and the states are numbered in the sequence $\epsilon_{i-2}\epsilon_{i-1}\epsilon_i = 000;\ 001;\ 011;\ 100;\ 101;\ 110;\ 111$.)

As can be seen, the elements of the matrix are different in the "physical" [eq. (9.13)] and geometric [eq. (9.58)] treatments. Their characteristic equations are identical, however; this is not surprising, since the two treatments must give absolutely equivalent results, and all the physical properties of the system are determined by the roots of the characteristic equation.

From eq. (9.56) it follows that the mean fraction of monomer units in the helical conformation is given by the expression

$$\xi = \frac{\partial \ln \lambda_1}{\partial \ln s} + \frac{\partial \ln \lambda_1}{\partial \ln \sqrt{\sigma}} = \vartheta + 2\eta \tag{9.59}$$

where ϑ is the mean fraction of monomer units bonded by hydrogen bonds [see eq. (9.15)], and η is the mean fraction of bonded monomer units, following free units. This equality is obvious, since each ordered region which contains bonded monomer units starts from two nonbonded units present in the helical conformation.

In this case, just as before (see section 9.3), the treatment may be simplified by neglecting the impossibility of having less than three monomer units in the helical conformation, as has been done by Lifson and Roig (30). Then, the conformations of only three consecutive monomer units are interdependent, and matrix G turns out to be a fourth-order matrix and can be reduced further into a third-order matrix. The results obtained in this way (30) differ little from those obtained from an examination of the exact partition function (9.57).

The mean-square dimensions of polypeptide chains during the helix–coil transition can be calculated by a geometric approach to the description of macromolecular structure by using the methods described in Chapter 5. The theory of polypeptide molecule dimensions (mean-square end-to-end distance and mean-square radius of gyration) has been developed by Nagai (24,25,29), who examined two conformational models. The bond lengths, valence angles, and restriction of rotation of chain elements were taken into account in the first, more rigorous, method. In the case of monomer units in the coiled conformation, rotations about individual bonds were assumed to be independent and were represented by the model of torsional oscillations close to equilibrium positions. It was assumed, furthermore, that the equilibrium positions correspond to a local conformation of the polypeptide chain, close to a β-conformation stretched to the limit, taking into account, however, the asymmetric structure of L-polypeptides. In the other, simplified, model of Nagai (29), each helical region, containing $\nu_{hel.}$ monomer units, was replaced by a rod of length $\nu_{hel.}l_{hel.}$ where $l_{hel.} = 1.5$ Å is the distance along the α-helix axis per monomer unit, while each coiled region, containing ν_{coil} monomer units, was replaced by a freely jointed chain of ν_{coil} segments with length l_{coil}. The value of l_{coil} was selected in such manner that the calculated value of the mean-square end-to-end distance of a completely coiled chain, described by the freely jointed chain model $\overline{h_{coil}^2} = nl_{coil}^2$ (n is the degree of polymerization) was consistent with the experimental data. The measurements of Doty, Bradbury, and Holtzer (41) have shown that $\overline{h_{coil}^2} = 7.92 \times 10^5$ Å^2 for poly-γ-benzyl-L-glutamate samples with $n = 1500$ in dichloroacetic acid at 25°C; this gives $l_{coil} = 23.0$ Å. As can be seen, the value of l_{coil} is much greater than that of $l_{hel.}$. This is due to the fact that an α-helix is tightly wound while a coiled molecule has a one-dimensional short-range order that corresponds to a structure close to a completely stretched β-structure of the chain. Furthermore, since dichloroacetic acid is a good solvent for poly-γ-benzyl-L-glutamate, the dimensions of the coiled molecule increase because of volume effects; this is effectively taken into account in the value of l_{coil}.

For the simple model under examination, using eq. (5.2) and remembering that the mean cosine of the angle between the ith and jth segments is equal to unity when both segments are part of the same helical region and zero in all other cases, we obtain:

$$\overline{h^2} = \sum_{i=1}^{n} \overline{r_i^2} + 2\sum_{i=2}^{n}\sum_{j=1}^{i-1} \overline{(\mathbf{r}_j, \mathbf{r}_i)}$$

$$= \sum_{i=1}^{n} [\bar{\epsilon}_i l_{\text{hel.}}^2 + (1 - \bar{\epsilon}_i) l^2_{\text{coil}}] + 2\sum_{i=2}^{n}\sum_{j=1}^{i-1} l_{\text{hel.}}^2 \overline{\prod_{k=j}^{i} \epsilon_k} \qquad (9.60)$$

where ϵ_i assume values of 1 and 0 for helical and coiled segments, respectively. For $n \gg 1$, and using only terms of order n, Nagai has derived (29) the eq. (9.61) for the mean dimensions of a macromolecule containing both helical and coiled regions:

$$\frac{\overline{h^2}}{h^2_{\text{coil}}} = 1 - \xi + \left\{\xi + 2\vartheta\left[3 + \frac{s^2}{\lambda_1(\lambda_1 - s)}\right]\right\}\frac{l_{\text{hel.}}^2}{l_{\text{coil}}^2} \qquad (9.61)$$

Here ξ is the mean fraction of helical monomer units in the molecule, defined by eq. (9.59); ϑ is the mean fraction of monomer units bonded by hydrogen bonds, defined by eq. (9.15); λ_1 is the largest root of eq. (9.14), and s is the equilibrium constant for the formation of a hydrogen bond in a monomer unit that follows a bonded unit [eq. (9.9)].

At small values of the cooperativeness parameter σ, for example for $\sigma \approx 2 \times 10^{-4}$, determined, as pointed out above, by comparing theory with experimental data on poly-γ-benzyl-L-glutamate (23,33), the results of the approximate theory practically coincide with those of the more rigorous theory of Nagai, which takes into account the real structure of the coiled regions of the chain. This is related to the fact that the applicability of the second, approximate model becomes better with an increase in the average number of monomer units present in the coiled region. As has been pointed out above [see eq. (9.28)], this quantity is equal in order of magnitude to $1/\sqrt{\sigma}$ in the transition region, i.e., for $\sigma \approx 2 \times 10^{-4}$ is sufficiently large.

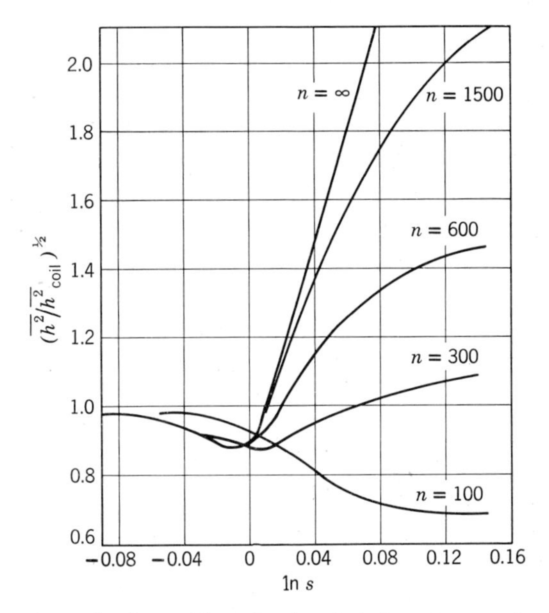

Fig. 9.6. Dimensions of polypeptide molecules of various degrees of polymerization n in the region of the helix–coil transition; $\sigma = 2 \times 10^{-4}$, $l_{coil} = 22.4$ Å., $l_{hel.} = 1.5$ Å; circles on the right are limiting values for α-helices.

Figure 9.6 shows the dependence of the mean-square length of macromolecules in the transition region (relative to the mean-square length of the coiled chain) $(\overline{h^2}/\overline{h^2_{coil}})^{1/2}$ on the logarithm of the equilibrium constant $\ln s$ (for $n \gg 1$) calculated with eq. (9.61). As can be seen, *the increase in chain dimensions during transition from a coiled structure into an α-helical one is preceded by a decrease in chain dimensions;* this results from the fact that the introduction into the chain of helical segments with a comparatively small number, m, of monomer units shortens the chain (this number is such that the dimensions of a helical region, $ml_{hel.}$, are smaller than the mean-square dimensions of a coiled region, $\sqrt{m}l_{coil}$, i.e., $m < l^2_{coil}/l^2_{hel.} \approx 200$), even though the number of hydrogen-bonded monomer units increases monotonically in this process. This effect has been observed experimentally by Doty, Wada, Yang, and Blout (42), who found that the intrinsic viscosity of poly-L-glutamic acid in a mixture of a $0.2M$ aqueous NaCl solution with dioxane (2:1) passes through a sharp minimum before the normal increase with a decrease in pH. Later, Applequist and Doty (58) obtained similar results for aqueous solutions of poly-L-lysine.

Nagai (29) has developed also the theory of polymer chain dimensions in the helix–coil transition region for chains of finite length. It was shown that the increase in dimensions during helix formation in the molecules must take place only for chains with $n > l_{\text{coil}}^2/l_{\text{hel.}}^2$. This conclusion is obvious and immediate. In the case of chains with $n \approx l_{\text{coil}}^2/l_{\text{hel.}}^2$, the dimensions of entirely helical and entirely coiled chains must be identical, while a minimum must be present in the region of transition (see Fig. 9.6). In fact, according to the experimental data of Doty and co-workers (11), the intrinsic viscosity of poly-γ-benzyl-L-glutamate samples with $n = 300$ is identical in the two limiting forms and changes in the transition region. (This is what Doty used to prove the fact that the transition does not follow the all-or-none principle.) It is interesting to note also that, with an increase in s, the dimensions of molecules with low degrees of polymerization attain values close to those of an entirely helical structure more rapidly than do the dimensions of molecules with a high degree of polymerization; this is consistent with the theory. The fraction of monomer units present in helical conformations, however, increases faster when n is large. This is the result of the fact that, in short molecules, hydrogen bonds break only at the ends of the molecules, while, in long chains, the high degree of coiling is determined by a small number of flexible monomer units with broken hydrogen bonds within the middle of the molecule.

It is not sufficient to consider only the interactions of nearest monomer units in examining polypeptide chains in the helix–coil transition region, and, particularly, the dimensions of the macromolecule in the transition region. In a coiled chain (particularly charged), the long-range interactions between monomer units which are normally distant but which have randomly approached each other during the thermal motion of chain segments also play an important role. These interactions, whose role increases with an increase in the fraction of monomer units in coiled conformations as well as of the mean dimensions of coiled regions, displace the region of transition toward higher temperature and broaden its range; this has been shown recently by Ptitsyn (43).

Ptitsyn and Skvortzov (60) have shown that long-range interactions exert a considerable influence on the dimensions of macromolecules in the region of the helix–coil transition. These interactions deepen the minimum in the plot of macromolecule dimensions as a function of the fraction of broken hydrogen bonds for the examined model in which the transition is initiated by the breaking of hydrogen bonds in any part of the chain. If the transition is initiated only by the breaking of hydrogen bonds at the ends of chains, long-range interactions lead to the result that the dimensions of the macromolecule pass through a maximum and not a minimum, in the process of melting.

References

1. Linderstrøm-Lang, K., and J. Schellman, in *The Enzymes*, Vol. I, P. D. Boyer, H. Lardy, and K. Myrback, Eds., Academic Press, New York, 1959, p. 443.
2. Pauling, L., R. B. Corey, and H. R. Branson, *Proc. Natl. Acad. Sci. U.S.*, **37**, 205 (1951).
3. Pauling, L., and R. B. Corey, *Proc. Natl. Acad. Sci. U.S.*, **37**, 235 (1951).
4. Crick, F. H., and J. D. Watson, *Proc. Roy. Soc.* (*London*), **A223**, 80 (1954).
5. Leach, S. J., *Revs. Pure Appl. Chem.*, **9**, 33 (1959); *Usp. Khim.*, **31**, 1104 (1962).
6. Rich, A., in *Sovremennye Problemy Biofiziki*, Vol. 1, IL, Moscow, 1961, p. 64 (originally published as *Biophysical Science: A Study Program*, J. L. Oncley, F. O. Schmitt, R. C. Williams, M. D. Rosenberg, and R. H. Bolt, Eds., Wiley, New York, 1959).
7. Rich, A., in *Sovremennye Problemy Biofiziki*, Vol. 1, IL, Moscow, 1961, p. 246 (originally published as *Biophysical Science: A Study Program*, J. L. Oncley, F. O. Schmitt, R. C. Williams, M. D. Rosenberg, and R. H. Bolt, Eds., Wiley, New York, 1959).
8. Kendrew, J., in *Sovremennye Problemy Biofiziki*, Vol. 1, IL, Moscow, 1961, p. 120 (originally published as *Biophysical Science: A Study Program*, J. L. Oncley, F. O. Schmitt, R. C. Williams, M. D. Rosenberg, and R. H. Bolt, Eds., Wiley, New York, 1959).
9. Katchalski, E., and I. Z. Steinberg, *Ann. Rev. Phys. Chem.*, **12**, 433 (1961).
10. Doty, P., A. M. Holtzer, J. H. Bradbury, and E. R. Blout, *J. Am. Chem. Soc.*, **76**, 4493 (1954).
11. Doty, P., in *Sovremennye Problemy Biofiziki*, Vol. 1, IL, Moscow, 1961 (originally published as *Biophysical Science*: *A Study Program*, J. L. Oncley, F. O. Schmitt, R. C. Williams, M. D. Rosenberg, and R. H. Bolt, Ed., Wiley, New York, 1959).
12. Scheraga, H. A., *Ann. Rev. Phys. Chem.*, **10**, 191 (1959).
13. Schellman, J. A., *Compt. Rend. Trav. Lab., Carlsberg, Ser. Chim.*, **29**, 230 (1955).
14. Schellman, J. A., *J. Phys. Chem.*, **62**, 1485 (1958).
15. Rice, S. A., A. Wada, and E. P. Geiduschek, *Discussions Faraday Soc.*, **25**, 130 (1958).
16. Zimm, B. H., and J. K. Bragg, *J. Chem. Phys.*, **28**, 1246 (1958).
17. Gibbs, J. H., and E. A. Di Marzio, *J. Chem. Phys.*, **28**, 1247 (1958).
18. Rice, S. A., and A. Wada, *J. Chem. Phys.*, **29**, 233 (1958).
19. Gibbs, J. H., and E. A. Di Marzio, *J. Chem. Phys.*, **30**, 271 (1959).
20. Hill, T. L., *J. Chem. Phys.*, **30**, 383 (1959).
21. Peller, L., *J. Phys. Chem.*, **63**, 1194 (1959).
22. Peller, L., *J. Phys. Chem.*, **63**, 1199 (1959).
23. Zimm, B. H., and J. K. Bragg, *J. Chem. Phys.*, **31**, 526 (1959).
24. Nagai, K., *Busseiron Kenkyu*, **2–5**, 677 (1959).
25. Nagai, K., *J. Phys. Soc. Japan*, **15**, 407 (1960).
26. Steiner, R. F., *J. Chem. Phys.*, **32**, 215 (1960).
27. Zimm, B. H., and S. A. Rice, *Mol. Phys.*, **3**, 391 (1960).
28. Zimm, B. H., *J. Chem. Phys.*, **33**, 1349 (1960).

29. Nagai, K., *J. Chem. Phys.*, **34,** 887 (1961).
30. Lifson, S., and A. Roig, *J. Chem. Phys.*, **34,** 1963 (1961).
31. Birshtein, T. M., *Vysokomol. Soedin.*, **4,** 605 (1962).
32. Birshtein, T. M., *Biofizika*, **7,** 513 (1962).
33. Zimm, B. H., P. Doty, and K. Iso, *Proc. Natl. Acad. Sci., U.S.*, **45,** 1601 (1959).
34. Hill, T. L., *J. Polymer Sci.*, **23,** 549 (1957).
35. Landau, L. D., and E. Lifshits, *Statisticheskaya Fizika* (Statistical Physics), Gostekhisdat, Moscow, 1951.
36. Hill, T. L., *Statisticheskaya Mekhanika*, IL, Moscow, 1960 (originally published as *Statistical Mechanics*, McGraw-Hill, New York, 1956).
37. Baur, M. E., and L. H. Nosanow, *J. Chem. Phys.*, **37,** 153 (1962).
38. Flory, P. J., *J. Polymer Sci.*, **49,** 105 (1961).
39. Sukhorukov, B. I., Yu. S. Moshkovskii, T. M. Birshtein, and V. N. Lystsov, *Biofizika*, **8,** 294 (1963).
40. Doty, P., and J. T. Yang, *J. Am. Chem. Soc.*, **78,** 498 (1956).
41. Doty, P., J. H. Bradbury, and A. M. Holtzer, *J. Am. Chem. Soc.*, **78,** 947 (1956).
42. Doty, P., A. Wada, J. T. Yang, and E. R. Blout, *J. Polymer Sci.*, **23,** 851 (1957).
43. Ptitsyn, O. B., *Biofizika*, **7,** 257 (1962).
44. De Voe, H., and I. Tinoco, Jr., *J. Mol. Biol.*, **4,** 500 (1962)
45. Zimm, B. H., and N. R. Kallenbach, *Ann. Rev. Phys. Chem.*, **13,** 171 (1962).
46. Urnes, P. J., and P. Doty, *Adv. Protein Chem.*, **16,** 401 (1961).
47. Marmur, J., R. Rownd, and C. L. Schildkraut, *Progr. Nucleic Acid Res.*, **1,** 231 (1963).
48. Applequist, J., *J. Chem. Phys.*, **38,** 934 (1963).
49. Ozaki, M., M. Tanaka, and E. Teramoto, *J. Phys. Soc. Japan*, **18,** 551 (1963).
50. Lifson, S., and B. H. Zimm, *Biopolymers*, **1,** 15 (1963).
51. Lifson, S., *Biopolymers*, **1,** 25 (1963).
52. Mizushima, S., *Adv. Protein Chem.*, **9,** 299 (1954).
53. Kauzmann, W., *Adv. Protein Chem.*, **14,** 1 (1959).
54. Scheraga, H. A., *J. Phys. Chem.*, **65,** 1071 (1961).
55. Nemethy, G., I. Z. Steinberg, and H. S. Scheraga, *Biopolymers*, **1,** 43 (1963).
56. Mizushima, S., and T. Shimanouchi, *Adv. Enzymol.*, **23,** 1 (1961).
57. Baur, M. E., and L. H. Nosanow, *J. Chem. Phys.*, **38,** 578 (1963).
58. Applequist, J., and P. Doty, in *Polyamino Acids, Polypeptides and Proteins*, M.. Stahmann, Ed., Univ. of Wisconsin Press, Madison, Wis., 1962, p. 161.
59. Bresler, S. E., *Vvedenie v Molekulyarnuyu Biologiyu* (Introduction to Molecular Biology), Izdatel'stvo Akad. Nauk SSSR, Moscow, 1963.
60. Ptitsyn, O. B., and A. M. Skvortsov, *Biofizika*, **10,** 6 (1965).
61. Nemethy, G., and H. A. Scheraga, *J. Chem. Phys.*, **36,** 3382 (1962).

Chapter 10

EFFECT OF EXTERNAL FACTORS ON CONFORMATIONAL TRANSITIONS IN POLYPEPTIDE CHAINS

10.1. Effect of Specific Interactions with the Solvent

In the preceding chapter we have presented the theory of conformational transitions (of the helix–coil type) which occur in polypeptide chains with changes in temperature. As has been shown experimentally, however, such transitions can occur also with a change in any other property of the surrounding medium which has an influence on the equilibrium constant of intramolecular hydrogen-bond formation. Thus, if the molecule is placed into a two-component solvent, one of the components of which is capable of forming hydrogen bonds with amino acid residues, such intermolecular bonding will be specific, i.e., it can take place only in monomer units which are not bonded by intramolecular hydrogen bonds. It is evident that the presence of intermolecular bonding will have an effect on the helix–coil transition. The theory of this effect can be developed by generalizing the method of developing the partition function of the macromolecule presented in the previous chapter.

In the presence of intramolecular bonding, each monomer unit of the chain can be present in one of three states: without a hydrogen bond or with an intramolecular or intermolecular hydrogen bond. If the intermolecular bonding is not cooperative, i.e., if it takes place independently in neighboring monomer units, then, in the development of the partition function of the chain, it is sufficient to consider that each monomer unit which is not bonded by an intramolecular hydrogen bond contributes to the partition function a factor of $(1 + a)$ and not 1, where $a = e^{\mu/kT}$ is the ratio of the activities of a monomer unit in the state in which it is bonded by an intermolecular hydrogen bond and in the free state, while μ is the difference between the chemical potentials of the monomer units in these two states (i.e., the change in free energy of a monomer unit in the course of intermolecular bonding); this was done in the papers of Gibbs and Di

Marzio (1) and Peller (2). Then each element of matrix G [see eq. (9.13)] contains either a factor $(1 + a)$, if the corresponding monomer unit is not bonded by an intramolecular hydrogen bond, or a factor s, if such a bond is formed.

Factoring $(1 + a)$ out of all the elements of matrix G, we find that

$$G(s, \sigma, a) = (1 + a)G(s^*, \sigma) \tag{10.1}$$

where $G(s^*, \sigma)$ is a matrix defined by eq. (9.13), with s replaced by

$$s^* = s/(1 + a) \tag{10.2}$$

Here, as before, s is the equilibrium constant between states of the monomer unit in which it is bonded by an intramolecular hydrogen bond and in which it is free, while s^* is the equilibrium constant between the states in which it is bonded by an intramolecular hydrogen bond and in which it is not bonded by such a bond (i.e., free or bonded by an intermolecular hydrogen bond). Consequently, the eigenvalues of matrix $G(s, \sigma, a)$ are equal to $(1 + a)\,\lambda\,(s^*, \sigma)$, where $\lambda(s^*, \sigma)$ are the roots of eq. (9.14) in which s has been replaced by s^*.

It is evident, therefore, that the condition for helix–coil transition is now not the equality $s = 1$, but the equality $s^* = 1$. For example, in the hypothetical limiting case of an entirely cooperative transition ($\sigma = 0$), the partition function of the chain is

$$Z = (1 + a)^n(1 + s^{*n}) = (1 + a)^n + s^n \tag{10.3}$$

so that (with $n \gg 1$)

$$Z = \begin{cases} s^n & \text{For } s > 1 + a, \text{ i.e., } s^* > 1 \\ (1 + a)^n & \text{For } s < 1 + a, \text{ i.e., } s^* < 1 \end{cases} \tag{10.4}$$

The condition for transition, $s^* = 1$, is a function of the ratio between the monomer unit activities in states in which it is bonded by an intermolecular hydrogen bond and in which it is free; this is equal to

$$a = Ka' \tag{10.5}$$

where K is the equilibrium constant for intermolecular bonding, while a, is the activity of the solvent component which is specifically bound. Therefore, *in the presence of specific intermolecular bonding, the helix–coil transition can be modulated not only by a change in temperature at a fixed solvent composition, but also by a change in the solvent composition at a fixed temperature.* In both cases, the transition takes place in the range $1 - \sqrt{\sigma} \leqslant s^* \leqslant 1 + \sqrt{\sigma}$, i.e., if the transition takes place over a narrow interval of change in s, it takes place as well over a narrow interval of change in concentration.

It is evident that, with an increase in the activity (i.e., concentration) of the solvent component which is bound specifically, the transition point T_m, is displaced in the direction of lower temperatures. From eqs. (9.9) and (10.2) and the condition that $s^* = 1$, we obtain (2)

$$T_m = \frac{\Delta H}{\Delta S - k \ln (1 + a)} = \frac{T_m^0}{1 - (kT_m^0/\Delta H) \ln (1 + a)} \tag{10.6}$$

where

$$T_m^0 = \Delta H/\Delta S \tag{10.7}$$

is the transition temperature in the absence of specific bonding with solvent molecules. Equation (10.6), which describes the change in the helix–coil transition temperature when a component which competes for hydrogen bonds with groups of the polypeptide chain is introduced into the composition of the solvent, was derived by Schellman (3,4) by a thermodynamic method and by Peller (2) from a statistical examination. Expanding eq. (10.6) in series in a for small values of a, we obtain (2)

$$\begin{aligned} T_m &= T_m^0[1 + (kT_m^0/\Delta H)a] \\ &= T_m^0[1 + (kT_m^0/\Delta H)Ka'] \end{aligned} \tag{10.8}$$

Equation (10.8) shows that (when $\Delta H < 0$) the introduction into the solvent of a specifically bound component usually decreases the temperature of melting; furthermore, this decrease is proportional to the activity a' (and to the concentration, at low values of a') of the component introduced. Equation (10.8) is equivalent to the usual equation for the lowering of the temperature of crystallization of the solvent when a substance insoluble in the solid phase is dissolved in it. The decrease in the temperature of the conformational change with an increase in the concentration of the solvent component which competes for hydrogen bonds with groups of the polypeptide chain has been observed in a large number of experimental studies. As was pointed out in section 9.1, the discovery of helix–coil transitions was made by Doty, Holtzer, Bradbury, and Blout (5) with a solution of poly-γ-benzyl-L-glutamate in a mixture of chloroform with dichloroacetic acid; this transition was determined by an increase in the content of dichloroacetic acid [see also (6)]. Later, conformational changes with a change in solvent composition were examined by a number of authors in solutions of different polypeptides (8–10,37,38). As an example, we give Figure 10.1, which is taken from the paper of Fasman (38), in which

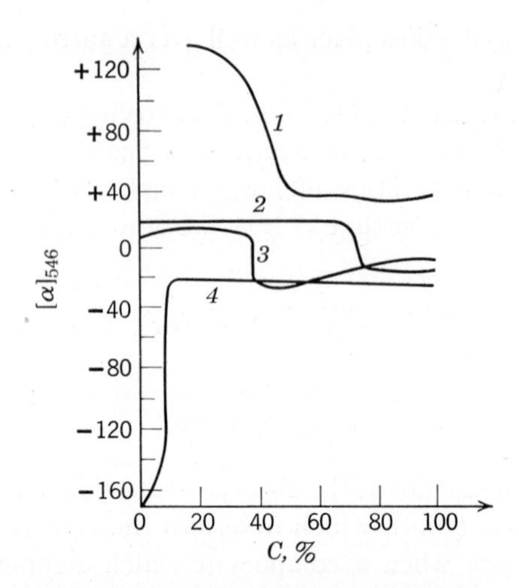

Fig. 10.1 Specific rotation of the plane of polarization $[\alpha]$ (at $\lambda = 546$ mμ) of a number of polypeptides as a function of the dichloroacetic acid content c of a chloroform–dichloroacetic acid mixed solvent: (*1*) poly-*O*-acetyl-L-serine; (*2*) poly-γ-benzyl-L-glutamate; (*3*) poly-ϵ-carbobenzoxy-L-lysine; (*4*) poly-β-benzyl-L-aspartate (38).

the dependence of the specific rotation of the plane of polarization $[\alpha]$ (at $\lambda = 546$ mμ) on the solvent composition in mixtures of dichloroacetic acid with chloroform is shown for a number of polypeptides. The breaks in the curves correspond to conformational transitions which take place, as has been pointed out above, with an increase in the content of dichloroacetic acid. From Figure 10.1 it is possible to judge the relative stability of the helical conformation in different polypeptides. For example, it can be seen from it that this conformation is more stable in poly-γ-benzyl-L-glutamate than in poly-ϵ-carbobenzoxy-L-lysine, since in the first case the helix–coil transition takes place at 68% dichloroacetic acid, while in the second case 36% dichloroacetic acid is sufficient.

10.2. Helix–Coil Transitions in Chains Which Contain Ionizable Groups

Interaction with solvent can have an effect on helix–coil transitions also in those cases in which, while it is not specific (i.e., it does not take place only in free monomer units), it nevertheless changes the energy and/or the entropy of melting of the helix. The most striking examples of such an interaction are met in polypeptide chains which contain ionizable groups, for example in polyaspartic acid $[-CO-CH(CH_2COOH)-NH-]_n$, polyglutamic acid $[-CO-CH(CH_2CH_2COOH)-NH-]_n$, polylysine

[—CO—CH$(CH_2)_4NH_2$—NH—]$_n$, etc. The acid or basic group in such chains can ionize with a change of the hydrogen ion concentration in solution, i.e., with a change in pH. The ionization of these groups changes in different ways the free energy of the chain in the coiled and helical states and, thus, displaces the temperature of the helix–coil transition. In such cases the transition can be investigated not only by methods based on a change in the fraction ϑ of chain monomer units bonded by intramolecular hydrogen bonds, but also by methods which measure the degree of ionization α (the fraction of charged chain monomer units), i.e., by studying the titration curves of the macromolecules. The statistical theory of helix–coil transitions in polypeptide chains which contain ionizable groups and also the titration theory of such chains were developed in the studies of Peller (2) and Zimm and Rice (11). Peller has calculated the partition function by the method of the largest term, while Zimm and Rice used the matrix method of the Ising model described above.

Following Zimm and Rice, let us write out the expression for the partition function of an ionizable polypeptide chain. The state of each monomer unit in the chain is characterized in this case by two sets of variables: (*1*) by the presence or absence of a hydrogen bond ($\mu_i = 1$ or 0) and (*2*) by the presence or absence of a charge on the ionizable group ($\eta_i = 1$ or 0). The partition function of the chain has the form:

$$Z = \sum_{\{\mu_i\}} e^{-F(\{\mu_i\})/kT} \sum_{\{\eta_i\}} \prod_{i=1}^{n} a^{\eta_i} e^{-F^{(e)}_{\{\mu_i\}}(\{\eta_i\})/kT} \tag{10.9}$$

where $F(\{\mu_i\})$ is the free energy of the uncharged chain at a given set of $\{\mu_i\}$ defined by eqs. (9.1)–(9.8), a is the ratio of activities of charged and uncharged monomer units, $F^{(e)}_{\{\mu_i\}}(\{\eta_i\})$ is the free energy of the electrostatic interaction of the charged groups, which is a function of $\{\mu_i\}$ and $\{\eta_i\}$, while summation is carried out over all possible states of intramolecular bonding in the chain $\{\mu_i\}$ and all possible states of ionization of the monomer units $\{\eta_i\}$. The quantity a is related to the hydrogen ion concentration in the solvent by the obvious relation [see eq. (10.5)]:

$$\log a = \pm (\mathrm{pH} - \mathrm{p}K) \tag{10.10}$$

where pH is the negative logarithm of the concentration of hydrogen ions in solution, and pK is the negative logarithm of the intrinsic dissociation constant of the ionizable group (in the absence of interactions with other groups). The plus and minus signs in eq. (10.10) refer to acid and basic ionizable groups, respectively.

Equation (10.9) takes into account the fact that the ionization of monomer units, which takes place with a change in pH, results in electrostatic repulsion between them; furthermore, the extent of this repulsion is a function of the conformations of the chain, defined by the quantities μ_i. It is easy to see that electrostatic repulsion between the nearest ionizable groups, which plays the main role, is on the average greater for helical than coiled regions of the chain. In fact, winding of the chain into an α-helix brings some of the nearest ionizable groups together to distances considerably smaller than in the coiled regions, in which the short-range order corresponds to chain conformations that are stretched to the limit. Thus, according to Zimm and Rice (11), in the case of polyglutamic acid, the distances between the charge of an ionizable COOH group and its four nearest neighbors are equal to, in the helical form, 10.1, 13.1, 7.9, and 7.5 Å, while in the coiled state these are ~10, ~10, ~10, and ~16 Å. It follows from this that *the electrostatic interaction in a charged polypeptide chain must stabilize the coiled structure.*

In the simplest case of $\sigma = 0$, eq. (10.9) obviously gives [compare eqs. (9.21) and (9.22)]

$$Z = Z_{\text{coil}}^{(e)} + s^n Z_{\text{hel.}}^{(e)} \tag{10.11}$$

where

$$Z_{\text{coil}}^{(e)} = \sum_{\{\eta_i\}} \prod_{i=1}^{n} a^{\eta_i} e^{-F_{\{0\}}^{(e)}(\{\eta_i\})/kT}$$

and (10.12)

$$Z_{\text{hel.}}^{(e)} = \sum_{\{\eta_i\}} \prod_{i=1}^{n} a^{\eta_i} e^{-F_{\{1\}}^{(e)}(\{\eta_i\})/kT}$$

are the ratios of the partition functions of partly charged and uncharged macromolecules in entirely coiled and entirely helical states, respectively. If in eq. (10.11) we take into account the electrostatic interaction of only a small number of m neighboring charged groups, then

$$F^{(e)}(\{\eta_i\}) = \sum_{i=1}^{n} F^{(e)}(\eta_{i-m}, \ldots, \eta_i)$$

and

$$Z_{\text{coil}}^{(e)} = \text{Sp}(G_{\text{coil}}^{(e)})^n = (\lambda_{\text{coil}}^{(e)})^n \tag{10.13}$$

$$Z_{\text{hel.}}^{(e)} = \text{Sp}(G_{\text{hel.}}^{(e)})^n = (\lambda_{\text{hel.}}^{(e)})^n$$

where $\lambda_{\text{coil}}^{(e)}$ and $\lambda_{\text{hel.}}^{(e)}$ are the largest eigenvalues of matrices $G_{\text{coil}}^{(e)}$ and $G_{\text{hel.}}^{(e)}$ respectively, composed of the quantities $a^{\eta_i}e^{-F^{(e)}(\eta_{i-m},\ldots,\eta_i)/kT}$ (see section 4.1). From eqs. (10.11) and (10.13), we have, with $n \gg 1$:

$$Z = \begin{cases} (\lambda_{\text{coil}}^{(e)})^n & \text{For } s\lambda_{\text{hel.}}^{(e)} < \lambda_{\text{coil}}^{(e)}, \text{ i.e., } s^* < 1 \\ s^{(n)}(\lambda_{\text{hel.}}^{(e)})^n & \text{For } s\lambda_{\text{hel.}}^{(e)} > \lambda_{\text{coil}}^{(e)}, \text{ i.e., } s^* > 1 \end{cases} \quad (10.14)$$

where

$$s^* = s(\lambda_{\text{hel.}}^{(e)}/\lambda_{\text{coil}}^{(e)}) \quad (10.15)$$

is the equilibrium constant between a monomer unit in the states in which it is bonded by a hydrogen bond and in which it is free in a partly charged chain.

We see that, in a partly charged chain, the helix–coil transition takes place at $s^* = 1$, i.e., at $s = \lambda_{\text{hel.}}^{(e)}/\lambda_{\text{coil}}^{(e)}$; however, $\lambda_{\text{hel.}}^{(e)} < \lambda_{\text{coil}}^{(e)}$ since the electrostatic interactions are larger in the helical than in the coiled chain. Therefore, in a partly ionized macromolecule, the helix–coil transition takes place at $s > 1$ (with $\Delta H < 0$), i.e., it is shifted towards lower temperatures. Since the ratio $\lambda_{\text{hel.}}^{(e)}/\lambda_{\text{coil}}^{(e)}$ decreases with a change in pH that results in an increase in the degree of ionization of the chain α, the shift is greater for larger α. In other words, the increasing of the degree of ionization of molecules at a solution temperature at which the molecule is present in the helical state but which is not very far from the transition temperature in uncharged chains results in a transition of the molecules into the coiled state.

The principal results, obtained above by an elementary analysis of the partition function of the ionizable polypeptide chain at $\sigma = 0$, remain valid also at values of σ which differ from zero. The calculation of the partition function (10.9) in this general case, however, meets serious difficulties, since, in calculating the states of the system, it is necessary to take into account all the possible combinations of the quantities μ_i and η_i which describe the presence or absence of hydrogen bonds and charges in different monomer units. This, obviously, raises the order of matrix G and renders more difficult the calculation of its eigenvalues. In order to obviate this difficulty, Zimm and Rice (11) have used a simplified model (compare section 9.1) in which the impossibility of breaking less than three consecutive hydrogen bonds is neglected. In this, the order of matrix G turns out to be 2×2^m, if the electrostatic interaction of monomer units with m neighbors on each side is taken into account (matrix G corresponding to the entire partition function would have had the order 7×2^m). In the paper

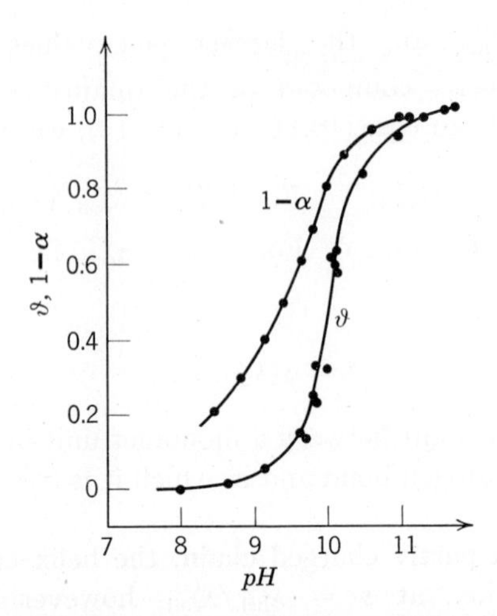

Fig. 10.2. Dependence of the fraction ϑ of monomer units bonded by hydrogen bonds on pH for aqueous solutions of poly-L-lysine and titration curve of the molecule (7).

of Zimm and Rice (11), $m = 4$, i.e., the "simplified" matrix G is of the 32nd order. The authors were able to calculate, with the help of an electronic computer, the largest eigenvalue of this matrix (at small σ) and to construct theoretical curves of the dependence of the fraction of bonded monomer units, ϑ, on temperature and pH of the medium. As should have been expected, with $\sigma \approx 10^{-4}$ [the value of σ in poly-γ-benzyl-L-glutamate, (see section 9.1)] the helix–coil transition occurs over a narrow pH range. This is confirmed in Figure 10.2, which shows the dependence of ϑ on pH of the medium for poly-L-lysine; these results were obtained by Applequist and Doty (7).

As has been pointed out above, conformational transitions in polypeptide chains can be studied as well from the dependence of the degree of ionization of the macromolecule on the pH of the solution, i.e., from the titration curves. The degree of ionization α of a macromolecule at a given pH can be obtained from the partition function of the chain, eq. (10.9), by differentiating it with respect to the ratio of activities of charged and uncharged monomer units.

$$\alpha = (1/n)\partial \ln Z/\partial \ln a \tag{10.16}$$

where the quantity a is related to the pH of the solution by eq. (10.10). In the absence of interactions between the charged groups, $F^{(e)}_{\{\mu_i\}}(\{\eta_i\}, = 0$, and from eqs. (10.9) and (10.16) it is easy to obtain $\alpha = a/(1 + a)$. In other words, in this case the activities of the charged and uncharged monomer units are equal to their concentrations in the chain, so that $a = \alpha/(1 - \alpha)$, and the titration curve has the form

$$\mathrm{pH} = \mathrm{p}K \pm \log [\alpha/(1 - \alpha)] \quad (10.17)$$

As before, the plus and minus signs refer to polyacid and polybase, respectively.

Because of the presence of interaction between charged groups, the ionization of each subsequent group requires the expenditure of additional work due to the increase in the energy of electrostatic repulsion between similarly charged groups of the chain. As a result, as the degree of ionization of the polyacid changes, the dissociation constant of each subsequent group turns out to be smaller than that of the previous one. Thus, as the chain becomes ionized, the effective dissociation constant K decreases while its negative logarithm, pK, increases. The titration curve of a macromolecule with interacting charged groups can then be written in the form

$$\mathrm{pH} = \mathrm{p}K_0 + \log \frac{\alpha}{1 - \alpha} + \Delta\mathrm{p}K(\alpha) \quad (10.18)$$

where $\Delta\mathrm{p}K(\alpha) = \mathrm{p}K(\alpha) - \mathrm{p}K_0$, and p$K_0$ is the value of pK extrapolated to $\alpha = 0$.

The increase in the energy of electrostatic repulsion in the macromolecule with an increase of α, which determines the increase of pK, is partly compensated by the decrease in the energy of the polymer–solvent system as a result of stronger attraction to the chain of low molecular weight gegenions retained in the neighborhood of the macromolecule by its electrostatic potential. Formally, this effect may be described as a decrease of the interactions of the charged groups of the chain as a result of their screening by gegenions. An approximate theory of the effect on pK of the interaction of the macromolecule with gegenions has been developed in the paper of Kotin and Nagasawa (36), in which the degree of bonding of gegenions by the ionized chain was calculated on the basis of a solution of the nonlinearized Poisson-Boltzmann equation.

The increase in the value of pK with an increase of α is determined first of all by the increase in the energy of repulsion of rather closely located charged groups of the chain as it becomes ionized (the effect of interactions between distant charged groups is apparently small). The theory of this effect (28–35) relates the quantity $\Delta\mathrm{p}K(\alpha)$ at high ionic strength to the distance between neighboring and nearest nonneighboring charged groups of the chain and, thus, to the conformations of monomer units.

Returning to polypeptide chains, let us note that, since in their case the electrostatic interactions between closely located charged groups are different for helical and coiled conformations, the titration curves of the two forms must also be different. For example, it follows from evaluations, cited above, of the distances between close charged groups in the helical and coiled chains that, at a given value of pH, a helical macromolecule must be less charged than a coiled one. Therefore, it is evident that, *in the region of a helix–coil transition initiation by a change of the pH of the solution, the degree of ionization of the macromolecule must increase rather sharply.* The relation between the degree of ionization of the molecule undergoing the conformational change and the degree of ionization of the two extreme conformations can be calculated easily in the case of an entirely cooperative system. From eqs. (10.11) and (10.13) we obtain

$$Z = Z_{\text{coil}}^{(e)}[1 + (s\lambda_{\text{hel.}}^{(e)}/\lambda_{\text{coil}}^{(e)})^n] = Z_{\text{coil}}^{(e)}Z_0(s^*) \tag{10.19}$$

where Z_0 has the form of the partition function of the nonionized macromolecule in which the equilibrium constant s has been replaced by equilibrium constant s^*, defined by eq. (10.15).

From eq. (10.19) it follows that

$$\begin{aligned} \alpha &= \frac{1}{n}\frac{\partial \ln Z}{\partial \ln a} \\ &= \frac{1}{n}\frac{\partial \ln Z_{\text{coil}}^{(e)}}{\partial \ln a} + \frac{1}{n}\frac{\partial \ln Z_0(s^*)}{\partial \ln s^*}\frac{\partial \ln s^*}{\partial \ln a} \\ &= \alpha_{\text{coil}} + \vartheta(\alpha_{\text{hel.}} - \alpha_{\text{coil}}) \end{aligned} \tag{10.20}$$

where $\alpha_{\text{hel.}}$ and α_{coil} are the degrees of ionization of purely helical and purely coiled molecules, respectively, at the given value of the solution pH, while ϑ is, as before, the fraction of monomer units bonded by hydrogen bonds. Thus, the degree of ionization of the molecule undergoing a conformational transition is simply the average degree of ionization of helical and coiled regions of the chain, and the averaging is carried out taking into account the fractions of monomer units in these regions (2):

$$\alpha = \vartheta\alpha_{\text{hel.}} + (1 - \vartheta)\alpha_{\text{coil}} \tag{10.21}$$

Equation (10.21) has been derived for macromolecules in which $\sigma = 0$, i.e., for chains in each of which the helix–coil transition takes place according to the all-or-none principle. For such chains, this equation is absolutely obvious, since in this case some of the molecules are present in the purely

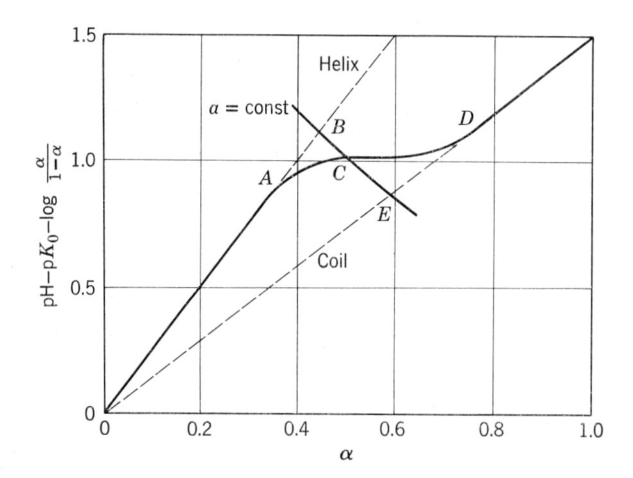

Fig. 10.3. Titration curve of a polyacid during helix–coil transition. Dashed lines are titration curves of a helix and a coil. The line BCE corresponds to a constant value of the activity a. The area OACD is equal to log s, the area OBE is equal to log $(\lambda_{coil}/\lambda_{hel.})$.

helical state, while others are in the purely coiled state in the region of transition. However, in real cases as well, when $\sigma \neq 0$, eq. (10.21) remains approximately valid if σ is sufficiently small, i.e., if the helical and coiled regions in each macromolecule are sufficiently long. In fact, in this case, junctions between helical and coiled regions are so few, that the difference in electrostatic interaction at the junctions from that within the regions does not make a significant contribution to the partition function of the chain.

From equation (10.21) it follows, for example, that since ϑ changes from 0 to 1 within a narrow pH interval (see above), *the titration curve of a polypeptide chain undergoes a more or less sharp transition from the titration curve of coiled chain to that of a helix.* The general form of the titration curve of a polypeptide chain containing acid groups and capable of helix–coil transition is shown in Figure 10.3. For the sake of convenience the quantity pH $-$ pK_0-log $[\alpha/(1-\alpha)]$, which describes directly the effect of the interaction of charged groups on the titration curve, is plotted along the ordinate, and not the pH. As expected, in the case of noninteracting groups, this quantity is reduced to zero at all degrees of ionization α, while for interacting groups, it increases with an increase of α, the increase being greater, the greater the electrostatic interaction between the groups. It can be seen from Figure 10.3 that, at some value of pH $-$ pK which

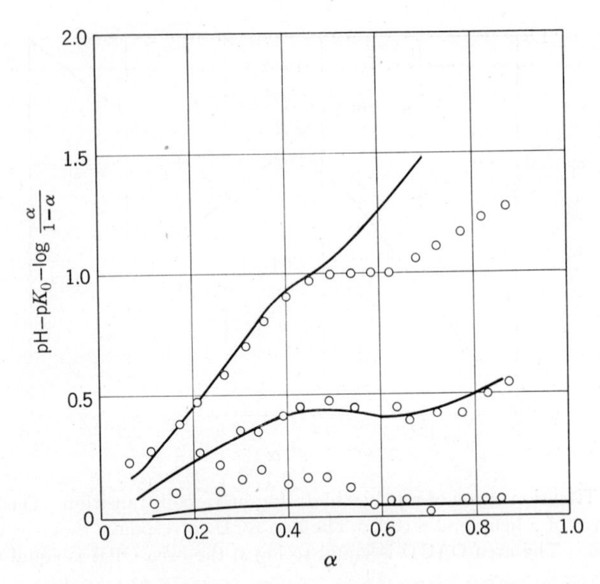

Fig. 10.4. Titration curves of polyglutamic acid in (*a*) $0.0133N$, (*b*) $0.133N$, and (*c*) $1.33N$ aqueous solutions of NaCl: (○) experimental data; (——) theoretical curves with $\sigma = 10^{-4}$ and $s = 1.114$.

depends on the value of the equilibrium constant s for an uncharged monomer unit, i.e., on the temperature, the curve of the dependence on α of the quantity $\mathrm{pH} - \mathrm{p}K_0 - \log [\alpha/(1 - \alpha)]$ undergoes an inflection which corresponds to the transition from the helical (at small α and small pH) to the coiled form of the molecule [see eq. (10.21)].

Interesting results have been obtained for poly-L-lysine (7), for which a comparison was made of the curves of the dependence of the fraction of hydrogen bonds ϑ and of the degree of ionization α on the solution pH (see Fig. 10.2). It was found that, in the case of an aqueous solution of poly-L-lysine (in the absence of low molecular weight ions), the change of α from 0.8 to 0.6 (as the pH increases from 8.4 to 9.2) occurs in an almost entirely coiled molecule ($\vartheta < 0.05$). A comparison of the experimental titration curve (7) at $\alpha < 0.6$ with the dependence of α_{coil} on pH, extrapolated by use of a semiempirical expression to the region of high pH, has shown that the entire titration curve has the form $\alpha = \alpha_{\mathrm{coil}}(1 - \vartheta)$, i.e., the ionization of the monomer units is practically entirely forbidden in a helix ($\alpha_{\mathrm{hel.}} \approx 0$) because of the large electrostatic interaction between close, charged groups. Addition of gegenions to the solution results in a departure of $\alpha_{\mathrm{hel.}}$ from zero.

Titration curves of real polypeptide chains with $\sigma \neq 0$ can be calculated by calculating their partition function by the method described above in connection with the calculation of the fraction of bonded monomer units.

Titration curves of polyglutamic acid, calculated by Zimm and Rice (11) using eqs. (10.9), (10.10), and (10.16), are shown on Figure 10.4; here the electrostatic interaction of the ionized groups with four neighbors in each direction was calculated, as has been pointed out already. The curves are compared with experimental data obtained by Wada (12,13)* in aqueous solutions of NaCl of different ionic strengths. The equilibrium constant s for uncharged groups, which enters into the theory, was selected in such a way as to obtain the best agreement with experiment ($s = 1.114$), while the cooperativeness parameter σ was taken from experimental data on the helix–coil transitions of poly-γ-benzyl-L-glutamate in nonaqueous solvents [$\sigma \approx 10^{-4}$, (16)] (see section 9.3). Considering the relative roughness of the starting assumptions, the agreement between theory and experiment is amazingly good. It shows, for example, that the degree of cooperativeness of the transition in poly-L-glutamic acid is close to that in poly-γ-benzyl-L-glutamate.

Let us note that the measurement of titration curves consists in the simultaneous determination of two canonically related quantities: the degree of ionization α and the ratio of the activities of charged and uncharged groups a, which are related to each other by eq. (10.16). As has been pointed out by Zimm and Rice (11), this permits one to determine the partition function of the chain by means of graphical integration of the experimental titration curves and to calculate from it the equilibrium constants of uncharged and partly charged monomer units s and $s^* = s\lambda_{\text{hel.}}^{(e)}/\lambda_{\text{coil}}^{(e)}$. Thus, the value of the logarithm of the equilibrium constant s for the uncharged chain is equal to the area enclosed between the curve of the dependence of $\text{pH} - \text{p}K_0 - \log[\alpha/(1-\alpha)]$ on α for a molecule which is undergoing a transition and of a similar curve for a hypothetically entirely coiled molecule. (The last curve is obtained by extrapolating the data obtained at large α to the region of small α.) The logarithm of the ratio $\lambda_{\text{hel.}}^{(e)}/\lambda_{\text{coil}}^{(e)}$ of the partition functions of a monomer unit in a purely helical and a purely coiled chain at a given $\text{pH} = \text{pH}_0$ is determined from the difference in the areas between the extrapolated titration curves for a pure helix and a pure coil, limited by the values of pH_0 (see Fig. 10.2). The measurement of titration curves at different temperatures permits, in principle, one to establish the temperature de-

* The titration curves of polyglutamic acid were studied by Goldstein and Katchalski also (14).

pendence of the constant s, i.e., to determine the heat of transition in an uncharged chain. Regrettably, such experiments have not been performed up to now. On the other hand, a study of the temperature dependence of melting curves of partly ionized macromolecules makes it possible (with known σ) to determine the temperature dependence of s^*, i.e., the heat of transition in a partly charged chain. As has been pointed out in section 9.3, the heats of transition of poly-L-glutamic acid and poly-L-lysine have been determined in this manner.

10.3. Effect of an External Force

Let us pass now to an examination of the effect of an external force on the helix–coil transition in polypeptide chains. The importance of this problem is determined by the fact, pointed out by Flory (17–21), that intramolecular conformational transitions in polypeptide chains determine the elastic properties of fibrous proteins (collagen, elastin, myosin) and, as a result, can be basically related to the mechanism of muscle contraction. For example, the strong shrinking of collagen fibers when they are heated to a given temperature (which is a function of the surrounding medium) is explained by a helix–coil transition in individual molecules, similar to the transition observed in highly dilute solutions (17,22). In order to treat quantitatively the effect of intramolecular conformational transitions on the elastic properties of fibrous proteins, it is necessary to extend the theory presented above by examining the effect of an external force on the helix–coil transition in polypeptide chains. Flory (18,23) [see also (24)] has presented a thermodynamic analysis of such an effect for uncharged polypeptide chains, while Birshtein, Vorobyov, and Ptitsyn (25) have examined qualitatively the case of charged polypeptide chains. Finally, Birshtein (26) has developed a statistical theory of the helix–coil transition in polypeptide chains which are present in a field of external force (for the model of a one-dimensional chain).

A general statistical treatment of the effect of an external force on helix–coil transitions can be carried out easily [compare (25)] in a manner similar to that used above for the effect of electrostatic interaction. For a chain located in a field of external force, we have

$$Z = \sum_{\{\mu_i\}} e^{-F\{\mu_i\}/kT} \sum_{\{\vartheta_i\}\,\{\mu_i\}} e^{-\Phi^{(f)}_{\{\mu_i\}}(\{\vartheta_i\})/kT} \tag{10.22}$$

where $F\{\mu_i\}$ is the thermodynamic potential of the chain in the absence of an external force (identical with its free energy), $\Phi^{(f)}_{\{\mu_i\}}\{\vartheta_i\}$ is the change of the thermodynamic potential of the chain in a field of external force f, while summation is carried out over all possible sets $\{\vartheta_i\}_{\{\mu_i\}}$ of orientations of monomer units in the field f consistent with the given set of their states $\{\mu_i\}$ and over all sets of $\{\mu_i\}$. In the simplest case of the absolute co-operativeness of the system ($\sigma = 0$), eq. (10.22) gives [see eqs. (10.11), (10.12)]:

$$Z = Z^{(f)}_{\text{coil}} + s^n Z^{(f)}_{\text{hel.}} \tag{10.23}$$

where

$$Z^{(f)}_{\text{coil}} = \sum_{\{\vartheta_i\}} e^{-\Phi^{(f)}_{\{0\}}(\{\vartheta_i\})/kT}$$

and (10.24)

$$Z^{(f)}_{\text{hel.}} = \sum_{\{\vartheta_i\}} e^{-\Phi^{(f)}_{\{1\}}(\{\vartheta_i\})/kT}$$

are the partition functions of the macromolecule in a field of external force (relative to the partition functions in the absence of an external force) in the totally coiled state and the totally helical state, respectively. Since the orientation of each monomer unit is determined by the orientation of a small number m of preceding monomer units,

$$\Phi^{(f)}_{\{\mu_i\}}(\{\vartheta_i\}) = \sum_{i=1}^{n} \Phi^{(f)}_{\{\mu_i\}}(\vartheta_{i-m},\ldots,\vartheta_i) \tag{10.25}$$

and

$$Z^{(f)}_{\text{coil}} = \text{Sp}\,(G^{(f)}_{\text{coil}})^n = (\lambda^{(f)}_{\text{coil}})^n$$

$$Z^{(f)}_{\text{hel.}} = \text{Sp}\,(G^{(f)}_{\text{hel.}})^n = (\lambda^{(f)}_{\text{hel.}})^n \tag{10.26}$$

[compare eqs. (10.13)], where $\lambda^{(f)}_{\text{coil}}$ and $\lambda^{(f)}_{\text{hel.}}$ are the largest eigenvalues of matrices $G^{(f)}_{\text{coil}}$ and $G^{(f)}_{\text{hel.}}$, respectively, composed of the quantities $\exp\{-\Phi^{(f)}_{\{\mu_i\}}(\vartheta_{i-m}, \ldots, \vartheta_i)/kT\}$.

From eqs. (10.23) and (10.26) we obtain, when $n \gg 1$,

$$Z = \begin{cases} (\lambda^{(f)}_{\text{coil}})^n & s\lambda^{(f)}_{\text{hel.}} < \lambda^{(f)}_{\text{coil}},\ \text{i.e.,}\ s^* < 1 \\ s^n(\lambda^{(f)}_{\text{hel.}})^n & s\lambda^{(f)}_{\text{hel.}} > \lambda^{(f)}_{\text{coil}},\ \text{i.e.,}\ s^* > 1 \end{cases} \tag{10.27}$$

where

$$s^* = s\lambda^{(f)}_{\text{hel.}}/\lambda^{(f)}_{\text{coil}} \tag{10.28}$$

is the equilibrium constant between a monomer unit of a chain located in a field of external force in the state in which the monomer unit is bonded by a hydrogen bond and the state in which it is free.

It follows from eq. (10.27) that the helix–coil transition in a chain which is under the influence of an external force will take place when $s^* = 1$, i.e., when $s = \lambda_{\text{coil}}^{(f)}/\lambda_{\text{hel}}^{(f)}$. In order to examine the quantity $\lambda_{\text{coil}}^{(f)}/\lambda_{\text{hel.}}^{(f)}$, let us note that the average projections of the distances between the ends of coiled and helical chains on the direction of the external force are equal to, respectively,

$$\begin{aligned} \bar{x}_{\text{coil}} &= nkTd \ln \lambda_{\text{coil}}^{(f)}/df \\ \bar{x}_{\text{hel.}} &= nkTd \ln \lambda_{\text{hel.}}^{(f)}/df \end{aligned} \tag{10.29}$$

Consequently,

$$\ln \frac{\lambda_{\text{coil}}^{(f)}}{\lambda_{\text{hel.}}^{(f)}} = \frac{1}{kT} \int_0^f (\bar{x}_{\text{coil}} - \bar{x}_{\text{hel.}}) df \tag{10.30}$$

Equation (10.30) shows that the effect of an external force on the helix–coil transition is determined by the dependencies of $\bar{x}$ on f for the coiled and helical chains. These dependencies are shown schematically in Figure 10.5, from which it is evident that when f is small, $\bar{x}_{\text{hel.}} > \bar{x}_{\text{coil}}$ (since it is easier to orient a rigid helix than to unwind a coil), while when f is large, $\bar{x}_{\text{coil}} > \bar{x}_{\text{hel.}}$ (since, in principle, the coil can be unwound to a state close to the completely stretched β-form). Therefore, when f is not very large (when $\bar{x}_{\text{coil}} < \bar{x}_{\text{hel.}}$), $\lambda_{\text{coil}}^{(f)} < \lambda_{\text{hel.}}^{(f)}$, i.e., the helix–coil transition takes place with $s < 1$; the external force stabilizes the helical conformation and shifts the helix–coil transition toward higher temperatures. The shift is maximal if the external force is such that $\bar{x}_{\text{coil}} = \bar{x}_{\text{hel.}}$ and then decreases with a further increase of the force [a positive term appears in the integral in

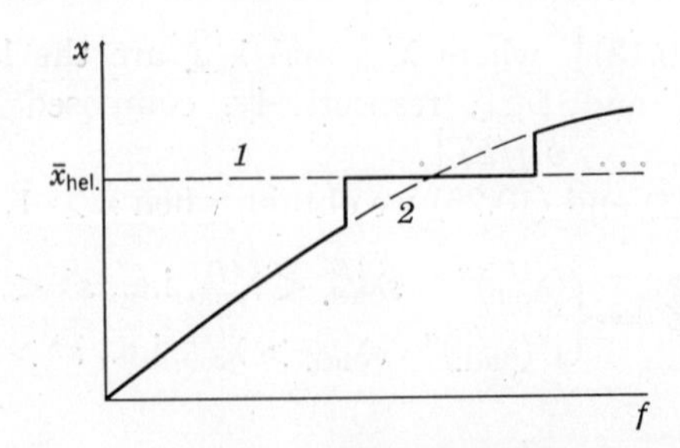

Fig. 10.5. Curves of the deformation of a polypeptide chain: (*1*) helical molecule; (*2*) coiled molecule; (——) molecule undergoing a conformational transition.

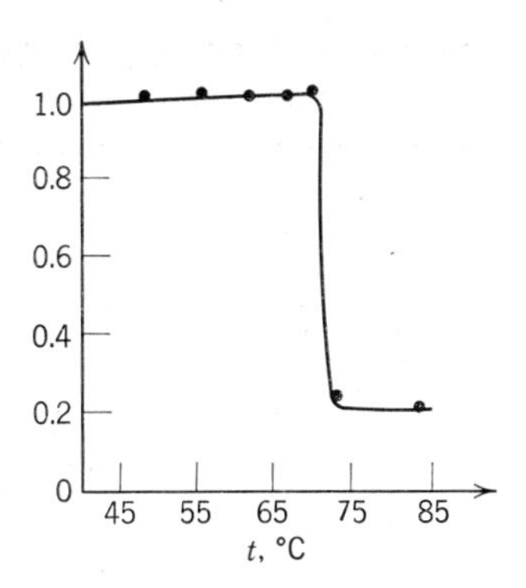

Fig. 10.6. Dependence on temperature of the length of a rat tail tendon treated with formaldehyde, under a constant small load (22).

the right-hand part of eq. (10.26) and compensates partly for the negative term, so that $\lambda_{\text{coil}}^{(f)}/\lambda_{\text{hel.}}^{(f)}$ passes through a minimum]. As a result the transition temperature increases with an increase of the applied force and passes through a maximum. In principle, such large forces are, of course, possible that for them $\lambda_{\text{coil}}^{(f)} > \lambda_{\text{hel.}}^{(f)}$, so that the transition occurs at $s > 1$ (it is shifted toward higher temperatures); however, in practice such forces can almost certainly not be attained since they exceed the breaking elongations of the samples. Thus, it is essentially possible to consider that the external force stabilizes the helical conformation of the chain.

Numerical evaluations have been carried out by Birshtein (26) for a one-dimensional chain in which each monomer unit can be oriented either parallel or antiparallel to the applied force; furthermore, the dimensions of a monomer unit are larger in the coiled than the helical state. It has been shown (26) that, when reasonable assumptions are made on the flexibility of a coiled chain, the helix–coil transition can occur with sufficiently strong forces at $s \approx 0.9$, and not $s = 1$, which corresponds to an increase in the transition temperature of ~15°C. when $\Delta H \approx -1$ kcal/mole. The sharpness of the transition is practically independent of the applied force.

The shift of the helix–coil transition temperature as the result of an applied force has been observed by Flory and co-workers (19,23) for collagen fibers. The existence of the transition was detected from the sharp shrinking of the fiber with an increase in temperature under constant external force (see, for example, Fig. 10.6). The shrinking of the fiber took place over a narrow temperature range; furthermore, the transition temperature increased with an increase in the applied force. This shift of the transition point has permitted a value of the heat of the helix–coil transition of collagen of ~1500 cal/mole to be obtained (19) by using a thermodynamic relation of the type of the Clausius-Clapeyron equation.

Let us examine now the deformation curves of polymer chains capable of undergoing a helix–coil transition. If the deformation of the chain takes place at a temperature which is higher than the transition temperature for an unstretched chain, but lower than the transition temperature for a chain with $\bar{x}_{\text{hel.}} = \bar{x}_{\text{coil}}$, then, as shown by Flory (22) [see also (24,25)], the theoretical curve of the deformation, $\bar{x}(f)$, has the shape shown by the steplike curve of Figure 10.6.

For small forces, we are dealing with the deformation of a coiled chain. *When the force attains a value at which the deformation temperature becomes equal to the transition temperature, the helix–coil transition takes place,* and the projection of the chain length on the direction of the external force increases sharply and then becomes independent of the magnitude of the applied force (since the helix cannot be deformed any more). Finally, with very large forces, when the transition temperature starts to decrease with an increase of the force, a reverse transition from the helix to a highly stretched coil becomes possible, and the last can become deformed with a further increase of the applied force. In all probability, it is difficult or even impossible to observe experimentally this reverse transition, since it takes place at elongations of the order of breaking elongations. As far as the first transition is concerned, i.e., the helix–coil transition under stretching, which results in a curve of the dependence of tension on deformation similar to a corresponding curve for crystallizable polymers, such transitions have been observed in experiments by Hill in the stretching of muscle fibers (27).

The effect of an external force on helix–coil transitions in charged polypeptide chains can be examined in a similar way. Considering as a first approximation that the electrostatic interaction of charged groups is a function only of whether the monomer units are present in a helical or coiled conformation (which is determined by the presence or absence of an intramolecular hydrogen bond) and that it is independent of the various possible conformations of monomer units in the coiled regions of the chain, we find that, in this case, the state of ionization of the chain and the external force affect the equilibrium constant s^* in independent ways. Combining eqs. (10.15) and (10.28), we find that the equilibrium constant between the state of the monomer unit in which it is bonded by a hydrogen bond and that in which it is free, in an ionizable chain located in a field of external force, is equal to

$$s^* = \frac{s\lambda_{\text{hel.}}^{(e)}}{\lambda_{\text{coil}}^{(e)}} \cdot \frac{\lambda_{\text{hel.}}^{(f)}}{\lambda_{\text{coil}}^{(f)}} \tag{10.31}$$

From the helix–coil transition condition $s^* = 1$, we find that at the transition point

$$s = s^{(f)} \cdot s^{(e)} \tag{10.32}$$

where $s^{(f)}$ is the value of the parameter s at the point of transition of an uncharged chain placed in a field of external force and defined by eq. (10.28) and $s^{(e)}$ is the value of the parameter s at the point of transition in a free charged chain, defined by eq. (10.15). As has been pointed out above (see section 10.2), the electrostatic interaction in polypeptide chains stabilizes the coiled form of the chain, so that the helix–coil transition may be due to an increase in pH and the simultaneous charging of the chain. In this way, $s^{(e)} > 1$. On the other hand, stretching of the chains stabilizes the helical form, i.e., $s^{(e)} < 1$. Since the point of helix–coil transition at a fixed value of s (fixed temperature and solvent composition) is a function of the magnitude of the external force applied, the degree of ionization of the chain α which is a function of the electrostatic interaction of neighboring charged groups, is also a function not only of the pH of the solution, but also of the external force.

References

1. Gibbs, J. H., and E. A. Di Marzio, *J. Chem. Phys.*, **30,** 271 (1959).
2. Peller, L., *J. Phys. Chem.*, **63,** 1199 (1959).
3. Schellman, J. A., *Compt. Rend. Trav. Lab. Carlsberg, Ser. Chim.*, **29,** 230 (1955).
4. Schellman, J. A., *J. Phys. Chem.*, **62,** 1485 (1958).
5. Doty, P., A. M. Holtzer, J. H. Bradbury, and E. R. Blout, *J. Am. Chem. Soc.*, **76,** 4493 (1954).
6. Blout, E. R., P. Doty, and J. T. Yang, *J. Am. Chem. Soc.*, **79,** 749 (1957).
7. Applequist, J., and P. Doty, in *Polyamino Acids, Polypeptides and Proteins,* M. A. Stahmann, Ed., Univ. Wisconsin Press, Madison, Wisc., 1962, p. 161.
8. Karlson, R. H., K. S. Norland, G. D. Fasman, and E. R. Blout, *J. Am. Chem. Soc.*, **82,** 2268 (1960).
9. Sela, M., I. Z. Steinberg, and E. Daniel, *Biochim. Biophys. Acta,* **46,** 433 (1961).
10. Perlmann, G., and E. Katchalski, in press.
11. Zimm, B. H., and S. A. Rice, *Mol. Phys.*, **3,** 391 (1960).
12. Doty, P., A. Wada, J. T. Yang, and E. R. Blout, *J. Polymer Sci.*, **23,** 851 (1957).
13. Wada, A., *Mol. Phys.*, **3,** 409 (1960).
14. Goldstein, L., and E. Katchalski, *Bull. Res. Council Israel,* **A9,** 138 (1960).
15. Doty, P., and J. T. Yang, *J. Am. Chem. Soc.*, **78,** 498 (1956).
16. Zimm, B. H., P. Doty, and K. Iso, *Proc. Natl. Acad. Sci., U.S.*, **45,** 1601 (1959).
17. Garrett, R. R., and P. J. Flory, *Nature,* **177,** 176 (1956).

18. Flory, P. J., *Science*, **124**, 53 (1956).
19. Oth, J. F. M., E. T. Dumitru, O. K. Spurr, Jr., and P. J. Flory, *J. Am. Chem. Soc.*, **79**, 3288 (1957).
20. Flory, P. J., and R. R. Garrett, *J. Am. Chem. Soc.*, **80**, 4836 (1958).
21. Flory, P. J., *J. Polymer Sci.*, **49**, 105 (1961).
22. Flory, P. J., *J. Cellular Comp. Physiol.* (*Suppl. 1*), **49**, 175 (1957).
23. Flory, P. J., *J. Am. Chem. Soc.*, **78**, 5222 (1956).
24. Zimm, B. H., in *Sovremennye Problemy Biofiziki*, Vol. 1, IL, Moscow, 1961, p. 159 (originally published as *Biophysical Science: A Study Program* J. L. Oncley, F. O. Schmitt, R. C. Williams, M. D. Rosenberg, and R. H. Bolt, Eds., Wiley, New York, 1959).
25. Birshtein, T. M., V. I. Vorobyov, and O. B. Ptitsyn, *Biofizika*, **6**, 524 (1961).
26. Birshtein, T. M., *Vysokomol. Soedin.*, **4**, 605 (1962).
27. Hill, A. V., *Proc. Roy. Soc.* (*London*), **B139**, 464 (1952).
28. Marcus, R. A., *J. Phys. Chem.*, **58**, 621 (1954).
29. Harris, F. E., and S. A. Rice, *J. Chem. Phys.*, **58**, 725, 733 (1954).
30. Katchalsky, A., J. Mazur, and P. Spitnik, *J. Polymer Sci.*, **23**, 513 (1957).
31. Lifson, S., *J. Chem. Phys.*, **26**, 727 (1957).
32. Lifson, S., B. Kaufman, and H. Lifson, *J. Chem. Phys.*, **27**, 1356 (1957).
33. Lifson, S., *J. Chem. Phys.*, **29**, 89 (1958).
34. Ptitsyn, O. B., *Vysokomol. Soedin.*, **2**, 463 (1960).
35. Birshtein, T. M., O. B. Ptitsyn, and E. A. Sokolova, *Vysokomol. Soedin.*, **6**, 158 (1964).
36. Kotin, L., and M. Nagasawa, *J. Chem. Phys.*, **36**, 873 (1962).
37. Fasman, G. D., M. Idelson, and E. R. Blout, *J. Am. Chem. Soc.*, **83**, 709 (1961).
38. Fasman, G., in *Polyamino Acids, Polypeptides and Proteins*, M. A. Stahmann, Ed., Univ. Wisconsin Press, Madison, Wisc., 1962, p. 221.

Chapter 11

THEORY OF CONFORMATIONAL TRANSITIONS IN POLYNUCLEOTIDE CHAINS

11.1. Conformational Partition Function of a DNA Molecule

Let us proceed now to a presentation of the theory of helix–coil transitions in molecules of deoxyribonucleic acid (DNA) and synthetic polynucleotides. The main chain of such polymers is a phosphoester polymer in which cyclic purine and pyrimidine bases are linked to the ribose rings (Fig. 11.1). DNA contains four types of such bases: adenine (A), thymine (T), guanine (G), and cytosine (C); the sequence of these bases codes the information contained in DNA [see, for example, (1)]. In ribonucleic acid molecules (RNA), thymine is replaced by uracil (U). In contrast to polypeptide chains, the helical structure of which is maintained by *intramolecular* hydrogen bonds, the helical structure of native DNA (as well as a number of synthetic polynucleotides) is determined by specific *intermolecular* hydrogen bonds between the purine and pyrimidine bases (adenine with thymine and uracil and guanine with cytosine).* As a result, molecules of native DNA are bound in pairs, their secondary structure being a Watson-Crick double helix (2) which consists of two antiparallel chains (Fig. 11.2). Similar structures are formed by complexes of a number of synthetic polynucleotides with complementary bases, i.e., such bases which can form specific hydrogen bonds (for example, complexes of polyadenine with polyuracil). The diameter of a Watson-Crick helix is ~20 Å, and the step along the helix axis is 3.4 Å. The double helix of native DNA is not ideally rigid. The molecule has some flexibility; this flexibility, however, is much smaller than in denatured DNA (i.e., DNA in which the molecules have undergone a helix–coil transition, determined by the breaking of the hydrogen bonds.)

The DNA molecules are polyelectrolytes; their phosphate groups are always ionized, while the purine and pyrimidine bases can also be ionized. Helix–coil transitions of DNA and synthetic polynucleotides can result

* See footnote at the beginning of section 9.1.

both from an increase in the temperature and a change in the solution pH. Let us examine first helix–coil transitions resulting from an increase in temperature (i.e., the thermal denaturation of DNA), without dwelling on the polyelectrolyte properties of the molecules. The theory of such transitions was developed in the papers of Gibbs and Di Marzio (3,4), Rice and Wada (5), Hill (6), Steiner (7), Zimm (8), Volkenshtein and Elyashevich (23), Ozaki, Tanaka, and Teramoto (26), and Lifson and Zimm (27). The results of Zimm's studies (8) are presented below; these make use of the matrix method of Ising's model. Following Zimm, we shall consider that the nucleotide residues of the chains in the helical state can combine with each other by hydrogen bonds in only one way, so that the kth residue of one chain combines with the $(n - k)$th residue of the antiparallel second chain (see Fig. 11.2). This assumption corresponds to the

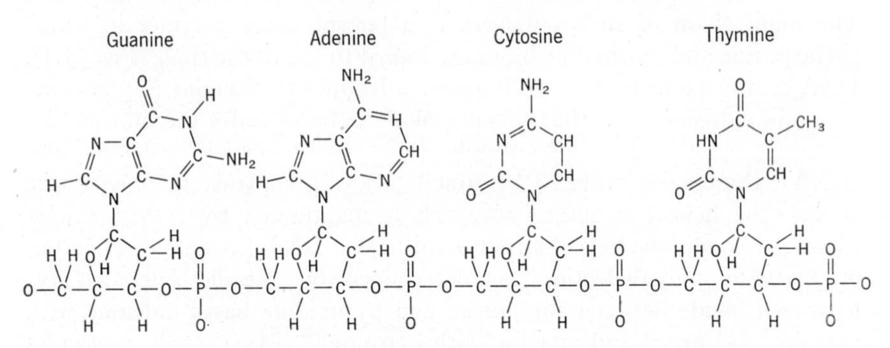

Fig. 11.1 Chemical structure of DNA.

real situation in native DNA, which is a copolymer of four different nucleotides; furthermore, their distribution along the chain is the result of evolutionary selection and is specific for the given type of DNA molecule. It is evident that, in such molecules, a double helix in which all hydrogen bonds possible are present can be formed only between such chains in which each base of a chain corresponds to a complementary base in the other chain; in this process, the double helix may form in a unique way. In synthetic polynucleotides, which are homopolymers, double helices can be formed from mutually complementary chains (for example, polyuracil with polyadenine). All the bases are complementary in such chains, so that it would be desirable to take into account in the theory the possibility of different ways of bonding between the chains. An analysis of this question (7,26) has shown that consideration of various ways of bonding between chains has no effect on the mean position of the helix–coil transition, but it does spread the transition interval somewhat. We shall neglect as well the heterogeneity of the composition of DNA molecules, i.e., the difference between the hydrogen bond energies for various nucleotide pairs. In reality, as has been shown by Marmur and Doty (9), the melting temperatures of homopolymeric adenine–thymine (A–T) and guanine–cytosine (G–C) complexes differ by $\approx 50°C$, so that the hydrogen bond energies of A–T and G–C must be different. This is not surprising, since three hydrogen bonds can form between guanine and cytosine and only two between adenine and thymine.* Simple evaluations show that the heterogeneity of DNA composition must also result in some broadening of the transition range; this is confirmed by experiment (24). Attempts at a quantitative evaluation of the effect of DNA composition heterogeneity on the breadth of the transition interval (26,28) have not been successful so far, since the solution of this problem meets with the general difficulties of the averaging of statistical quantities which characterize macromolecules that are nonhomogeneous in composition or in structure (compare section 5.1).

Following the paper of Zimm (8), let us turn to the development of the partition function of a DNA molecule. Each pair of bases in a double molecule of DNA or synthetic polynucleotides can be either bonded by a hydrogen bond (state $\mu_i = 1$) or nonbonded (state $\mu_i = 0$). Expressions for the partition function or the free energy of the system must take into account the fact that a change in the latter with the formation of each hydrogen bond depends significantly on the states of all the preceding base pairs. In fact, if the preceding base pair is bonded, the free energy change during the bonding of the next pair is the sum of the free energy of formation of the hydrogen bond and the free energy change due to the positioning of the given pair of bonded bases above the preceding pair and to the loss of the freedom of rotation in two bonded monomer units. If j preceding pairs are not bonded, then the formation of the hydrogen bond in the $(j + 1)$th pair results in the formation of a ring in a chain of j pairs of unbonded bases; this imposes some restrictions on the conformations of all monomer units in the ring; the corresponding free energy change can be included in the free energy of formation of the hydrogen bond in the $(j + 1)$th base pair. Finally, if all the monomer units preceding the base pair under examination are not bonded, the free energy change during hydrogen bond formation must include the entropy loss during the formation of the first crosslink between the two chains.

* Evaluations of the energy of the dipole–dipole interactions of guanine–cytosine and adenine–thymine pairs (25) result as well in a stronger G–C than A–T bond.

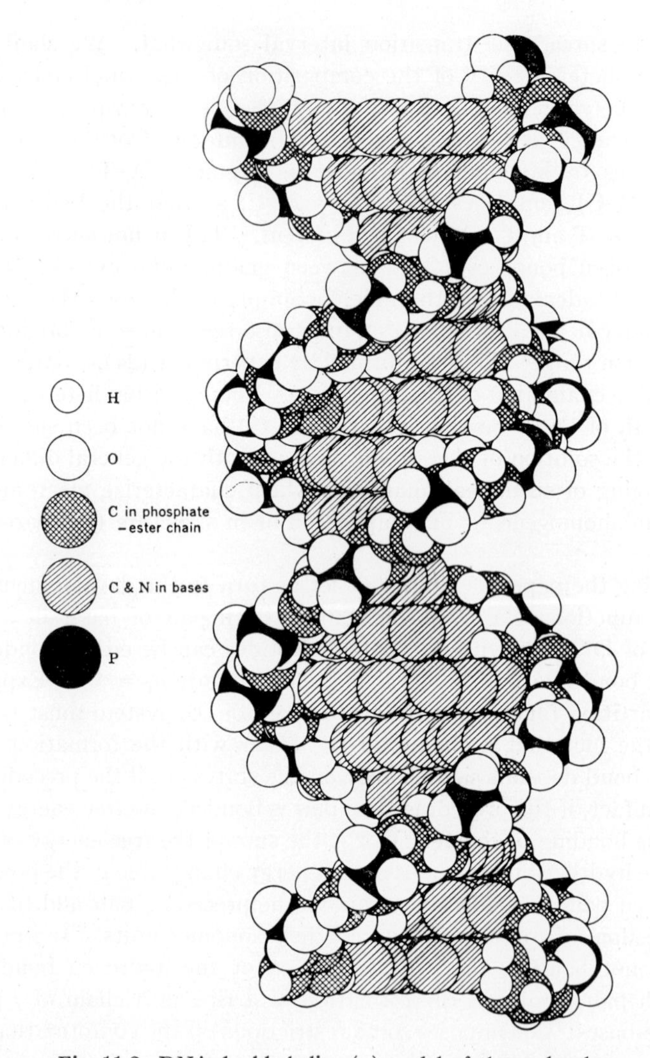

Fig. 11.2. DNA double helix: (*a*) model of the molecule.

In accordance with this, the free energy of a DNA molecule can be written in the form

$$F(\mu_1, \mu_2, \ldots, \mu_n) = \sum_{i=1}^{n} F(\mu_1, \ldots, \mu_{i-1}; \mu_i) \tag{11.1}$$

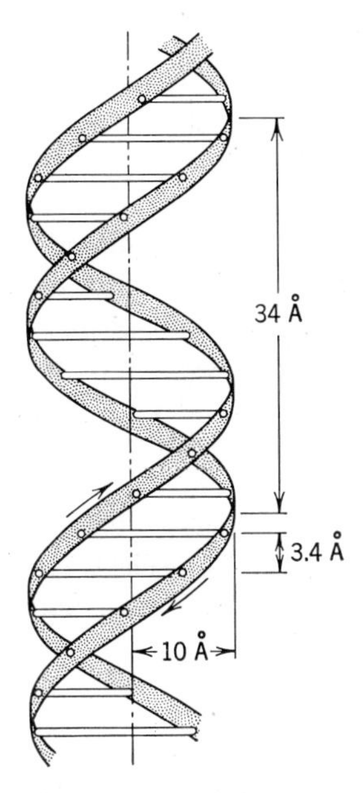

Fig. 11.2. DNA double helix: (*b*) schematic representation of the molecule.

where $F(\mu_1, \ldots, \mu_{i-1}; \mu_i)$ is the free energy of the ith pair of monomer units in state μ_i, which is actually a function of the states of all preceding pairs. We have

$$\begin{aligned} F(\mu_1, \ldots, \mu_{i-1}; 0) &\equiv F_{\text{free}} \\ F(\mu_1, \ldots, \mu_{i-2}, 1; 1) &\equiv F_{\text{bonded}} \\ F(\mu_1, \ldots, \mu_{i-j-2}, 1, \underbrace{0, \ldots, 0}_{j}; 1) &\equiv F_{\text{bonded}} + (F_j)_{\text{init.}} \\ F(0, \ldots, 0; 1) &\equiv F_{\text{bonded}} + F_{\text{init.}} \end{aligned} \tag{11.2}$$

It is evident that the quantity

$$\Delta F \equiv F_{\text{bonded}} - F_{\text{free}} \tag{11.3}$$

is the free energy change when the sequence of bonded pairs of monomer units increases by one pair at the expense of the neighboring region of unbonded pairs of units; this is just as in the case of polypeptide chains. The quantities $(F_j)_{\text{init.}}$ and $F_{\text{init.}}$ are additional free energy changes during the formation of a hydrogen bond following a ring of j pairs of unbonded bases and the formation of the first hydrogen bond between two chains, respectively. In addition to the contributions due to entropy losses from the restriction of the conformations of all the monomer units in the ring and from the first crosslinking of chains, respectively, these quantities must also contain contributions which take into account the fact that, when a hydrogen bond is formed following a nonbonded pair of monomer units, the free energy change does not include terms due to the positioning of the base pairs above each other. As shall be seen from what follows, it is precisely this last factor which determines principally the cooperative nature of the helix–coil transition in DNA molecules.

The partition function of the macromolecule can be calculated by summing over all the 2^n states of monomer unit pairs. Furthermore, the contribution of each state of the double chain to the partition function is determined by the product of factors selected according to the following rules: (*1*) factor 1 for state 0 of a pair of monomer units (this means that the free energy of a pair of nonbonded monomer units is taken as zero, $F_{\text{free}} = 0$); (*2*) factor s

$$s = e^{-\Delta F/kT} = e^{-(\Delta H - T\Delta S)/kT} \tag{11.4}$$

for state 1 of a pair of monomer units, where s is the equilibrium constant for the process of increasing the helical region by one pair of monomer units at the expense of a neighboring region of nonbonded units; (*3*) an additional factor τ

$$\tau = e^{-F_{\text{init.}}/kT} \tag{11.5}$$

for the first pair of monomer units in state 1; this factor includes, in particular, the ratio of the volume available to the center of masses of one of the bonded chains when the center of masses of the other chain is fixed to the total volume of the system; (*4*) factor σ_j

$$\sigma_j = e^{-(F_j)_{\text{init.}}/kT} \tag{11.6}$$

for a ring of j nonbonded monomer units of each chain.

Rule *2*, just as the similar rule in the case of a polypeptide chain, states that the free energy of a sequence of bonded monomer units is proportional to the number of bonded units with the effect of chain ends neglected; this effect is taken into account by rules *3* and *4* and determines the cooperativeness of the system. The quantity ΔH which determines the temperature dependence of the equilibrium constant s includes the energy gains when the nucleotide–solvent hydrogen bonds are replaced by nucleotide–nucleotide and solvent–solvent hydrogen bonds (see section 9.2) and

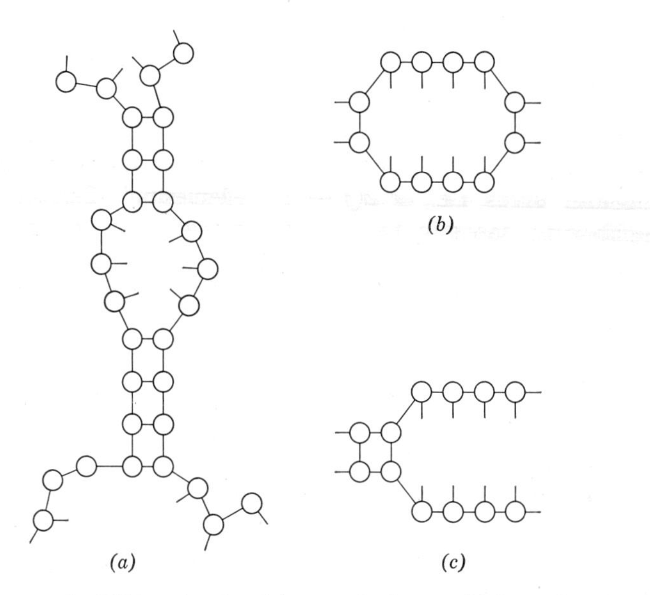

Fig. 11.3. States of a DNA molecule: (*a*) general scheme; (*b*) formation of a hydrogen bond following a ring; (*c*) formation of a hydrogen bond following a pair of bonded nucleotides.

when a pair of bonded bases is placed above the previous pair, at the expense of the energy of their interaction. On the other hand, this quantity includes the energy loss due to the increase of the repulsive energy between the negative charges of the phosphate groups* when the distance between them decreases as a result of the winding of the chain into the double helix. The quantity ΔS includes the entropy decrease during the loss of conformational degrees of freedom in a pair of bonded monomer units. The values of ΔH and ΔS are negative for all nucleic acids, as has been shown experimentally. Let us note that, since the molecules of the nucleic acids are almost always charged, the change in the state of the solvent during helix–coil transition (see section 9.1) must include the free energy change of the gegenions. As a result, the equilibrium constant of the helix–coil transition in nucleic acids is a function of the ionic strength of the solvent.

The quantities σ_j, which determine the degree of cooperativeness of the system, are equilibrium constants for the formation of rings from j pairs of unbonded monomer units without changing the total whole number of

* The phosphate groups are charged at all usual pH's so that their ionization is independent of pH.

hydrogen bonds, i.e., for a transition from state c to state b (see Fig. 11.3). It is evident that

$$\sigma_j = Z_{2(j+1)}/Z_2 \tag{11.7}$$

where $Z_{2(j+1)}$ is the partition function of a ring from j pairs of nonbonded monomer units, i.e., of $2(j+1)$ "elements" (flexible regions which connect neighboring bases in the chain), while Z_2 is the partition function of the "ring" of two such elements formed during the bonding of a pair of bases which directly follows a bonded pair. Partition function Z_2 includes the stacking energy, i.e., the energy of interaction, ϵ, of two consecutive pairs of bonded bases located one above the other, while quantity $Z_{2(j+1)}$ does not contain this term. Therefore,

$$\sigma_j = Z_{2(j+1)}/Z_2'e^{-\epsilon/kT} \tag{11.8}$$

where Z_2' is the conformational component of the partition function of the ring of two elements. Since the partition function of the ring of $2(j+1)$ elements, $Z_{2(j+1)}$ also has a conformational character, we have

$$\sigma_j = e^{\epsilon/kT}W_{2(j+1)}(0)/W_2(0) \tag{11.9}$$

where $W_{2(j+1)}(0)$ and $W_2(0)$ are the probabilities of a zero distance between the ends of "chains" of $2(j+1)$ and 2 elements, respectively. In a very rough approximation, *a priori* not valid for small j but which gives the correct result for large j, the distribution functions which enter into the right-hand side of eq. (11.9) can be regarded as Gaussian, so that [see (10)]:

$$W_{2(j+1)}(0) \sim 1/[2(j+1)^{3/2}] \tag{11.10}$$

Substituting eq. (11.10) into eq. (11.9) we obtain

$$\sigma_j = \sigma_0/(j+1)^{3/2} \tag{11.11}$$

where the parameter σ_0 contains as a multiplier $e^{\epsilon/kT}$, and also takes into account corrections related to the nonapplicability of a Gaussian distribution function for a "chain" of two elements. Since the stacking of consecutive pairs of bonded bases is energetically favorable because of the forces of attraction which act between them [see, for example, the theoretical calculations carried out by De Voe and Tinoco (25)], the quantity $\epsilon < 0$ and consequently, $e^{\epsilon/kT} < 1$. As is shown experimentally for nucleic acids $\sigma_0 \ll 1$, i.e., the degree of cooperativeness is quite large. Unfortunately, at present there is no satisfactory theoretical evaluation of the value of σ_0. Equation (11.11), proposed by Zimm, takes into account correctly the dependence of σ_j on j (for large j) and contains the cooperativeness parameter σ_0 which is determined by comparing theory with experiment.

As shall be seen from what follows, the value of the quantity τ, which also has an effect on the cooperativeness of the system, is essentially not reflected in the helix–coil transition curve.

11.2. Calculation of the Partition Function and Theory of the Thermal Denaturation of DNA

We will now proceed to a calculation of the partition function for the general case of arbitrary τ and σ_j. Since the possibility of formation of rings of any size determines the interdependence of the states of all pairs of monomer units of the chain and each such pair can exist in one of two states, it is possible to construct a matrix G of order 2^n, each element of which is indexed by the states of pairs of monomer units $(0, 1, 2, \ldots, n-1)$ and $(1, 2, 3, \ldots, n)$ and gives the contribution to the partition function of the nth pair of monomer units when the states of all the preceding pairs are fixed. It is evident that in each row (and each column) of such a matrix there will be only two nonzero elements which correspond to the two possible states of the nth (or zeroth) pair of monomer units when the states of all the preceding pairs are fixed. Numbering the states of unit pairs in the sequence 000...000; 000...001; 000...010; 000...011; 000...100; 000...101; 000...110; 000...111, etc. (where 0 denotes a nonbonded pair of monomer units, 1 is a bonded pair) and writing out only the nonzero elements of the matrix, we obtain eq. (11.12).

$G =$ (11.12)

	00...000	00...001	00...010	00...011	00...100	00...101	00...110	00...111	...	11...1000	11...1001	11...1010	11...1011	11...1100	11...1101	11...110	11...111
00...000	1	$s\tau$							⋮								
00...001			1	s					⋮								
00...010					1	$s\sigma_1$			⋮								
00...011							1	s	⋮								
....	...	...	...	...	...	...	...	...	...	...	...	...	...	...	...	...	...
011...100									⋮	1	$s\sigma_2$						
011...101									⋮			1	s				
011...110									⋮					1	$s\sigma_1$		
011...111									⋮							1	s
100...000	1	$s\sigma_{n-1}$							⋮								
100...001			1	s					⋮								
100...010					1	$s\sigma_1$			⋮								
100...011							1	s	⋮								
....	...	...	...	...	...	...	...	...	...	...	...	...	...	...	...	...	...
11...100									⋮	1	$s\sigma_2$						
11...101									⋮			1	s				
11...110									⋮					1	$s\sigma_1$		
11...111									⋮							1	s

Notwithstanding such a high order of correlation, the partition function of the chain, just as before, can be expressed in the form of a linear combination of elements of matrix G^n. In fact, let us add to the beginning of the chain n hypothetical pairs of segments with numbers $-n+1$, $-n+2$, ..., 0 and let us assume that all these segments are always nonbonded. Since the states of the added segments are fixed, the free energy of the nonbonded state is taken as zero and the energy of any state is independent of the number of preceding nonbonded segments, such an operation is not accompanied by any change either in the set of states of the chain or in the energy of these states. The partition function Z can be expressed in the form:

$$Z = \sum_{\{\mu_i\}} \{G\}_{\mu_{-n+1},\ldots,\mu_0;\ \mu_{-n+2},\ldots,\mu_1} \{G\}_{\mu_{-n+2},\ldots,\mu_1;\ \mu_{-n+3},\ldots,\mu_2} \ldots \{G\}_{\mu_0,\ldots,\mu_{n-1};\ \mu_1,\ldots,\ \mu_n}$$

$$= \sum_{\{\mu_i\}} \{G^n\}_{\mu_{-n+1},\ldots,\mu_0;\ \mu_1,\ldots,\mu_n} \tag{11.13}$$

where $\mu_i = 0, 1$ and the summation is carried out over all permissible values of $\mu_i(-n+1 \leqslant i \leqslant n)$.

The first index of matrix G^n characterizes the state of the added segments, the second the state of the real double chain. It is evident that cyclic conditions cannot be imposed in this case, since their imposition would mean that the state of n segments would be fixed and not that of a single segment (as in a polypeptide chain). Expanding matrix G^n in eigenvectors $\mathbf{v}$ and $\tilde{\mathbf{u}}$ of matrix G, we have [see eq. (4.34)]:

$$Z = \sum_{\{\mu_i\}} \sum_{\nu} [\mathbf{v}(\lambda_\nu)\tilde{\mathbf{u}}(\lambda_\nu)]_{\mu_{-n+1},\ldots,\mu_0;\ \mu_1,\ldots,\mu_n} \cdot \lambda_\nu^n = \sum_{\nu} c_\nu \lambda_\nu^n \tag{11.14}$$

where λ_ν are the eigenvalues of matrix G. Restricting ourselves, just as before, to the case that $n \gg 1$, we obtain

$$Z = c_1 \lambda_1^n \tag{11.15}$$

where λ_1 is the largest eigenvalue of matrix G, while the value of c_1 depends on the boundary conditions selected (the states of the zeroth and nth segments). Since the physical properties of the system are determined by $\ln Z$ and its derivatives, factor c_1 can be omitted with a precision up to terms of order n; thus, in this case also, the problem of construction of the partition function is reduced to the determination of the largest root of matrix G.

The construction of a secular equation for matrix G of order $2^n \times 2^n$ seems, at first, to be an impossible task. Zimm, however, solved this problem in the following manner. It is well known that a system of 2^n equations [see eq. (4.21)]

$$\tilde{\mathbf{u}}(\lambda_\nu)G = \lambda_\nu \tilde{\mathbf{u}}(\lambda_\nu) \tag{11.16}$$

makes possible the determination both of the components of eigenvector $\tilde{\mathbf{u}}(\lambda_\nu)$ and of the corresponding eigenvalue λ_ν. Usually, eigenvalues λ_ν are found by setting the determinant of matrix $G - \lambda\mathbf{I}$ equal to zero, after which there remain in system (11.16) only $2^n - 1$ independent equations. In the present case, it is not possible to obtain an expression for the determinant of matrix $G - \lambda\mathbf{I}$; it is possible, however, to construct system (11.16) and to rearrange it into such a form that one of the equations would contain only the variable λ_ν.

Such an equation can be constructed from the equations for two components of vector $\mathbf{u}_\nu = \mathbf{u}(\lambda_\nu)$ (which is indexed just as the elements of matrix G):

$$\begin{aligned} \lambda u_{000\cdots00} &= u_{000\cdots00} + u_{100\cdots00} \\ \lambda u_{100\cdots00} &= u_{110\cdots00} + u_{010\cdots00} \end{aligned} \tag{11.17}$$

(where subscripts ν are omitted). We obtain from the first of eqs. (11.17), setting in it $u_{000\cdots00} = 1$ without limiting the generality,

$$u_{100\cdots00} = \lambda - 1 \tag{11.18}$$

component $u_{010\cdots00}$, which enters into the second of eqs. (11.17), can be expressed by means of λ and the parameters of matrix G in the following way. From the system of equations

$$\begin{aligned} \lambda u_{010\cdots00} &= u_{0010\cdots00} + u_{1010\cdots00} \\ \lambda u_{0010\cdots00} &= u_{00010\cdots00} + u_{10010\cdots00} \\ &\cdots\cdots\cdots\cdots \\ \lambda u_{000\cdots010} &= u_{000\cdots001} + u_{100\cdots001} \end{aligned} \tag{11.19}$$

it is evident that component $u_{010\cdots00}$ can be expressed by means of $u_{000\cdots001}$ and also by means of $u_{1010\cdots00}$, $u_{10010\cdots00}$, $u_{100010\cdots00}$, $u_{100\cdots01}$. For $u_{000\cdots001}$, we have

$$\lambda u_{000\cdots001} = s\tau u_{000\cdots000} + s\sigma_{n-1} u_{100\cdots000} \tag{11.20}$$

or, taking into account eq. (11.18) and the fact that $u_{000\cdots00} = 1$,

$$u_{000\cdots001} = \frac{1}{\lambda}\,[s\tau + s\sigma_{n-1}(\lambda - 1)] \tag{11.21}$$

The quantities

$$u_{1\underbrace{0\cdots0}_{k}10\cdots00}$$

which contain $k(= 1, 2, \ldots n - 2)$ zeros between two ones in the subscript, are equal to

$$u_{1\underbrace{0\cdots0}_{k}10\cdots00} = u_{10\cdots00}s\sigma_k = (\lambda - 1)s\sigma_k \tag{11.22}$$

In fact, we have for $u_{10\cdots01}$, for example,

$$\lambda u_{100\cdots01} = s\sigma_{n-2}(u_{010\cdots00} + u_{110\cdots00}) \tag{11.23}$$

and since $u_{010\cdots00} + u_{110\cdots00} = \lambda u_{100\cdots00}$, then

$$u_{100\cdots01} = s\sigma_{n-2}u_{100\cdots00} = s\sigma_{n-2}(\lambda - 1) \tag{11.24}$$

Using eqs. (11.19), (11.21), and (11.22), we obtain

$$u_{010\cdots00} = \left[\frac{\tau}{\lambda^{n-1}} + (\lambda - 1)\sum_{j=1}^{n=1}\frac{\sigma_j}{\lambda_j}\right]s \tag{11.25}$$

It can be shown that for component $u_{110\cdots00}$, which also enters into the second of eqs. (11.17), that *

$$u_{110\cdots00} = su_{100\cdots00} \tag{11.26}$$

From eqs. (11.17), (11.18), (11.25), and (11.26) we find finally the equation relative to λ, i.e., the secular equation for matrix G:

$$(\lambda - s)(\lambda - 1) = s(\lambda - 1)\sum_{j=1}^{n-1}\sigma_j\lambda^{-j} + s\tau/\lambda^{n-1} \tag{11.27}$$

The problem is reduced now to the determination of the roots of this equation.

Equation (11.27) includes as a particular case eqs. (9.14) and (9.39) which describe the melting of a polypeptide chain. Actually, if one sets

$$\tau = \sigma$$
$$\sigma_j = \begin{cases}\sigma & j \geqslant 3\\ 0 & j = 1, 2\end{cases} \tag{11.28}$$

as has been done in the development of the theory of melting of a polypeptide chain, then, upon summation in j, eq. (11.27) becomes eq. (9.14).

* An equality of the type of eq. (11.26), obvious for the relation between $u_{000\cdots011}$ and $u_{000\cdots001}$, can be obtained by means of recurrence for any $u_{\cdots110\cdots00}$ and $u_{\cdots100\cdots00}$, among them for $u_{110\cdots00}$ and $u_{100\cdots00}$.

We obtain the result of the simplified theory of melting of a polypeptide chain [eq. (9.39)] after setting

$$\tau = \sigma_j = \sigma \tag{11.29}$$

When $\sigma_j = \tau = 0$ (absolute cooperativeness), eq. (11.27) assumes the form

$$(\lambda - s)(\lambda - 1) = 0 \tag{11.30}$$

In accordance with this, the partition function of the system consists of the sum of two terms, which correspond respectively to a totally helical and a totally coiled chain [eq. (9.21) and (9.22)]. The largest root of eq. (11.27) is

$$\lambda_1 = \begin{cases} s & s > 1 \\ 1 & s < 1 \end{cases} \tag{11.31}$$

Consequently, the fraction of base pairs bonded by hydrogen bonds is

$$\vartheta = \frac{\partial \ln \lambda_1}{\partial \ln s} \approx \begin{cases} 1 & s > 1 \\ 0 & s < 1 \end{cases} \tag{11.32}$$

i.e., at the point $s = 1$, a helix–coil transition takes place which occurs according to the all-or-none principle. On the other hand, if $\sigma_j = \tau = 1$, i.e., if cooperativeness is completely absent, eq. (11.27) assumes the form

$$(\lambda - s)(\lambda - 1) = s \tag{11.33}$$

from which $\lambda_1 = 1 + s$ and

$$\vartheta = s/(1 + s) \tag{11.34}$$

i.e., the fraction of base pairs bonded by hydrogen bonds is described by an equation for a unimolecular reaction (the transition is not cooperative and is diffused over a wide temperature range).

In the general case, substituting into eq. (11.27) the quantities σ_j in form (11.11), we obtain

$$(\lambda - s)(\lambda - 1) = \sigma_0 s(\lambda - 1)g_{n-1}(\lambda) + \tau s \lambda^{-n+1} \tag{11.35}$$

where

$$g_{n-1}(\lambda) = \sum_{j=1}^{n-1} \frac{1}{(j + 1)^{3/2} \lambda^j} \tag{11.36}$$

If the largest root of eq. (11.30) is larger than unity, then, in determining it when $n \gg 1$, it is possible to drop the last term on the right-hand side of the equation and to replace $g_{n-1}(\lambda)$ by $g_\infty(\lambda)$; this results in eq. (11.37):

$$\lambda - s = \sigma_0 s g_\infty(\lambda) \tag{11.37}$$

Using the values tabulated by Truesdell (11) of a function related by a simple relation with the function $g_\infty(\lambda)$, Zimm (8) finds

$$g_\infty(\lambda) = 1.612 - 3.545(\lambda - 1)^{1/2} + 4.072(\lambda - 1) + \ldots g_\infty(\infty) = 0 \quad (11.38)$$

A further investigation carried out by Zimm by use of a graphic method shows that eq. (11.37) [and, consequently, also eq. (11.35)] has a largest root greater than unity when

$$s > s_c = 1/(1 + 1.612\sigma_0) \quad (11.39)$$

This can be clarified on the basis of the fact that, with a precision up to terms of order σ_0, eq. (11.37) has a single root $\lambda = s[1 + \sigma_0 g_\infty(s)]$, which is the largest root of the starting equation, eq. (11.35), when $\lambda > 1$, i.e., when $s > 1/[1 + \sigma_0 g_\infty(s)]$. Since in the right-hand side of the last inequality

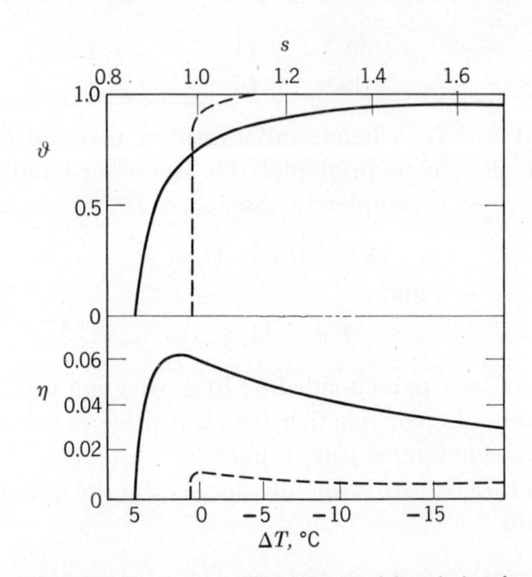

Fig. 11.4. Dependence of the average fraction ϑ of bonded pairs of monomer units and of the average fraction η of helix–coil junctions on the equilibrium constant s and the deviation of the temperature ΔT from the transition temperature ($s = 1$): (——) $\Delta H = -5$ kcal/mole, $\sigma_0 = 0.1$; (– –) $\Delta H = -5$ kcal/mole, $\sigma_0 = 0.01$.

it can be considered that $s = 1$ with precision up to terms of order σ_0, using eq. (11.38), we obtain eq. (11.39). Investigation of the largest root of equation (11.35) is difficult when $s < s_c$; as will be seen, (see Fig. 11.4) however, the part of the helix–coil transition which is of interest lies almost entirely at $s > s_c$.

Differentiating eq. (11.37) with respect to λ, we find that the fraction of base pairs bonded by hydrogen bonds is equal to

$$\vartheta = \partial \ln \lambda_1/\partial \ln s = 1/[1 - \sigma_0 s g_\infty'(\lambda)] \qquad (11.40)$$

where

$$g_\infty'(\lambda) = dg_\infty(\lambda)/d\lambda.$$

The dependence of ϑ on s, calculated with eq. (11.40) is shown in Figure 11.4 for two values of σ_0 (0.1 and 0.01). The change in the temperature T, relative to T at $s = 1$, calculated with eq. (9.9) at $\Delta H = -5$ kcal/mole, is also shown on the abscissa.

We see that, near $s = s_c$, ϑ decreases sharply with an increase in temperature, i.e., the helix–coil transition takes place over a narrow temperature interval. Figure 11.4 also shows the dependence on s and temperature of the average fraction of base pairs located at a helix–coil junction (or, equivalently, the average fraction of base pairs located at a coil–helix junction), which can be represented, on the basis of expressions (11.37) and (11.40), in the form:

$$\eta = \partial \ln \lambda_1/\partial \ln \sigma_0 = \vartheta(\lambda_1 - s)/\lambda_1 \qquad (11.41)$$

It is evident that, at $\sigma_0 = 0.01$ and a temperature one degree below the melting temperature, approximately 1% of the base pairs are located at helix–coil junctions.

An exact profile of the melting curve can obviously be determined only when rigorous expressions for the quantities σ_j are available. The existence of a critical value of s equal to s_c, however, and the shape of the part of the curve in the region where ϑ is considerably less than one are determined essentially by the values of σ_j with large j (since $g_\infty(\lambda)$ is determined in this region principally by terms with large j) for which approximation (11.11) is apparently sufficiently good. In the region in which ϑ is close to unity, the average dimensions of the rings become small, and eq. (11.11) ceases to be valid quantitatively. As a result, as is pointed out by the author himself, the Zimm theory does not describe quantitatively the shape of the DNA melting curve in the region close to the purely helical state. Let us recall that the cooperativeness parameter σ_0 is not calculated theoretically, but enters into the theory as an empirical parameter, just as in the case of polypeptide chains.

Experimental investigations of the thermal denaturation of DNA have been carried out in a large number of studies [reviews of these studies can be found for example in the monograph of Steiner and Beers (29) and in

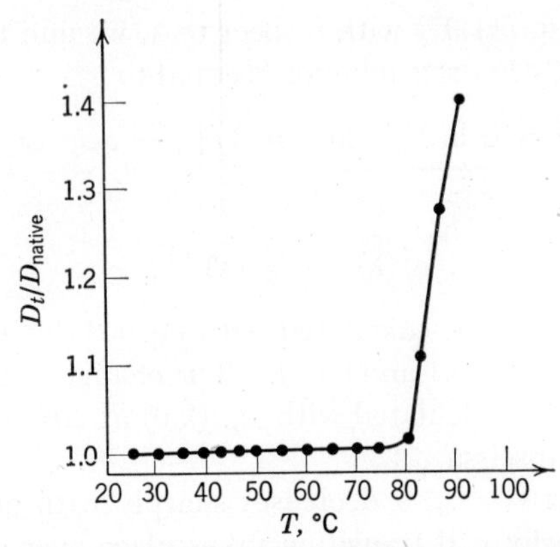

Fig. 11.5. Dependence on temperature of the ultraviolet absorption at $\lambda \approx 260$ mμ of calf thymus DNA (pH = 7, solution of 0.015M NaCl + 0.015M sodium citrate) (36). D = optical density.

various review articles (13,30,31)]. As an example, the temperature dependence of the ultraviolet absorption (at $\lambda \approx 260$ mμ) of calf thymus DNA in a saline aqueous solution is shown in Figure 11.5. The ratio, plotted on the ordinate, of the ultraviolet absorption at the temperature of the experiment to the ultraviolet absorption at 25°C (when the DNA molecules are in the native helical state) is a measure of the number of pairs of monomer units with broken hydrogen bonds [see, for example, (32)]. In this case the transition takes place over an interval of ~10°C; in the case of bacterial DNA and especially phage DNA, however, which are more homogeneous in composition, the transition is much sharper and takes place in an interval of 1–2°C.

Just as in the case of polypeptide chains, the magnitude of the temperature interval of the transition depends on one hand on the heat of transition $-\Delta H$ and on the other hand on the cooperativeness parameter σ_0. The quantity $-\Delta H$ can be measured directly by calorimetry and also determined from the dependence of the transition temperature on the concentration of hydrogen ions (see section 11.3). Calorimetric measurements carried out by Sturtevant, Rice, and Geiduschek (12) on salmon testis DNA which had been subjected to acid denaturation at pH = 2.5, a temperature of 25°C, and an ionic strength of the solution of 0.1M gave a heat of transition of 5 kcal/mole of base pair. In order to determine the heat of melting of DNA in a neutral medium, it is necessary to add to this quantity the heat of ionization of the purine and pyrimidine bases which takes place simultaneously with the acid denaturation of DNA (see section

11.3). This last quantity has been evaluated by De Voe and Tinoco (25), who, using the heat of ionization of monodeoxyribonucleotides (33), found that the enthalpy change during the titration of bases in the coiled form from pH = 2.5 to pH = 7 is equal to 3.2 kcal/mole of base pair. Consequently, the heat of melting of a helix in a neutral medium is equal to 8 kcal/mole of base pair. Similar values of the heats of melting have been obtained calorimetrically also for complexes of poly A + poly U. It has been shown by Steiner and Kitzinger (34) that in these complexes, at pH = 6.6, a temperature of 25°C, and an ionic strength of 0.1–1M, the heat of melting is 5–6 kcal/mole. A value of ~7 kcal/mole was found for the same complexes in the study of Ross and Sturtevant (35).

Using the value of the heat of transition in an acid medium, ~5 kcal/-mole of base pair, Zimm (8) evaluated the cooperativeness parameter σ_0 of DNA from the temperature dependence of the melting curves; its value was found to lie between 10^{-1} and 10^{-2} for samples homogeneous in composition.

The values of the heats of melting of DNA and poly A + poly U complexes in neutral medium, determined calorimetrically, are close to values obtained (14,15,19) from experimental data on the dependence of the denaturation temperature of DNA on the pH of the solution (see section 11.3). Let us note that the large (~10 kcal/mole) values of the heats of denaturation of DNA are probably an additional indication that the stability of DNA doubles helices is determined not only by hydrogen bonds but also by the additional forces of attraction between the hydrophobic groups.

11.3. Theory of the Acid and Alkaline Denaturations of DNA

Up to now, we have discussed only the thermal denaturation of DNA, which is characterized by the fact that the denatured coiled conformation is favorable entropically. The energy of molecules of DNA and other nucleic acids is lower in the helical state which is, therefore, stable at sufficiently low temperatures. The energetic balance of nucleic acid molecules receives considerable contributions not only from intra- and intermolecular hydrogen bonds and from interactions of hydrophobic groups, but also from electrostatic interactions of charged groups of the chain. As a result, the temperature of denaturation of nucleic acids is a function of the degree of ionization of the macromolecules determined by the concentration of hydrogen ions and also of the ionic strength of the solution, i.e., of the concentration of other low molecular weight ions.

It is known, for example, that native DNA in solution can undergo denaturation not only with a change in temperature, but also with a change in the concentration of hydrogen ions, i.e., a change in the pH of the medium. At room temperature DNA is stable in aqueous solution in the pH ranges of $\approx$3.5–4.5 and 9–11.5 (12,14).* In similar manner, complexes of polyadenylic and polyurydilic acids (poly A + poly U), which have a regular double helical structure, are stable in the pH interval from $\approx$4.5 to $\approx$10. Complexes are not formed in the pH ranges outside of the regions indicated, and the molecules of DNA or of polyadenine and polyuracil have coiled structures. Transition from the helical to the coiled conformation takes place over a narrow pH range and has a cooperative character.

The effect of pH on the conformations of polynucleotide chains in solution is due to the fact that the hydrogen bonds which stabilize the helical structure are formed in these molecules between groups which can ionize; as a result, the ionization of just one group that participates in the formation of a hydrogen bond means the simultaneous rupture of the latter; this results in a change in the conformation of the macromolecule. In this case, we have a good example of specific interactions which have been discussed above in connection with polypeptides (see sections 10.1 and 10.2). In fact, the ionization of bases, i.e., the process of dissociation or binding of a proton (for acid and basic ionizable groups, respectively), takes place only in the absence of hydrogen bonds; this process does not occur in the helical form. The purine and pyrimidine bases in DNA and in the synthetic polynucleotides form hydrogen bonds between the amino group and a ring nitrogen atom on one hand and a —NH—CO— group on the other hand. The negative logarithms of the dissociation constants of these groups are respectively equal to (17): $pK_{NH_2} \approx$ 2.4–2.9 (guanine), 3.7–3.8 (adenine), 4.5–4.8 (cytosine); $pK_{NH-CO} \approx$ 9.5–11.4 (guanine, thymine, uracil). Since an amino group binds a proton while a —NH—CO— group releases it, the first is charged at $pH < pK_{NH_2}$, while the second is charged at $pH > pK_{NH-CO}$. As a result, the purine and pyrimidine bases are not charged in the interval $pK_{NH_2} < pH < pK_{NH-CO}$, and in this range the helical conformation of the molecule can exist. An interesting special case is found in polyadenine (poly A) molecules which, as has been shown by Steiner and Beers (18), exist in a helical conformation in solution at $pH < 6$ and in a coiled conformation at $pH > 6$. This is due to the fact that the helical conformation of poly A molecules can exist only when the adenine $—NH_2$ groups are ionized, since hydrogen bonds are insufficient to stabilize it and it is necessary to have also electrostatic interactions

* The exact values of pH at which denaturation takes place depend on the ionic strength of the solution.

between the purine bases and the charged phosphate groups of the polynucleotide chain.

Steiner (7) and Birshtein (19) have studied theoretically the effect of base ionization on the helix–coil transition in a polynucleotide chain, and also the effect of such a transition on titration curves, i.e., curves of the dependence of the degree of ionization α of a macromolecule on the value of the solution pH. Let us assume, as before, that the nucleotide residues of two chains can combine with each other in a unique manner and let us neglect the heterogeneity of the composition of the molecule. Each base pair in the molecule can exist in one of three states: state 0, in which the pair of monomer units is not bonded by a hydrogen bond and is not charged; state $0'$, in which the pair of monomer units is not bonded by hydrogen bonds and is charged; state 1, in which the pair of monomer units is bonded by a hydrogen bond and is not charged. Since we consider ionization without simultaneous breaking of the hydrogen bond impossible, we shall not examine state $1'$, in which the pair of monomer units is charged and bonded by a hydrogen bond. Here we assign to each pair of bases a single charged state, since the ionization constants of $—NH_2$ and —NH—CO— groups are greatly different, so that their titration regions do not overlap and they can be examined independently. We shall consider, for the sake of clarity, that it is the acid group —NH—CO— which becomes charged, i.e., we shall discuss the alkaline region of pH's. As before, we shall not consider the ionization of phosphate groups, since their ionization does not change in the pH range under examination. The energy of the electrostatic interaction of the phosphate groups with the charges of the purine and pyrimidine bases, being a function of the ionic strength of the solution, can be included in the ionization constant of these bases.

The total number of states of the ionizable chain is 3^n; furthermore, each term of the partition function must be developed according to the rules presented during the examination of thermal denaturation and contains, besides, an additional factor which represents the ratio a of the activities of charged and uncharged groups raised to a power equal to the number of charged groups in the chain [compare eq. (10.9)]. The ratio of activities a is related by eq. (10.10) to the pH of the medium and the negative logarithm of the intrinsic dissociation constant, pK, of the ionizable group (in the absence of interactions with other groups). In doing this we assume, for the sake of simplicity, that there is no electrostatic interaction between the charged groups. Such an interaction can, in principle, be taken into account (19), but it does not change the basic results.

As in the cases examined above, in the absence of cooperativeness ($\sigma_j = \tau = 1$), the partition function of the ionizable macromolecule is equal to the product of the partition functions of all base pairs

$$Z = (1 + a + s)^n \tag{11.42}$$

and the fraction of bonded monomer units obeys the equation of a unimolecular reaction:

$$\vartheta = (1/n)\, \partial \ln Z/\partial \ln s = s^*/(1 + s^*) \tag{11.43}$$

where

$$s^* = s/(1 + a) \tag{11.44}$$

is the constant of formation of a hydrogen bond between a pair of ionizable groups [see eq. (10.2)]. In the opposite limiting case of a completely cooperative transition, which occurs according to the all-or-none principle ($\sigma_j = \tau = 0$), the partition function is the sum of two terms which correspond to completely helical and completely coiled chains [compare eq. (10.3)]:

$$Z = (1 + a)^n + s^n \approx \begin{cases} s^n & s^* > 1 \\ (1 + a)^n & s^* < 1 \end{cases} \tag{11.45}$$

where s^* is defined by eq. (11.44). From this

$$\vartheta = \begin{cases} 1 & s^* > 1 \\ 0 & s^* < 1 \end{cases} \tag{11.46}$$

we see that in this case, when $s^* = 1$, an infinitely sharp transition takes place from the helical ($s^* > 1$) to the coiled ($s^* < 1$) state of the chain.

In the intermediate case, in which the transition is cooperative but the cooperativeness is not absolute ($\sigma_j, \tau \neq 0$), bonded and nonbonded pairs of monomer units can coexist in one pair of molecules. In developing the partition function, just as in the case of specific bonding in polypeptide chains (see section 10.1), we can start from the partition function of the unionized molecule, remembering that each pair of monomer units in the nonbonded state contributes to the partition function a factor of $1 + a$ and not 1. Then, each element of matrix G [eq. (11.12)] contains either a factor $(1 + a)$, if the corresponding pair of monomer units is not bonded, or a factor s, if this pair is bonded by a hydrogen bond. It is evident (compare section 10.1) that in this case the eigenvalues λ of matrix G will be defined, as before, by eq. (11.27) in which s has been replaced by s^* [eq. (11.44)] and λ by λ^*:

$$\lambda^* = \lambda/(1 + a) \tag{11.47}$$

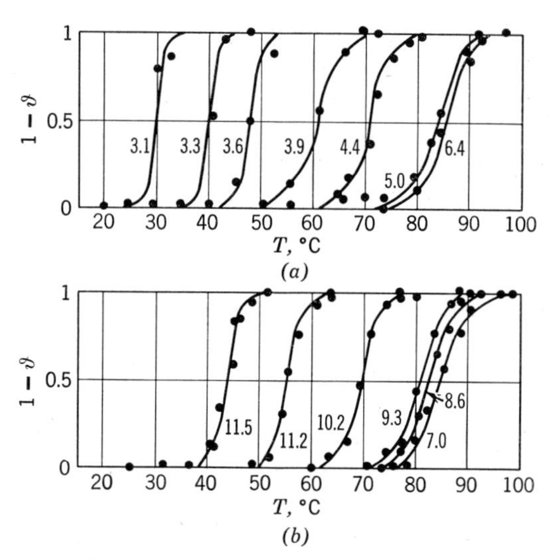

Fig. 11.6. Helix–coil transition curves in rat thymus DNA in (*a*) acid pH and (*b*) alkaline pH ranges (14). The numbers on the curves are values of pH.

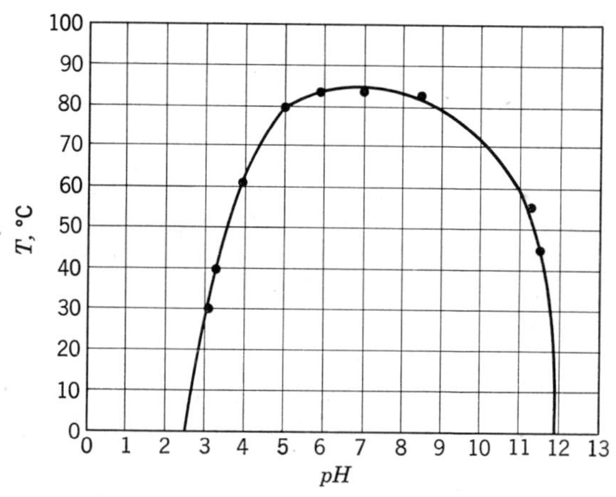

Fig. 11.7. Dependence of the melting temperature of rat thymus DNA on the pH of the medium (14).

From this

$$\vartheta = \partial \ln \lambda_1 / \partial \ln s = \vartheta^{(0)}{}_{s=s^*} \tag{11.48}$$

Here $\vartheta^{(0)}{}_{s=s^*}$ is the fraction of bonded pairs in the unionized molecule with value of s equal to the value of s^* for the ionizable molecule.

As can be seen, accounting for the ionization of purine and pyrimidine bases results in dependence of the equilibrium constant s^* both on temperature and on the pH of the medium; these two factors complement each other in their influence on the helix–coil transitions of DNA and synthetic polynucleotides. The dependence of the temperature of the helix–coil transition in DNA on the pH of the medium has been investigated in the studies of Cox and Peacocke (20), Cavalieri and Rosenberg (21), Sturtevant, Rice, and Geiduschek (12), and Sukhorukov, Moshkovskii, Birshtein and Lystsov (14). As an example, in Figure 11.6 are shown curves of the helix–coil transition at acid and alkaline pH's in rat thymus DNA in an $0.15M$ aqueous solution of NaCl, studied by the change of the intensity of ultraviolet absorption (14). The dependence obtained from these curves of the "melting temperature" (the mean point of the region of transition) on the pH of the medium is shown in Figure 11.7. The region of relative stability of native DNA (at pH 5–9) and the regions of acid (pH < 5) and alkaline (pH > 9) denaturation of DNA are clearly seen.

The condition of transition at any combinations of temperature and pH is the equality $s^* = 1$, i.e.,

$$s_m \equiv e^{-(\Delta H - T_m \Delta S)/kT_m} = 1 + a_m \tag{11.49}$$

where a_m is the value of the ratio of activities of charged and uncharged groups at the melting point related by eq. (10.10) to the value of the pH at the melting point. Therefore, by measuring the dependence of the melting temperature T_m of DNA double helices on pH (i.e., on a_m), it is possible to determine the changes in the energy and entropy which accompany an increase of the bonded region of the macromolecule by one pair of monomer units. Using this method, Warner (15) and Birshtein (19) determined ΔH and ΔS for poly A + poly U complexes from the experimental data of Steiner and Beers (16), who investigated absorption in the ultraviolet region, and of Warner (15) who investigated the titration curves of these complexes in 0.1–$0.2M$ aqueous solutions of KCl. The dependence of $\ln(1 + a_m)$ on $1/T_m$ in the pH interval investigated (6–10.4) is well represented by a straight line (Fig. 11.8) in accordance with eq. (11.49). The heat of melting, $-\Delta H$, per adenine–uracil nucleotide pair in a neutral medium, as determined from the slope of this straight line, is 8 ± 1 kcal/mole, while the entropy of melting, $-\Delta S \approx 25$ cal/mole-deg.

In the study of Sukhorukov et al. (14), it was similarly shown that the dependence of $\ln(1 + a_m)$ on $1/T_m$ for DNA is also well represented by a single straight line for the acid and alkaline regions of denaturation (see

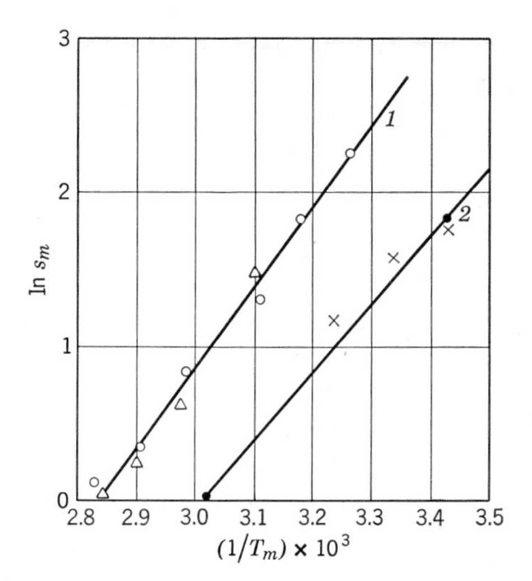

Fig. 11.8. Dependence of ln s_m on $1/T_m$ for molecules of (*1*) DNA and (*2*) poly A+ poly U: (O) acid denaturation of DNA (14); (Δ) alkaline denaturation of DNA (14); (×, ●) alkaline denaturation of poly A + poly U (15,16).

Fig. 11.8). In this case the heat of melting, $-\Delta H$, per base pair in neutral medium was found to be 10–11 kcal/mole, while the increase in entropy during the breaking of these bonds was $-\Delta S \approx 30$ cal/deg-mole. We see that the heats of transition both of native DNA and of poly A and poly U complexes, determined from the dependence of the temperature of melting on the pH of the medium, turned out to be close to those determined calorimetrically (see section 11.2). As was pointed out in section 11.2, with a known ΔH, it is possible to determine the cooperativeness parameter σ_0 from the sharpness of the helix–coil transition.

Such an evaluation, has shown (14) that the value of σ_0 is approximately equal to 0.1 at neutral pH; this is consistent with the estimate of Zimm (8) (see section 11.2). The value of σ_0 decreases in the acid and alkaline regions.

Helix–coil transitions in ionizable molecules of DNA and synthetic polynucleotides also manifest themselves in the titration curves of these substances and can be investigated, therefore, for example, by the potentiometric method. Using the general expression for a titration curve eq. (10.16), and eq. (11.47), we obtain

$$\alpha = \frac{\partial \ln \lambda_1}{\partial \ln a} = \frac{\partial \ln \lambda_1^*}{\partial \ln a} + \frac{a}{1 + a} \tag{11.50}$$

where λ_1^* is the largest root of eq. (11.27), in which s has been replaced by s^*, and $\lambda_1 = \lambda_1^*(1 + a)$. Taking into consideration that λ_1^* depends on a only through s^*, and using eq. (11.44), we obtain (19) [compare eq. (10.21)]:

$$\begin{aligned} \alpha &= \frac{\partial \ln \lambda_1^*}{\partial \ln s^*} \cdot \frac{\partial \ln s^*}{\partial \ln a} + \frac{a}{1 + a} \\ &= \frac{a}{1 + a} (1 - \vartheta) \\ &= \alpha_{\text{coil}}(1 - \vartheta) \end{aligned} \tag{11.51}$$

where α_{coil} is the degree of ionization of a coiled chain at a given pH. We see that, in agreement with our starting assumptions (independence of the ionization of monomer units in the helical state and absence of electrostatic interaction between charged monomer units), the titration curve of partly helical DNA is nothing but the titration curve of its coiled part; the fraction of monomer units in the coiled state is, in its turn, a function of the pH of the medium, i.e., it changes during titration.

For example, for a noncooperative macromolecule in which ϑ depends on temperature and pH according to a unimolecular reaction equation [eq. (11.43)], we have

$$\alpha = a/(1 + \tilde{a}) \tag{11.52}$$

where

$$\tilde{a} = a/(1 + s) \tag{11.53}$$

In other words, in this case the titration curve of acid groups has the form, taking eq. (10.10) into account,

$$\log [\alpha/(1 - \alpha)] = \text{pH} - \text{p}\tilde{K} \tag{11.54}$$

where pK = pK + log $(1 + s)$. This means that the effect of hydrogen bonds on the titration curve of a noncooperative macromolecule is reduced to a change in the ionization constant, as has been pointed out by Tanford (22). In the opposite limiting case of a completely cooperative macromolecule, in which $\vartheta = 1$ with $s^* > 1$ and $\vartheta = 0$ with $s^* < 1$ [eq. (11.46)], we obtain:

$$\alpha = \begin{cases} 0 & s^* > 1 \\ a/(1 + a) & s^* < 1 \end{cases} \tag{11.55}$$

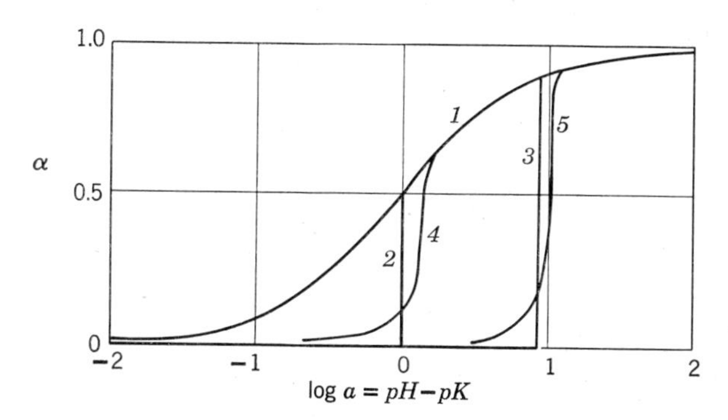

Fig. 11.9. Theoretical titration curves of DNA: (*1*) coiled DNA; (*2*) all or none transition $\sigma_0 = 0$, $s = 2$; (*3*) $\sigma_0 = 0$, $s = 10$; (*4*) $\sigma_0 = 0.1$, $s = 2$; (*5*) $\sigma_0 = 0.1$, $s = 10$.

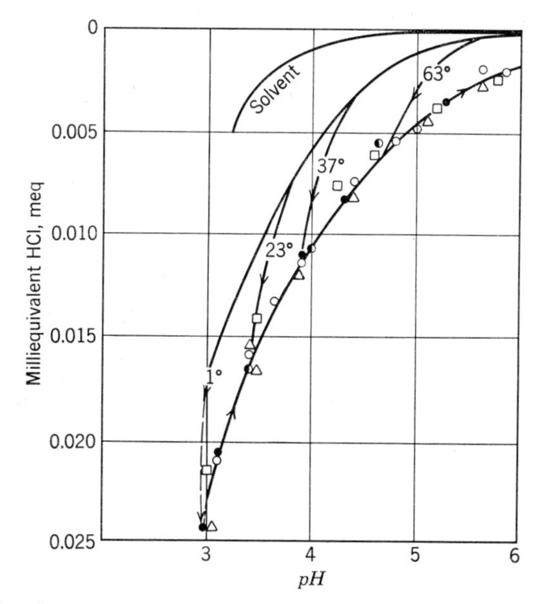

Fig. 11.10. Titration curves of DNA solutions at an ionic strength of 0.017*M* (21): (O) direct titration at 75°C; (□) reverse titration at 1°C; (◐) reverse titrations at 23°C; (●) reverse titration at 37°C; (Δ) reverse titration at 63°C. Curves with arrows denote direct titration; numbers on curves give temperature of the solution.

i.e., the titration curve changes abruptly from the titration curve of a helix to that of a coil. In the general case, this transition takes place over a finite interval of pH, in which ϑ decreases from 1 to 0 [see eq. (11.51)]. It can be seen from this that the cooperativeness of the process of hydrogen bond breaking determines the cooperativeness of the process of ionization of monomer units directly related to it and results, therefore, in a sudden change in the titration curves.

Theoretical titration curves calculated with the equations presented above are shown in Figure 11.9. From this figure it can be seen that the titration curves can be broken down essentially into two parts: $\alpha = 0$ at pH values which are insufficient to initiate the helix–coil transition ($s^* > 1$), and $\alpha = \alpha_{\text{coil}} = a/(1 + a)$ at pH values at which helical molecules cannot exist ($s^* < 1$). Depending on the value of s, i.e., on temperature, the transition between these two regions takes place at different values of pH. At a temperature not far removed from the transition temperature of an unionized molecule, the transition takes place at pH values not too far from pK, when $\alpha_{\text{coil}} < 1$. As the pH increases further, α increases from this value of α_{coil} to unity; furthermore, this increase with an increase in pH proceeds along the titration curve of the coiled molecule. The entire titration curve turns out to be asymmetric. If the temperature is considerably lower than the transition temperature of an unionized molecule, then the value of the transition pH is much higher than the pK (in the case of acid groups), and α increases sharply from zero to unity.

Experimental data are in complete agreement with the predictions of the theory presented above. Titration curves of DNA studied by Cavalieri and Rosenberg (21) are shown as an example in Figure 11.10 for the pH range 3–6 at various temperatures in the range from 1 to 75°C. From these curves it can be seen that, at a given pH value which depends on temperature, a sharp transition takes place from the titration curve of native DNA to the titration curve of denatured DNA. Let us mention that native DNA can ionize to some extent, especially at low temperature; according to the opinion of Steiner (7) this is related to structural defects.

References

1. Crick, F. H., *Biofizika*, **8**, 529 (1963).
2. Crick, F. H., and J. D. Watson, *Proc. Roy. Soc.* (*London*), **A223**, 80 (1954).
3. Gibbs, J. H., and E. A. Di Marzio, *J. Chem. Phys.*, **28**, 1247 (1958).
4. Gibbs, J. H., and E. A. Di Marzio, *J. Chem. Phys.*, **30**, 271 (1959).
5. Rice, S. A., and A. Wada, *J. Chem. Phys.*, **29**, 233 (1958).
6. Hill, T. L., *J. Chem. Phys.*, **30**, 383 (1959).
7. Steiner, R. F., *J. Chem. Phys.*, **32**, 215 (1960).
8. Zimm, B. H., *J. Chem. Phys.*, **33**, 1349 (1960).
9. Marmur, J., and P. Doty, *Nature*, **183**, 1427 (1959).
10. Jacobson, H., and W. H. Stockmayer, *J. Chem. Phys.*, **18**, 1600 (1950).
11. Truesdell, C., *Ann. Math.*, **46**, 144 (1945).

12. Sturtevant, J. M., S. A. Rice, and E. P. Geiduschek, *Discussions Faraday Soc.*, **25**, 138 (1958).
13. Doty, P., in *Sovremennye Problemy Biofiziki*, Vol. 1, IL, Moscow, 1961, p. 138 (originally published as *Biophysical Science: A Study Program*, J. C. Oncley, F. O. Schmitt, R. C. Williams, M. D. Rosenberg, and R. H. Bolt, Eds., Wiley, New York 1959.
14. Sukhorukov, B. I., Yu. S. Moshkovskii, T. M. Birshtein, and V. N. Lystsov, *Biofizika*, **7**, 294 (1963).
15. Warner, R. C., and E. Breslow, *Proc. Intern. Congr. Biochem. Vienna*, **1958**, **9**, 157.
16. Steiner, R. F., and R. F. Beers, Jr., *Biochim. Biophys. Acta*, **33**, 470 (1959).
17. Jordan, D., in *The Nucleic Acids*, Vol. 1, Butterworths, London, 1955, p. 447.
18. Steiner, R. F., and R. F. Beers, Jr., *Biochim. Biophys. Acta*, **32**, 166 (1959).
19. Birshtein, T. M., *Biofizika*, **7**, 513 (1962).
20. Cox, R. A., and A. R. Peacocke, *J. Chem. Soc.*, **1956**, 2499.
21. Cavalieri, L. F., and B. H. Rosenberg, *J. Am. Chem. Soc.*, **79**, 5352 (1957).
22. Tanford, C., *J. Am. Chem. Soc.*, **83**, 1628 (1961).
23. Volkenshtein, M. V., and A. M. Elyashevich, *Biofizika*, **6**, 513 (1961).
24. Geiduschek, E. P., *J. Mol. Biol.*, **4**, 467 (1962).
25. De Voe, H., and I. Tinoco, Jr., *J. Mol. Biol.*, **4**, 500 (1962).
26. Ozaki, M., M. Tanaka, and E. Teramoto, *J. Phys. Soc. Japan*, **18**, 551 (1963).
27. Lifson, S., and B. H. Zimm, *Biopolymers*, **1**, 15 (1963).
28. Lifson, S., *Biopolymers*, **1**, 25 (1963).
29. Steiner, R. F., and R. F. Beers, Jr., *Polynucleotides*, Elsevier, Amsterdam–London–New York, 1961.
30. Zimm, B. H., and N. R. Kallenbach, *Ann. Rev. Phys. Chem.*, **13**, 171 (1962).
31. Marmur, J., R. Rownd, and C. L. Schildkraut, *Progr. Nucleic Acid Res.*, **1**, 231 (1963).
32. Bresler, S. E., *Vvedenie v Molekulyarnuyu Biologiyu* (Introduction to Molecular Biology), Izdatel'stvo Akad. Nauk SSSR, Moscow, 1963.
33. Rawitscher, M., and J. M. Sturtevant, *J. Am. Chem. Soc.*, **82**, 3739 (1960).
34. Steiner, R. F., and C. Kitzinger, *Nature*, **194**, 1172 (1962).
35. Ross, P., and J. Sturtevant, paper presented at American Chemical Society Meeting, 1962; *Abstracts of Papers*, p. 57c (1962).
36. Doty, P., H. Boedtker, J. R. Fresco, R. Haselkorn, and M. Litt, *Proc. Natl. Acad. Sci. U.S.*, **45**, 482 (1959).

CONCLUSION

This book is devoted to two different, but closely connected problems, namely, the conformational statistics of ordinary macromolecules and the theory of helix–coil transitions in biopolymer molecules. The general approach to these problems consists in an examination of macromolecules as linear cooperative systems, the states of the elements (i.e., monomer units) of which are mutually dependent. Accordingly, both types of problems are examined by a single mathematical method, the matrix method of the Ising model.

At the same time, we see from this monograph that the conformational statistics of ordinary macromolecules and the theory of helix–coil transitions in biopolymer molecules are, at present, in different stages of development. The nature of the flexibility of macromolecules can be understood qualitatively without using the concept of a macromolecule as a linear cooperative system. Therefore, the development of the modern conformational statistics of ordinary macromolecules, presented in this book, was preceded by a qualitative investigation of the flexibility of polymer chains based on the existence of internal rotation of bonds in the macromolecule. The statistical physics of linear cooperative systems was needed only in the solution of the next problem of the theory: the expression in quantitative terms of the concepts on the flexibility of macromolecules. This problem consisted, on one hand, in the determination of the relations between the parameters that characterize the flexibility of the chain, with their observed properties (dimensions, dipole moments, thermomechanical curves, etc.) and, on the other hand, in the direct calculation of flexibility parameters on the basis of presently available information on the potential of interaction of nonbonded atoms and atomic groups. Both of these problems have essentially been solved, and, at present, we have detailed concepts on the conformations and mechanism of flexibility of ordinary macromolecules (see section 8.5) and we can predict, with a satisfactory degree of accuracy, their crystalline conformations and properties in solution and in the highly elastic state using only parameters that describe the individual atoms of the chains.

A considerably different situation exists in the theory of helix–coil transitions. Due to the fact that the very existence of such transitions is determined by the interdependence of the states of individual monomer units of the macromolecule, it was found necessary to use the statistics of one-dimensional cooperative systems at the very beginning in the development of the model theory. The existing theories of helix–coil transitions in molecules of polypeptides and polynucleotides claim only a qualitative interpretation of the sharpness of transitions, the dependence of the transition temperature on solvent composition, pH, and solution ionic strength, the external force, etc. They do not have as their aim the evaluation of parameters that characterize the heat and entropy of transition, as well as the degree of its cooperativeness. In fact, the existing theories only illustrate the fact that the helix–coil transition has a sharper character the greater the free energy of initiation of a helical region of the chain; they do not attempt to explain why this free energy is so large in real polymer chains.

Furthermore, individual differences between single macromolecules, which manifest themselves in differences in the temperatures, heats, and degrees of sharpness of transitions in different biopolymers, are outside the realm of these theories. For example, the theory of helix–coil transitions in DNA molecules does not take into consideration the heterogeneity of DNA and consequently cannot describe the dependence of the temperature and sharpness of melting of the double helix on its composition. The theory of helix–coil transitions in polypeptide chains does not explain, for example, the striking difference between the heats of melting of poly-γ-benzyl-L-glutamate helices, on one hand, and poly-L-glutamic acid and poly-L-lysine, on the other. (As is known, see section 8.5, these heats differ in order of magnitude and even in sign.) The transition from a model theory of helix–coil transitions, which explains only the general aspects of the phenomenon, to a theory relating the specificity of transitions in different macromolecules with their chemical structure is still a task for the future. In this endeavor theoreticians will meet with considerable difficulties, since, if the degree of cooperativeness of the transition appears to be interpretable essentially in terms of an examination only of intramolecular interactions, the evaluation of the heats and entropies of transitions will probably require that changes in the state of the entire solution be taken into account; this immediately increases manyfold the difficulty of the problem. Nevertheless, it is so important to go on to a detailed quantitative theory of conformational transitions in polypeptides and nucleic acids that it is certain that these difficulties will be surmounted successfully.

As has been noted with such perspicacity by the French physicist, Sadron, polymer physics has two possibilities for development: in technology and in biology. At present, the only branch of the statistical physics of polymers which has been subjected to a more or less detailed development is the statistical physics of macromolecules. Its "exit into biology" is, first of all, the development of the theory of the conformations and conformational transitions of biopolymer molecules. We have seen that considerable success has already been attained in this area, even though the development of the proper statistical theory has only started and the solution of the basic problems still lies ahead. This branch of statistical physics is certainly destined for an important future, since biopolymers perform their biological functions to a great extent on the molecular level; thus, the physics of biopolymer molecules may have a direct biological significance.

On the other hand, the "exit into technology" of the statistical physics of macromolecules is possible via only one route: the theory of polymers in the bulk state. The key problem in this field seems to be the development of the theory of supermolecular structures, i.e., of the elements of ordering in polymers in bulk. The concepts of the supermolecular structure, which are being developed at the present time in the Soviet Union by V. A. Kargin and his school, as well as by a number of authors in other countries, encompass a vast domain of phenomena, from the elements of orientational order in the highly elastic state of polymers to the phenomena of their crystallization. A very large amount of experimental material has been accumulated in this realm, and numerous quite important theoretical studies are available; these have been carried out by Flory, Gibbs, and Di Marzio (see section 7.1); however, we are still only approaching an all-encompassing examination of these most important problems. The transition of polymer physics from the molecular to the supermolecular level will certainly be of enormous importance to the technological physics of rubbers, plastics, and fibers. On the other hand, the investigation of the supermolecular structures will have a great significance also for molecular biophysics, for example, for such a field as the study of muscle action.

How is the solution of the problems of the statistical physics listed above, related to the already solved questions of macromolecular physics? As far as the theory of biopolymeric molecules is concerned, its close relation to the general theory of macromolecules is unquestionably evident and requires no elucidation. At first glance, the theory of polymers in bulk is less directly related to the theory of individual macromolecules. From the concepts of Flory, Gibbs, and Di Marzio, presented briefly in section 7.1, however, it follows that, in this case as well, the stiffness of definite segments of macromolecules plays the principal role in the formation of all sorts of types of supermolecular structures as a result of which it is possible to trace a strong analogy between many properties of polymers and of liquid crystals. As a result, it is possible to imagine that the concepts and methods of the conformational statistics of macromolecules, presented in this book, will be of great importance also in new branches of polymer theory—namely, in the theory of molecules of biopolymers and in the theory of supermolecular structures.

APPENDIX

We shall show that all the elements of the averaged matrix of the cosines of the angles between the axes of systems of coordinates linked to two different monomer units of the polymer chain tend to zero as the distance between the monomer units increases. We shall carry out the proof for the case of independent rotations about bonds of neighboring monomer units. Then, the matrix of the cosines of the angles between the axes of the local systems of coordinates, linked with the kth and $(k + m)$th monomer units, is equal to S^m, where S is the matrix of the cosines of the angles between the axes of systems of coordinates linked to neighboring monomer units, averaged over the conformations. We shall consider, for the sake of simplicity, that the set of conformations of monomer units is discrete. Then

$$S = \sum_{\alpha} w(\Omega^{(\alpha)}) S(\Omega^{(\alpha)}) \tag{A.1}$$

Here

$$w(\Omega^{(\alpha)}) = \frac{e^{-U(\Omega^{(\alpha)})/kT}}{\sum_{\alpha} e^{-U(\Omega^{(\alpha)})/kT}} \tag{A.2}$$

is the statistical weight of conformation $\Omega^{(\alpha)}$, which has an energy of $U(\Omega^{(\alpha)})$. It is evident that

$$\sum_{\alpha} w(\Omega^{(\alpha)}) = 1 \tag{A.3}$$

In order to investigate the question of the behavior of matrix S^m when $m \to \infty$, let us introduce the concept of the norm of the matrix (see, for example, (69,71) in Chapter 5). The norm of a square matrix A is a nonnegative number $\|A\|$ comparable to this matrix, which satisfies the conditions:

$$\|A\| > 0 \quad \text{when} \quad A \neq 0$$

and

$$\|A\| = 0 \quad \text{when} \quad A = 0 \tag{A.4}$$

$$\|cA\| = |c| \, \|A\| \tag{A.5}$$

$$\|A + B\| \leqslant \|A\| + \|B\| \tag{A.6}$$

$$\|AB\| \leqslant \|A\| \, \|B\| \tag{A.7}$$

The norm of matrix $||A||$ can be developed in many ways. For example, it can be defined as the largest modulus of the totality of vectors $A\mathbf{x}$, where $\mathbf{x}$ is an arbitrary unit vector

$$||A|| = \max_{|x| = 1} |A\mathbf{x}| \tag{A.8}$$

From condition (A.4) it follows that the necessary and sufficient condition that

$$\lim_{m \to \infty} S^m = 0 \tag{A.9}$$

is the equality to zero of the limit of the norm of matrix S^m

$$\lim_{m \to \infty} ||S^m|| = 0 \tag{A.10}$$

From condition (A.7) it follows that, for the validity of eq. (A.10), it is sufficient that the norm of matrix S be not greater than 1. In fact

$$||S^m|| \leqslant ||S||\,||S^{m-1}|| \leqslant \cdots \leqslant ||S||^m \tag{A.11}$$

Therefore, if $||S|| < 1$, then $||S^m|| < 1$, and consequently $S^m \to 0$.

It is easy to show that the norm of matrix S, developed in accordance with condition (A.1), is not greater than 1. In fact, using eqs. (A.5) and (A.6), we have

$$\begin{aligned} ||S|| &= ||\sum_\alpha w(\Omega^{(\alpha)})S(\Omega^{(\alpha)})|| \leqslant \sum_\alpha ||w(\Omega^{(\alpha)})S(\Omega^{(\alpha)})|| \\ &= \sum_\alpha w(\Omega^{(\alpha)})||S(\Omega^{(\alpha)})|| \end{aligned} \tag{A.12}$$

Matrices $S(\Omega^{(\alpha)})$ are matrices of unitary transformation and their norm is $||S(\Omega^{(\alpha)})|| = 1$ [this follows, for example, from eq. (A.8)]. Consequently, us'ng eq. (A.3), we have

$$||S|| \leqslant \sum w(\Omega^{(\alpha)}) = 1 \tag{A.13}$$

If $||S|| < 1$, then, in accordance with eq. (A.11), $\lim_{m \to \infty} ||S^m|| = 0$ and, consequently, $\lim_{m \to \infty} S^m = 0$. In the case that $||S|| = 1$, conditions (A.9) and (A.10) may be not fulfilled.

Let us examine this case. Let $||S|| = 1$; then, according to eq. (A.8), there exists such a unit vector $\mathbf{x}$, that $|S\mathbf{x}| = 1$. Moreover, from eqs. (A.1), (A.3) and the inequality of triangles for vectors $|\mathbf{x} + \mathbf{y}| \leqslant |\mathbf{x}| + |\mathbf{y}|$, we have

$$|S\mathbf{x}| \leqslant \sum_\alpha w(\Omega^{(\alpha)})|S(\Omega^{(\alpha)})\mathbf{x}| = \sum_\alpha w(\Omega^{(\alpha)}) = 1 \tag{A.14}$$

It is evident that the equality sign in eq. (A.14) can be valid only if all the unit vectors $S(\Omega^{(\alpha)})\mathbf{x}$ are parallel to each other, i.e., if

$$S(\Omega^{(\alpha)})\mathbf{x} = \mathbf{y} \tag{A.15}$$

where $\mathbf{y}$ is independent of α. In this way, $\|S\| = 1$, if all the rotation matrices $S(\Omega^{(\alpha)})$ transform a certain unit vector $\mathbf{x}$ into an identical unit vector $\mathbf{y}$. This can take place either if all $S(\Omega^{(\alpha)})$ are identical with each other (then $\mathbf{x}$ can be any unit vector), or if all $S(\Omega^{(\alpha)})$ describe a rotation about a single axis (then vector $\mathbf{x}$ is directed along this axis and $\mathbf{y} = \mathbf{x}$), or if $S(\Omega^{(\alpha)})$ describe a rotation of 180° about axes which lie in a single plane, in other words, if they correspond to a reflection in this plane (then vector $\mathbf{x}$ is perpendicular to this plane and $\mathbf{y} = -\mathbf{x}$). It is only in these cases that $\|S\| = 1$ and $\lim_{m\to\infty} S^m$ can be not equal to zero. It is evident that only the first case has a practical significance for polymer chains; in this case, all $S(\Omega^{(\alpha)})$ are identical with each other, i.e., each monomer unit has only one conformation. The second and third cases are true if the valence angle is equal to 180° or 0°, respectively.

Let us note that condition (A.9) means that all the eigenvalues of matrix S are less than unity in modulus

$$|\lambda_1|,\ |\lambda_2|,\ |\lambda_3| < 1 \tag{A.16}$$

The proof of this statement is particularly easy in the case in which matrix S is reduced to the diagonal form by a similarity transformation

$$S = T\Lambda T^{-1} \tag{A.17}$$

where Λ is a diagonal matrix composed of the eigenvalues of matrix S. It is evident that in such a case

$$S^m = T\Lambda^m T^{-1} \tag{A.18}$$

and, in order to fulfill equality (A.9), it is necessary and sufficient that $\lim_{m\to\infty} \Lambda^m = 0$; for this, it is necessary and sufficient that condition (A.16) be fulfilled in its turn.

AUTHOR INDEX*

* *Italic* numbers refer to reference pages.

C

H

I

J

K

L

M

N

O

T

SUBJECT INDEX